I

Glory Be to the Father

GLORIA PATRI

Source unknown, 2nd century

Henry W. Greatorex, 1813-1858

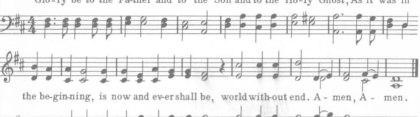

Glo-ry be to the Fa-ther and to the Son and to the Ho-ly Ghost, As it was in

the be-gin-ning, is now and ev-er shall be, world with-out end. A - men, A - men.

II

GLORIA PATRI

Charles Meineke, 1782-1850

Glo - ry be to the Fa-ther and to the Son and to the Ho-ly Ghost, As it was in

the be-gin-ning, is now and ev-er shall be, world without end. A-men, A-men.

Great Hymns of the Faith

Compiled and edited by
JOHN W. PETERSON

Editorial Committee
NORMAN JOHNSON
HAROLD DeCOU   CHARLES VAN HORN
REV. CHARLES WICKMAN   KENNETH OSBECK

Singspiration® Inc.
WORLD DISTRIBUTORS
ZONDERVAN PUBLISHING HOUSE
GRAND RAPIDS, MICHIGAN 49506

PRINTED IN U.S.A.
Eleventh printing 1971

TABLE OF CONTENTS

Great Hymns of the Faith

O Worship the King

LYONS

ROBERT GRANT, 1779-1838

Arr. from J. MICHAEL HAYDN, 1737-1806

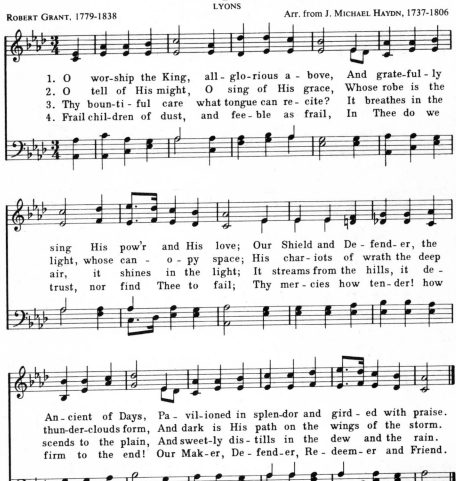

1. O wor-ship the King, all - glo-rious a - bove, And grate-ful - ly
2. O tell of His might, O sing of His grace, Whose robe is the
3. Thy boun-ti - ful care what tongue can re - cite? It breathes in the
4. Frail chil-dren of dust, and fee - ble as frail, In Thee do we

sing His pow'r and His love; Our Shield and De - fend- er, the
light, whose can - o - py space; His char - iots of wrath the deep
air, it shines in the light; It streams from the hills, it de -
trust, nor find Thee to fail; Thy mer - cies how ten - der! how

An - cient of Days, Pa - vil-ioned in splen-dor and gird - ed with praise.
thun-der-clouds form, And dark is His path on the wings of the storm.
scends to the plain, And sweet-ly dis - tills in the dew and the rain.
firm to the end! Our Mak- er, De - fend- er, Re - deem- er and Friend.

This tune in a lower key: 45

2 Love Divine

BEECHER

CHARLES WESLEY, 1707-1788

JOHN ZUNDEL, 1815-1882

1. Love di-vine, all loves ex-cel-ling, Joy of heav'n, to earth come down;
2. Breathe, O breathe Thy lov-ing Spir-it In-to ev-'ry trou-bled breast!
3. Come, al-might-y to de-liv-er, Let us all Thy life re-ceive;
4. Fin-ish then Thy new cre-a-tion, Pure and spot-less let us be;

Fix in us Thy hum-ble dwell-ing, All Thy faith-ful mer-cies crown.
Let us all in Thee in-her-it, Let us find that sec-ond rest.
Sud-den-ly re-turn, and nev-er, Nev-er-more Thy tem-ples leave.
Let us see Thy great sal-va-tion Per-fect-ly re-stored in Thee:

Je-sus, Thou art all com-pas-sion, Pure, un-bound-ed love Thou art;
Take a-way our bent to sin-ning, Al-pha and O-me-ga be;
Thee we would be al-ways bless-ing, Serve Thee as Thy hosts a-bove,
Changed from glo-ry in-to glo-ry, Till in heav'n we take our place,

Vis-it us with Thy sal-va-tion, En-ter ev-'ry trem-bling heart.
End of faith, as its be-gin-ning, Set our hearts at lib-er-ty.
Pray and praise Thee with-out ceas-ing, Glo-ry in Thy per-fect love.
Till we cast our crowns be-fore Thee, Lost in won-der, love and praise.

Sing Praise to God Who Reigns Above

MIT FREUDEN ZART

3

Johann J. Schütz, 1640-1690
Trans. by Frances E. Cox, 1812-1897

From the Bohemian Brethren's
Kirchengesänge, 1566

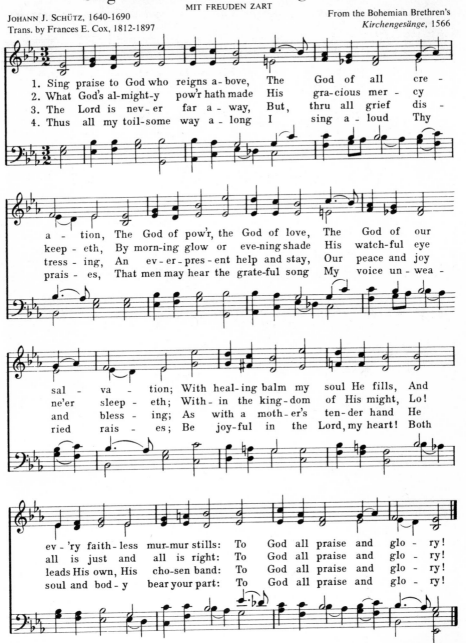

1. Sing praise to God who reigns a-bove, The God of all cre-a - tion, The God of pow'r, the God of love, The God of our sal - va - tion; With heal-ing balm my soul He fills, And ev - 'ry faith - less mur-mur stills: To God all praise and glo - ry!

2. What God's al-might-y pow'r hath made His gra-cious mer - cy keep - eth, By morn-ing glow or eve-ning shade His watch-ful eye ne'er sleep - eth; With-in the king-dom of His might, Lo! all is just and all is right: To God all praise and glo - ry!

3. The Lord is nev - er far a - way, But, thru all grief dis - tress - ing, An ev - er-pres - ent help and stay, Our peace and joy and bless - ing; As with a moth-er's ten-der hand He leads His own, His cho-sen band: To God all praise and glo - ry!

4. Thus all my toil-some way a - long I sing a - loud Thy prais - es, That men may hear the grate-ful song My voice un - wea - ried rais - es; Be joy-ful in the Lord, my heart! Both soul and bod - y bear your part: To God all praise and glo - ry!

4

Praise Ye the Triune God!

FLEMMING

Elizabeth R. Charles, 1828-1896

Friedrich F. Flemming, 1778-1813

1. Praise ye the Fa - ther for His lov-ing-kind-ness, Ten - der - ly
2. Praise ye the Sav - ior— great is His com-pas-sion, Gra-cious-ly
3. Praise ye the Spir - it, Com-fort-er of Is - rael, Sent of the

cares He for His err-ing chil-dren; Praise Him, ye an - gels,
cares He for His cho-sen peo-ple; Young men and maid - ens,
Fa - ther and the Son to bless us; Praise ye the Fa - ther,

praise Him in the heav - ens, Praise ye Je - ho - vah!
ye old men and chil - dren, Praise ye the Sav - ior!
Son, and Ho - ly Spir - it— Praise ye the Tri - une God!

5

Begin, My Tongue, Some Heavenly Theme

MANOAH

Isaac Watts, 1674-1748

From Greatorex's *Collection*, 1851

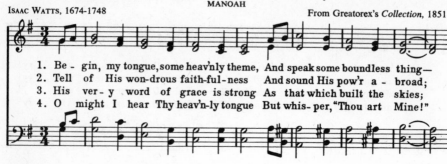

1. Be - gin, my tongue, some heav'nly theme, And speak some boundless thing—
2. Tell of His won-drous faith-ful-ness And sound His pow'r a - broad;
3. His ver - y word of grace is strong As that which built the skies;
4. O might I hear Thy heav'n-ly tongue But whis-per, "Thou art Mine!"

This tune in a lower key: 192

Begin, My Tongue, Some Heavenly Theme

The might-y works or might-ier name Of our e-ter-nal King.
Sing the sweet prom-ise of His grace, The love and truth of God.
The voice that rolls the stars a-long Speaks all the prom-is-es.
Those gen-tle words should raise my song To notes al-most di-vine.

Come, Thou Almighty King

6

ITALIAN HYMN

Source unknown, c. 1757

FELICE DE GIARDINI, 1716-1796

1. Come, Thou Al-might-y King, Help us Thy name to sing,
2. Come, Thou In-car-nate Word, Gird on Thy might-y sword,
3. Come, Ho-ly Com-fort-er, Thy sa-cred wit-ness bear
4. To the great One in Three E-ter-nal prais-es be,

Help us to praise: Fa-ther, all-glo-ri-ous, O'er all vic-
Our prayer at-tend: Come and Thy peo-ple bless, And give Thy
In this glad hour: Thou who al-might-y art, Now rule in
Hence ev-er-more: His sov-'reign maj-es-ty May we in

to-ri-ous, Come and reign o-ver us, An-cient of Days.
word suc-cess- Spir-it of ho-li-ness, On us de-scend.
ev-'ry heart, And ne'er from us de-part, Spir-it of pow'r.
glo-ry see, And to e-ter-ni-ty Love and a-dore.

Another harmonization of this tune, in a lower key: 60

7

Praise Our God

KENT

JOHN W. PETERSON, 1921-
Based on Revelation 19:5

JOHN W. PETERSON, 1921-

1. Praise our God, all ye His serv-ants, Ye that fear Him, small and great;
2. Praise our God, all ye His serv-ants, For His con - de - scend-ing grace,
3. Praise our God, all ye His serv-ants, Him whom an-gel hosts ac -claim;

With a sac - ri - fice of wor-ship In His glo-rious pres-ence wait.
For His love that brought sal - va - tion To a sin - ful, fall - en race.
Let us join the ser - aph cho - rus And His worth to all pro-claim.

REFRAIN

Al - le - lu - ia, Al - le-lu - ia, Al - le - lu - ia— Praise our God!

8

All People That on Earth Do Dwell

OLD HUNDREDTH

From Psalm 100
Attr. to William Kethe, late 16th century — alt.

LOUIS BOURGEOIS, c. 1510 - c. 1561
in the *Genevan Psalter*, 1551

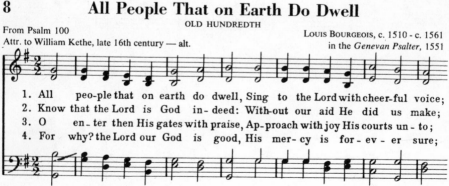

1. All peo-ple that on earth do dwell, Sing to the Lord with cheer-ful voice;
2. Know that the Lord is God in-deed: With-out our aid He did us make;
3. O en - ter then His gates with praise, Ap-proach with joy His courts un - to;
4. For why? the Lord our God is good, His mer - cy is for - ev - er sure;

The DOXOLOGY may also be sung to this meter.

All People That on Earth Do Dwell

Him serve with fear, His praise forth-tell, Come ye be-fore Him and re-joice.
We are His folk, He doth us feed, And for His sheep He doth us take.
Praise, laud and bless His name al-ways, For it is seem-ly so to do.
His truth at all times firm-ly stood, And shall from age to age en-dure.

His Loving-Kindness 9

LOVING-KINDNESS

SAMUEL MEDLEY, 1738-1799

WILLIAM CALDWELL, 19th century

1. A-wake, my soul, to joy-ful lays, And sing thy great Re-deem-er's praise;
2. He saw me ru-ined by the fall, Yet loved me not-with-stand-ing all;
3. Tho nu-m'rous hosts of might-y foes, Tho earth and hell my way op-pose,
4. When trou-ble, like a gloom-y cloud, Has gath-ered thick and thundered loud,

He just-ly claims a song from me— His lov-ing-kind-ness, O how free!
He saved me from my lost es-tate— His lov-ing-kind-ness, O how great!
He safe-ly leads my soul a-long— His lov-ing-kind-ness, O how strong!
He near my soul has al-ways stood— His lov-ing-kind-ness, O how good!

Lov-ing-kind-ness, lov-ing-kind-ness, His lov-ing-kind-ness, O how free!
Lov-ing-kind-ness, lov-ing-kind-ness, His lov-ing-kind-ness, O how great!
Lov-ing-kind-ness, lov-ing-kind-ness, His lov-ing-kind-ness, O how strong!
Lov-ing-kind-ness, lov-ing-kind-ness, His lov-ing-kind-ness, O how good!

10 **O God, Our Help in Ages Past**

ST. ANNE

From Psalm 90
ISAAC WATTS, 1674-1748

Attr. to William Croft, 1678-1727

1. O God, our help in a - ges past, Our hope for years to come,
2. Un - der the shad-ow of Thy throne Still may we dwell se - cure;
3. Be - fore the hills in or-der stood Or earth re-ceived her frame,
4. Time, like an ev - er - roll-ing stream, Bears all its sons a - way;
5. O God, our help in a - ges past, Our hope for years to come,

Our shel-ter from the storm - y blast, And our e - ter - nal home!
Suf - fi - cient is Thine arm a - lone, And our de - fense is sure.
From ev - er-last-ing Thou art God, To end-less years the same.
They fly, for-got-ten, as a dream Dies at the ope - ning day.
Be Thou our guide while life shall last, And our e - ter - nal home.

11 **When All Thy Mercies, O My God**

BELMONT

JOSEPH ADDISON, 1672-1719

From Gardiner's *Sacred Melodies,* 1812

1. When all Thy mer - cies, O my God, My ris - ing soul sur - veys,
2. Un - num-bered com-forts to my soul Thy ten - der care be - stowed,
3. When worn with sick-ness, oft hast Thou With health re-newed my face;
4. Thru ev - 'ry pe - riod of my life Thy good-ness I'll pur - sue,

Trans-port-ed with the view, I'm lost In won - der, love and praise.
Be - fore my in - fant heart con-ceived From whom those com-forts flowed.
And, when in sins and sor-rows bowed, Re - vived my soul with grace.
And aft - er death, in dis-tant worlds, The glo - rious theme re - new.

Great God of Wonders!

SAMUEL DAVIES, 1723-1761   JOHN NEWTON, 1725-1807

1. Great God of won-ders! all Thy ways Are match-less, God-like,
2. In won-der lost, with trem-bling joy, We take the par-don
3. O may this strange, this match-less grace, This God-like mir-a-

and di-vine; But the fair glo-ries of Thy grace More God-like
of our God: Par-don for crimes of deep-est dye, A par-don
cle of love, Fill the whole earth with grate-ful praise, And all th'an-

and un-ri-valed shine, More God-like and un-ri-valed shine.
bought with Je-sus' blood, A par-don bought with Je-sus' blood.
gel-ic choirs a-bove, And all th'an-gel-ic choirs a-bove.

CHORUS

Who is a par-d'ning God like Thee? Or who has grace so

rich and free? Or who has grace so rich and free? free?

13 Praise Ye the Lord, the Almighty

LOBE DEN HERREN

JOACHIM NEANDER, 1650-1680
Trans. by Catherine Winkworth, 1827-1878

From *Stralsund Gesangbuch*, 1665
Arr. in Crüger's *Praxis Pietatas Melica*, 1668

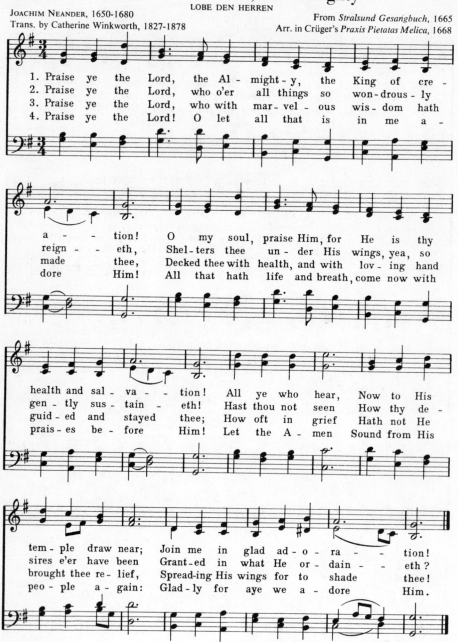

1. Praise ye the Lord, the Al - might - y, the King of cre -
a - - tion! O my soul, praise Him, for He is thy
health and sal - va - - tion! All ye who hear, Now to His
tem - ple draw near; Join me in glad ad - o - ra - - tion!

2. Praise ye the Lord, who o'er all things so won - drous - ly
reign - - eth, Shel - ters thee un - der His wings, yea, so
gen - tly sus - tain - eth! Hast thou not seen How thy de -
sires e'er have been Grant - ed in what He or - dain - - eth?

3. Praise ye the Lord, who with mar - vel - ous wis - dom hath
made thee, Decked thee with health, and with lov - ing hand
guid - ed and stayed thee; How oft in grief Hath not He
brought thee re - lief, Spread - ing His wings for to shade thee!

4. Praise ye the Lord! O let all that is in me a -
dore Him! All that hath life and breath, come now with
prais - es be - fore Him! Let the A - men Sound from His
peo - ple a - gain: Glad - ly for aye we a - dore Him.

God of Everlasting Glory

BRETON ROAD

JOHN W. PETERSON, 1921-

JOHN W. PETERSON, 1921-

1. God of ev-er-last-ing glo-ry, Fill-ing earth and sky,
2. As we push man's fron-tiers for-ward In-to out-er space,
3. In the o-pen book of na-ture Faith re-mains un-moved—
4. Thru the course of hu-man his-t'ry Has Thy pur-pose run,

Ev-'ry-where Thy won-ders o-pen To our search-ing eye:
Reach-ing for the stars and plan-ets, Still Thy hand we trace;
Pat-terns of the Mas-ter-Build-er By each fact are proved;
And in sub-stance have we seen Thee In Thy glo-rious Son:

In our tel-e-scop-ic prob-ing— Light years from our world,
In the lab-'ra-to-ry's si-lence, Where Thy se-crets hide,
So with rev-'rent hearts we pon-der All the grand de-sign
He it was who came to save us And our hopes to raise—

In the at-om's theo-ried struc-ture Sci-ence has un-furled.
There the mar-vels of cre-a-tion Are for us sup-plied.
Of the u-ni-verse a-round us, Wrought by hands di-vine.
God of ev-er-last-ing glo-ry, Thy great name we praise!

15 Brethren, We Have Met to Worship

HOLY MANNA

GEORGE ATKINS, 19th century

Attr. to William Moore, 19th century
in *Columbian Harmony*, 1825

1. Breth-ren, we have met to wor-ship And a-dore the Lord our God;
2. Breth-ren, see poor sin-ners round you Slum-b'ring on the brink of woe;
3. Sis-ters, will you join and help us? Mo-ses' sis-ter aid-ed him;
4. Let us love our God su-preme-ly, Let us love each oth-er too;

Will you pray with all your pow-er, While we try to preach the Word?
Death is com-ing, hell is mov-ing— Can you bear to let them go?
Will you help the trem-bling mour-ners Who are strugg-ling hard with sin?
Let us love and pray for sin-ners Till our God makes all things new.

All is vain un-less the Spir-it Of the Ho-ly One comes down;
See our fa-thers and our moth-ers And our chil-dren sink-ing down;
Tell them all a-bout the Sav-ior— Tell them that He will be found;
Then He'll call us home to heav-en, At His ta-ble we'll sit down;

Breth-ren, pray, and ho-ly man-na Will be show-ered all a-round.
Breth-ren, pray, and ho-ly man-na Will be show-ered all a-round.
Sis-ters, pray, and ho-ly man-na Will be show-ered all a-round.
Christ will gird Him-self and serve us With sweet man-na all a-round.

The Lord Is King!

ALL IS WELL

Norman Johnson, 1928-
Freely adapted from
Josiah Conder, 1789-1855

Adapted from J. T. White, 19th century
The Sacred Harp, 1844
Arr. by Norman Johnson, 1928-

1. The Lord is King! Lift up, lift up thy voice— Sing His praise, sing His praise!
2. The Lord is King! Let all His worth de-clare— Great is He, great is He!
3. The Lord is King! And bow to Him ye must— God is great, God is good!
4. The Lord is King! Thru-out His vast do-main He is all, all in all!

All heav'n and earth be-fore Him now re-joice— Sing His praise, sing His praise!
Bow to His will and trust His ten-der care— Great is He, great is He!
The Judge of all to all is ev-er just— God is great, God is good!
The Lord Je-ho-vah ev-er-more shall reign— He is all, all in all!

From world to world the joy shall ring, For He a-lone is God and King;
Nor mur-mur at His wise de-crees, Nor doubt His stead-fast prom-is-es;
Ho-ly and true are all His ways: Let ev-'ry crea-ture shout His praise;
Thru earth and heav'n one song shall ring, From grate-ful hearts this an-them spring:

From sky to sky His ban-ners fling— Sing His praise, sing His praise!
In hum-ble faith fall on thy knees— Great is He, great is He!
The Lord of Hosts, An-cient of Days— God is great, God is good!
A-rise, ye saints, sa-lute thy King— All thy days, sing His praise!

17
Come, Thou Fount

NETTLETON

ROBERT ROBINSON, 1735-1790

JOHN WYETH, 1770-1858
Arr. by Norman Johnson, 1928-

1. Come, Thou Fount of ev-'ry bless-ing, Tune my heart to sing Thy grace;
2. Here I raise mine Eb-en-e-zer— Hith-er by Thy help I'm come;
3. O to grace how great a debt-or Dai-ly I'm con-strained to be!

Streams of mer-cy, nev-er ceas-ing, Call for songs of loud-est praise.
And I hope by Thy good pleas-ure Safe-ly to ar-rive at home.
Let Thy good-ness like a fet-ter Bind my wan-d'ring heart to Thee:

Teach me some me-lo-dious son-net Sung by flam-ing tongues a-bove;
Je-sus sought me when a strang-er Wan-d'ring from the fold of God;
Prone to wan-der—Lord, I feel it— Prone to leave the God I love;

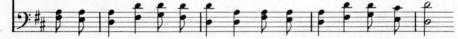

Praise the mount—I'm fixed up-on it— Mount of Thy re-deem-ing love.
He to res-cue me from dan-ger In-ter-posed His pre-cious blood.
Here's my heart— O take and seal it, Seal it for Thy courts a-bove.

Effective with other tunes of 87. 87. D. meter.

Now Thank We All Our God

NUN DANKET

Martin Rinkart, 1586-1649
Trans. by Catherine Winkworth, 1827-1878

Johann Crüger, 1598-1662
Arr. by Eldon Burkwall, 1928-

1. Now thank we all our God With hearts and hands and voic - es,
2. O may this boun-teous God Thru all our life be near us,
3. All praise and thanks to God The Fa - ther now be giv - en,

Who won-drous things hath done, In whom His world re - joic - es;
With ev - er joy - ful hearts And bless - ed peace to cheer us;
The Son and Him who reigns With Them in high-est heav - en—

Who from our moth - ers' arms Hath blessed us on our way
And keep us in His grace, And guide us when per - plexed,
The one e - ter - nal God Whom earth and heav'n a - dore—

With count - less gifts of love, And still is ours to - day.
And free us from all ills In this world and the next.
For thus it was, is now, And shall be ev - er - more.

19   The God of Abraham Praise

LEONI

Thomas Olivers, 1725-1799
Based on the revised *Yigdal*
of Daniel ben Judah, 14th century

From a Hebrew melody
Arr. by Meyer Lyon (Leoni), 1751-1797

1. The God of A-braham praise, Who reigns en-throned a - bove,
2. The God of A-braham praise, At whose su-preme com-mand
3. He by Him-self hath sworn— I on His oath de - pend;
4. The whole tri - um-phant host Give thanks to God on high;

An - cient of ev - er - last-ing days, And God of love.
From earth I rise and seek the joys At His right hand.
I shall, on ea - gles' wings up-borne, To heav'n as - cend.
"Hail, Fa - ther, Son and Ho - ly Ghost!" They ev - er cry.

Je - ho - vah, great I AM, By earth and heav'n con - fessed,
I all on earth for - sake, Its wis - dom, fame and pow'r,
I shall be - hold His face, I shall His pow'r a - dore,
Hail, A-braham's God and mine! I join the heav'n - ly lays;

I bow and bless the sa - cred Name For - ev - er blest.
And Him my on - ly por - tion make, My shield and tow'r.
And sing the won-ders of His grace For - ev - er - more.
All might and maj - es - ty are Thine, And end - less praise.

We Praise Thee, O God, Our Redeemer

20

KREMSER

JULIA C. CORY, 1882-1963

Netherlands melody, before 1625
Arr. by Edward Kremser, 1838-1914

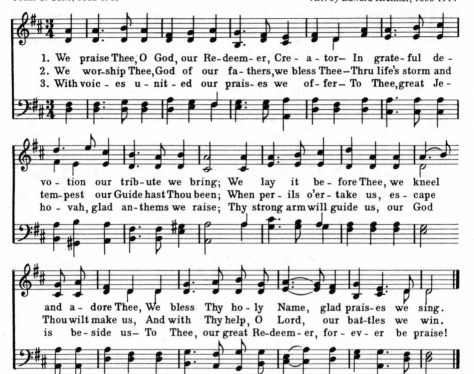

1. We praise Thee, O God, our Re-deem-er, Cre-a-tor— In grate-ful de-vo-tion our trib-ute we bring; We lay it be-fore Thee, we kneel and a-dore Thee, We bless Thy ho-ly Name, glad prais-es we sing.

2. We wor-ship Thee, God of our fa-thers, we bless Thee—Thru life's storm and tem-pest our Guide hast Thou been; When per-ils o'er-take us, es-cape Thou wilt make us, And with Thy help, O Lord, our bat-tles we win.

3. With voic-es u-nit-ed our prais-es we of-fer— To Thee, great Je-ho-vah, glad an-thems we raise; Thy strong arm will guide us, our God is be-side us— To Thee, our great Re-deem-er, for-ev-er be praise!

We Gather Together

21

Netherlands folk song, before 1625
Trans. by Theodore Baker, 1851-1934

To be sung to the above tune

1. We gather together to ask the Lord's blessing,
   He chastens and hastens His will to make known;
   The wicked oppressing now cease from distressing:
   Sing praises to His name— He forgets not His own.

2. Beside us to guide us, our God with us joining,
   Ordaining, maintaining His kingdom divine;
   So from the beginning the fight we were winning:
   Thou, Lord, was at our side— all glory be Thine!

3. We all do extol Thee, Thou Leader triumphant,
   And pray that Thou still our defender wilt be;
   Let Thy congregation escape tribulation:
   Thy name be ever praised! O Lord, make us free!

22

Ancient of Days

ANCIENT OF DAYS

William C. Doane, 1832-1913

J. Albert Jeffery, 1855-1929

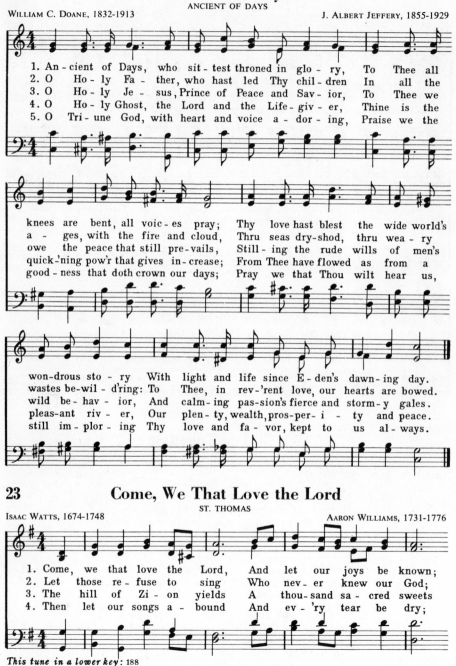

1. An - cient of Days, who sit - test throned in glo - ry, To Thee all
2. O Ho - ly Fa - ther, who hast led Thy chil - dren In all the
3. O Ho - ly Je - sus, Prince of Peace and Sav - ior, To Thee we
4. O Ho - ly Ghost, the Lord and the Life - giv - er, Thine is the
5. O Tri - une God, with heart and voice a - dor - ing, Praise we the

knees are bent, all voic - es pray; Thy love hast blest the wide world's
a - ges, with the fire and cloud, Thru seas dry-shod, thru wea - ry
owe the peace that still pre - vails, Still - ing the rude wills of men's
quick - 'ning pow'r that gives in - crease; From Thee have flowed as from a
good - ness that doth crown our days; Pray we that Thou wilt hear us,

won-drous sto - ry With light and life since E - den's dawn - ing day.
wastes be - wil - d'ring: To Thee, in rev - 'rent love, our hearts are bowed.
wild be - hav - ior, And calm - ing pas - sion's fierce and storm - y gales.
pleas-ant riv - er, Our plen - ty, wealth, pros - per - i - ty and peace.
still im - plor - ing Thy love and fa - vor, kept to us al - ways.

23

Come, We That Love the Lord

ST. THOMAS

Isaac Watts, 1674-1748

Aaron Williams, 1731-1776

1. Come, we that love the Lord, And let our joys be known;
2. Let those re - fuse to sing Who nev - er knew our God;
3. The hill of Zi - on yields A thou-sand sa - cred sweets
4. Then let our songs a - bound And ev - 'ry tear be dry;

This tune in a lower key: 188

Come, We That Love the Lord

Join in a song with sweet ac-cord, And thus sur-round the throne.
But chil-dren of the heav'n-ly King May speak their joys a-broad.
Be-fore we reach the heav'n-ly fields Or walk the gold-en streets.
We're march-ing thru Em-man-uel's ground To fair-er worlds on high.

We Magnify Our Father God 24

MONTROSE

DAVID GEORGE BALL, 1936-   JOHN W. PETERSON, 1921-

1. We mag-ni-fy our Fa-ther God With songs of thought-ful praise; As
2. We glo-ri-fy the Ho-ly Ghost For fel-low-ship and aid; In

grate-ful chil-dren we con-fess How per-fect are His ways. We wor-ship
chang-ing times we find our-selves Se-cure and un-a-fraid. The love of

Je-sus Christ our Lord Who saw our sin and pain And with the Great Phy-
God will nev-er change Thru-out e-ter-ni-ty; In rev-'rence and

CODA

si-cian's skill Re-stored our health a-gain.
thank-ful-ness We bless the Trin-i-ty! We bless the Trin-i-ty!

25

The Great Creator

LANDGRAF

DAVID GEORGE BALL, 1936-

JOHN H. LANDGRAF, 1937-

1. How I praise the great Cre - a - tor, Who did make this world so fair;
2. In the steep and on the hill - top, There I find His roy - al throne;
3. Ti - ny bud and love - ly flow - er, All the fra - grant bloom of spring,
4. Bub-bling spring and swirl-ing riv - er, Lap-ping lake and toss - ing sea,
5. How I praise the great Cre - a - tor, Who did make this world so fair;

As I scan the realm of na - ture I can see His im - age there.
And the God who made the moun-tain Ev - er loves me as His own.
Show the sweet-ness and the beau-ty Of my Sov-'reign and my King.
All de - clare the might and great-ness Of the One who cares for me.
For I too am His cre - a - tion, And I love Him for His care.

26

Rejoice, Ye Pure in Heart

MARION

EDWARD H. PLUMPTRE, 1821-1891

ARTHUR H. MESSITER, 1834-1916

1. Re - joice, ye pure in heart, Re - joice, give thanks and sing;
2. Bright youth and snow-crowned age, Strong men and maid - ens meek,
3. With voice as full and strong As o - cean's surg-ing praise,
4. With all the an - gel choirs, With all the saints on earth,
5. Still lift your stand-ard high, Still march in firm ar - ray,

Your fes - tal ban-ner wave on high, The cross of Christ your King:
Raise high your free, ex - ult - ing song, God's won-drous prais - es speak:
Send forth the hymns our fa - thers loved, The psalms of an - cient days:
Pour out the strains of joy and bliss, True rap - ture, no - blest mirth:
As war-riors thru the dark - ness toil Till dawns the gold - en day:

REFRAIN

Rejoice, Ye Pure in Heart

Re - joice, re - joice, Re - joice, give thanks and sing.

Re - joice, re - joice,

I Sing the Mighty Power of God 27

ELLACOMBE

Isaac Watts, 1674-1748 — alt.

From *Gesangbuch der Herzogl,*
Württemberg, 1784

1. I sing the might-y pow'r of God That made the moun-tains rise,
2. I sing the good-ness of the Lord That filled the earth with food;
3. There's not a plant or flow'r be - low But makes Thy glo - ries known;

That spread the flow-ing seas a - broad And built the loft - y skies.
He formed the crea-tures with His word And then pro-nounced them good.
And clouds a - rise and tem-pests blow By or - der from Thy throne;

I sing the wis - dom that or - dained The sun to rule the day;
Lord, how Thy won-ders are dis-played Wher- e'er I turn my eye:
While all that bor-rows life from Thee Is ev - er in Thy care,

The moon shines full at His com-mand, And all the stars o - bey.
If I sur - vey the ground I tread Or gaze up - on the sky!
And ev - 'ry - where that man can be, Thou, God, art pres - ent there.

This tune in a lower key: 107

28 Holy God, We Praise Thy Name

GROSSER GOTT

Te Deum, c. 4th century
Attr. to Ignace Franz, 1719-1790
Trans. by Clarence Walworth, 1820-1900

From *Katholisches Gesangbuch*,
Vienna, c. 1774

1. Ho - ly God, we praise Thy name—
   All on earth Thy scep - ter claim,

2. Hark, the loud ce - les - tial hymn
   Cher - u - bim and Ser - a - phim,

3. Lo, the ap - os - tol - ic train
   Proph-ets swell the glad re-frain,

4. Ho - ly Fa - ther, Ho - ly Son,
   While in es - sence on - ly One,

Lord of all, we bow be - fore Thee!
All in heav'n a - bove a - dore Thee:
An - gel choirs a - bove are rais - ing;
In un - ceas - ing cho - rus prais-ing,
Joins Thy sa - cred name to hal - low;
And the white-robed mar - tyrs fol - low;
Ho - ly Spir - it, Three we name Thee;
Un - di - vid - ed God we claim Thee,

In - fi - nite Thy vast do-main,
Fill the heav'ns with sweet ac - cord,
And, from morn to set of sun,
And a - dor - ing bend the knee,

Ev - er - last - ing is Thy reign.
Ho - ly, ho - ly, ho - ly Lord!
Thru the Church the song goes on.
While we sing our praise to Thee.

29 Praise the Lord! Ye Heavens, Adore Him

LEDO

From Psalm 148
Foundling Hospital Collection, 1796

JOHN W. PETERSON, 1921-

1. Praise the Lord! ye heav'ns, a - dore Him—Praise Him, an-gels in the height;
   Sun and moon, re - joice be - fore Him—Praise Him, all ye stars of . . . light.

2. Praise the Lord! for He is glo-rious—Nev - er shall His prom-ise fail;
   God hath made His saints vic - to-rious—Sin and death shall not pre - - vail.

Praise the Lord! for He hath spo-ken—Worlds His might-y voice o - beyed;
Praise the God of our sal - va-tion! Hosts on high, His pow'r pro-claim;

Alternate tune: HYFRYDOL — 84

Praise the Lord! Ye Heavens, Adore Him

Laws which nev-er can be bro-ken For their guid-ance He hath made.
Heav'n and earth and all cre-a-tion, Laud and mag-ni-fy His name!

Bless the Lord
30

JOHN W. PETERSON, 1921-
Chorus — Psalm 103:1

JOHN W. PETERSON, 1921-

1. Bless the Lord and sing His prais-es, Bless the Lord now, O my soul;
2. Bless the Lord for love vic-to-rious, Love that con-quered on the tree;
3. Bless the Lord, He walks be-side me And He lights the path be-fore;
4. Bless the Lord for truth He's giv-en— For the word of proph-e-cy

Join the song all heav-en rais-es, Let the an-them loud-ly roll!
For His grace so great and glo-rious Flow-ing out from Cal-va-ry.
Ev-'ry need is now sup-plied me From His boun-teous heav'n-ly store.
That has drawn the veil from heav-en And re-vealed my des-ti-ny.

CHORUS

Bless the Lord, O my soul, Bless the Lord, O my soul; Bless the

Lord, O my soul, And all that is with-in me Bless His ho-ly name.

31 All Creatures of Our God and King

LASST UNS ERFREUEN

Francis of Assisi, 1182-1226
Trans. by William H. Draper, 1855-1933

From *Geistliche Kirchengesäng*, 1623
Arr. by Norman Johnson, 1928-

1. All creatures of our God and King, Lift up your voice and with us sing Alleluia, Alleluia! Thou burning sun with golden beam, Thou silver moon with softer gleam: O praise Him! O praise Him! Alleluia, Alleluia, Alleluia!
2. Thou rushing wind that art so strong, Ye clouds that sail in heav'n along, O praise Him! Alleluia! Thou rising morn, in praise rejoice, Ye lights of evening, find a voice: O praise Him! O praise Him! Alleluia, Alleluia, Alleluia!
3. Dear mother earth, who day by day Unfoldest blessings on our way, O sing ye! Alleluia! The flow'rs and fruits that in thee grow, Let them His glory also show: O praise Him! O praise Him! Alleluia, Alleluia, Alleluia!
4. And all ye men of tender heart, Forgiving others, take your part, O sing ye! Alleluia! Ye who long pain and sorrow bear, Praise God and on Him cast your care: O praise Him! O praise Him! Alleluia, Alleluia, Alleluia!
5. Let all things their Creator bless, And worship Him in humbleness, O praise Him! Alleluia! Praise, praise the Father, praise the Son, And praise the Spirit, Three in One: O praise Him! O praise Him! Alleluia, Alleluia, Alleluia!

Praise God, from whom all blessings flow, Praise Him, all creatures here below, Alleluia, Alleluia! Praise Him above, ye heav'nly host, Praise Father, Son and Holy Ghost: Alleluia, Alleluia! Alleluia! Alleluia, Alleluia! Alleluia!

Blessed Be the Name

W. H. CLARK, 19th century
Chorus — Ralph E. Hudson, 1843-1901

RALPH E. HUDSON, 1843-1901
Arr. by William J. Kirkpatrick, 1838-1921

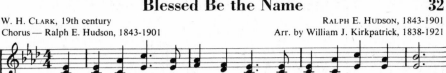

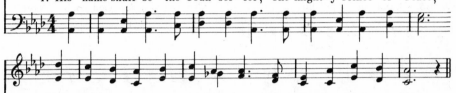

1. All praise to Him who reigns a-bove In maj-es-ty su-preme,
2. His name a-bove all names shall stand, Ex-alt-ed more and more,
3. Re-deem-er, Sav-ior, Friend of man Once ru-ined by the fall,
4. His name shall be the Coun-sel-lor, The might-y Prince of Peace,

Who gave His Son for man to die, That He might man re-deem!
At God the Fa-ther's own right hand, Where an-gel-hosts a-dore.
Thou hast de-vised sal-va-tion's plan, For Thou hast died for all.
Of all earth's king-doms Con-quer-or, Whose reign shall nev-er cease.

CHORUS

Bless-ed be the name, bless-ed be the name, Bless-ed be the name of the Lord! Bless-ed be the name, bless-ed be the name, Bless-ed be the name of the Lord!

33 ## Stand Up and Bless the Lord

ALTUS

JAMES MONTGOMERY, 1771-1854

JOHN WILLARD, 1921-

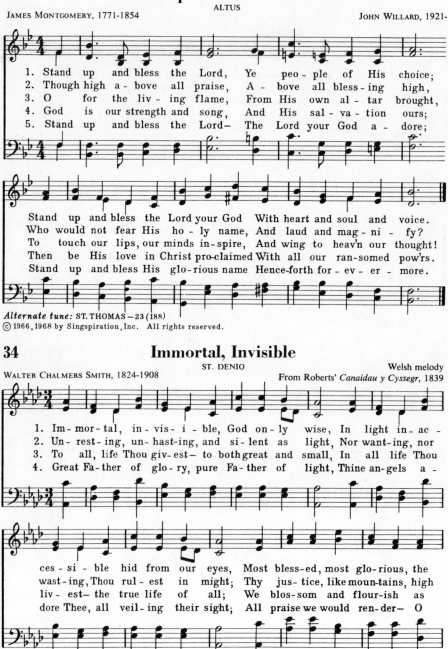

1. Stand up and bless the Lord, Ye peo - ple of His choice;
2. Though high a - bove all praise, A - bove all bless - ing high,
3. O for the liv - ing flame, From His own al - tar brought,
4. God is our strength and song, And His sal - va - tion ours;
5. Stand up and bless the Lord— The Lord your God a - dore;

Stand up and bless the Lord your God With heart and soul and voice.
Who would not fear His ho - ly name, And laud and mag - ni - fy?
To touch our lips, our minds in - spire, And wing to heav'n our thought!
Then be His love in Christ pro-claimed With all our ran-somed pow'rs.
Stand up and bless His glo-rious name Hence-forth for - ev - er - more.

Alternate tune: ST.THOMAS — 23 (188)

34 ## Immortal, Invisible

ST. DENIO

WALTER CHALMERS SMITH, 1824-1908

Welsh melody
From Roberts' *Canaidau y Cyssegr,* 1839

1. Im - mor - tal, in - vis - i - ble, God on - ly wise, In light in - ac -
2. Un - rest - ing, un - hast-ing, and si - lent as light, Nor want-ing, nor
3. To all, life Thou giv - est— to both great and small, In all life Thou
4. Great Fa - ther of glo - ry, pure Fa - ther of light, Thine an - gels a -

ces - si - ble hid from our eyes, Most bless-ed, most glo - rious, the
wast - ing, Thou rul - est in might; Thy jus - tice, like moun-tains, high
liv - est— the true life of all; We blos-som and flour-ish as
dore Thee, all veil - ing their sight; All praise we would ren-der— O

Alternate tune: FOUNDATION — 268

Immortal, Invisible

An-cient of Days, Al-might-y, vic-to-rious— Thy great name we praise.
soar-ing a-bove Thy clouds,which are foun-tains of good-ness and love.
leaves on the tree, And with-er and per-ish— but naught chang-eth Thee.
help us to see 'Tis on-ly the splen-dor of light hid-eth Thee!

Praise, My Soul, the King of Heaven   **35**

ZION

From Psalm 103
HENRY F. LYTE, 1793-1847   THOMAS HASTINGS, 1784-1872

1. { Praise, my soul, the King of heav-en, To His feet thy trib-ute bring;
    { Ran-somed,healed,re-stored,for-giv-en, Ev-er-more His prais-es sing:

2. { Fa-ther-like, He tends and spares us, Well our fee-ble frame He knows;
    { In His hands He gen-tly bears us, Res-cues us from all our foes:

3. { An-gels in the height, a-dore Him, Ye be-hold Him face to face;
    { Sun and moon,bow down be-fore Him, Dwellers all in time and space:

Al-le-lu-ia! Praise the Ev-er-last-ing King!
Al-le-lu-ia! Wide-ly yet His mer-cy flows!
Al-le-lu-ia! Praise with us the God of grace!

Al-le-lu-ia! Praise the Ev-er-last-ing King!
Al-le-lu-ia! Wide-ly yet His mer-cy flows!
Al-le-lu-ia! Praise with us the God of grace!

Alternate tunes: CWM RHONDDA—291, REGENT SQUARE—99 (both require adaptation of text)

36 A Mighty Fortress Is Our God

EIN' FESTE BURG

MARTIN LUTHER, 1483-1546
Trans. by Frederick H. Hedge, 1805-1890

MARTIN LUTHER, 1483-1546

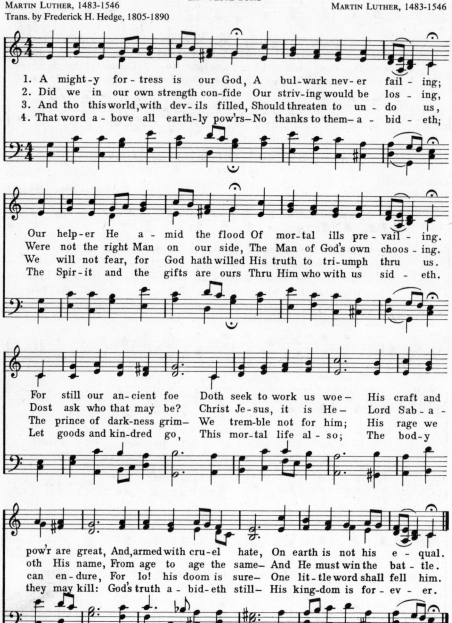

1. A might-y for-tress is our God, A bul-wark nev-er fail - ing;
2. Did we in our own strength con-fide Our striv-ing would be los - ing,
3. And tho this world, with dev-ils filled, Should threaten to un - do us,
4. That word a - bove all earth-ly pow'rs— No thanks to them— a - bid - eth;

Our help-er He a - mid the flood Of mor-tal ills pre-vail - ing.
Were not the right Man on our side, The Man of God's own choos - ing.
We will not fear, for God hath willed His truth to tri-umph thru us.
The Spir-it and the gifts are ours Thru Him who with us sid - eth.

For still our an-cient foe Doth seek to work us woe— His craft and
Dost ask who that may be? Christ Je-sus, it is He— Lord Sab - a -
The prince of dark-ness grim— We trem-ble not for him; His rage we
Let goods and kin-dred go, This mor-tal life al - so; The bod-y

pow'r are great, And, armed with cru-el hate, On earth is not his e - qual.
oth His name, From age to age the same— And He must win the bat - tle.
can en-dure, For lo! his doom is sure— One lit-tle word shall fell him.
they may kill: God's truth a - bid-eth still— His king-dom is for - ev - er.

How Great Thou Art!

O STORE GUD

Carl Boberg, 1859-1940
Trans. by Stuart K. Hine, 1899-

Swedish melody
Arr. by Manna Music, Inc.

1. O Lord my God, when I in awe-some won-der Con-sid-er
2. When thru the woods and for-est glades I wan-der And hear the
3. And when I think that God, His Son not spar-ing, Sent Him to
4. When Christ shall come with shout of ac-cla-ma-tion And take me

all the worlds Thy hands have made, I see the stars, I hear the roll-ing
birds sing sweet-ly in the trees, When I look down from loft-y moun-tain
die, I scarce can take it in— That on the cross, my bur-den glad-ly
home, what joy shall fill my heart! Then I shall bow in hum-ble ad-o-

REFRAIN

thun-der, Thy pow'r thru-out the un-i-verse dis-played!
gran-deur And hear the brook and feel the gen-tle breeze,
bear-ing, He bled and died to take a-way my sin!
ra-tion And there pro-claim, my God, how great Thou art!

Then sings my

soul, my Sav-ior God, to Thee; How great Thou art, how great Thou art! Then sings my

soul, my Sav-ior God, to Thee; How great Thou art, how great Thou art!

*Translator's original words are "works" and "mighty."

38

Joyful, Joyful, We Adore Thee

HYMN TO JOY

Henry van Dyke, 1852-1933

Melody from *Ninth Symphony*
Ludwig van Beethoven, 1770-1827

1. Joy-ful, joy-ful, we a-dore Thee, God of glo-ry, Lord of love;
2. All Thy works with joy sur-round Thee, Earth and heav'n re-flect Thy rays,
3. Thou art giv-ing and for-giv-ing, Ev-er bless-ing, ev-er blest,
4. Mor-tals, join the might-y cho-rus Which the morn-ing stars be-gan;

Hearts un-fold like flow'rs be-fore Thee, Hail Thee as the sun a-bove.
Stars and an-gels sing a-round Thee, Cen-ter of un-bro-ken praise;
Well-spring of the joy of liv-ing, O-cean-depth of hap-py rest!
Fa-ther-love is reign-ing o'er us, Broth-er-love binds man to man.

Melt the clouds of sin and sad-ness, Drive the dark of doubt a-way;
Field and for-est, vale and moun-tain, Bloss-'ming mea-dow, flash-ing sea,
Thou the Fa-ther, Christ our Broth-er— All who live in love are Thine:
Ev-er sing-ing, march we on-ward, Vic-tors in the midst of strife;

Giv-er of im-mor-tal glad-ness, Fill us with the light of day!
Chant-ing bird and flow-ing foun-tain Call us to re-joice in Thee.
Teach us how to love each oth-er, Lift us to the joy di-vine.
Joy-ful mu-sic lifts us sun-ward In the tri-umph song of life.

This Is My Father's World

TERRA BEATA

MALTBIE D. BABCOCK, 1858-1901

FRANKLIN L. SHEPPARD, 1852-1930
Arr. by Norman Johnson, 1928-

1. This is my Fa-ther's world, And to my list-'ning ears
2. This is my Fa-ther's world— The birds their car-ols raise;
3. This is my Fa-ther's world— O let me ne'er for-get

All na-ture sings, and round me rings The mu-sic of the spheres.
The morn-ing light, the lil-y white, De-clare their Mak-er's praise.
That tho the wrong seems oft so strong God is the Rul-er yet.

This is my Fa-ther's world! I rest me in the thought Of
This is my Fa-ther's world! He shines in all that's fair; In the
This is my Fa-ther's world! The bat-tle is not done; Je-

rocks and trees, of skies and seas— His hand the won-ders wrought.
rus-tling grass I hear Him pass— He speaks to me ev-'ry-where.
sus who died shall be sat-is-fied, And earth and heav'n be one.

40   # Great Is Thy Faithfulness

THOMAS O. CHISHOLM, 1866-1960   WILLIAM M. RUNYAN, 1870-1957

1. Great is Thy faith-ful-ness, O God my Fa-ther! There is no
2. Sum-mer and win-ter, and spring-time and har-vest, Sun, moon and
3. Par-don for sin and a peace that en-dur-eth, Thine own dear

shad-ow of turn-ing with Thee; Thou chang-est not, Thy com-
stars in their cours-es a-bove, Join with all na-ture in
pres-ence to cheer and to guide, Strength for to-day and bright

pas-sions, they fail not: As Thou hast been Thou for-ev-er wilt be.
man-i-fold wit-ness To Thy great faith-ful-ness, mer-cy and love.
hope for to-mor-row—Bless-ings all mine, with ten thou-sand be-side!

CHORUS

Great is Thy faith-ful-ness! Great is Thy faith-ful-ness! Morn-ing by

morn-ing new mer-cies I see; All I have need-ed Thy

Great Is Thy Faithfulness

hand hath pro-vid-ed— Great is Thy faith-ful-ness, Lord, un-to me!

Oh, He's a Wonderful Savior 41

JOHN W. PETERSON, 1921-

JOHN W. PETERSON, 1921-

1. Oh, He's a won-der-ful Sav-ior— Glo-ry to Him we as-cribe;
2. Oh, He's a won-der-ful Sav-ior— He nev-er leaves us a-lone;
3. Oh, He's a won-der-ful Sav-ior— Tho once re-ject-ed by men;

Oh, He's a won-der-ful Sav-ior— Who can His mer-cies de-scribe?
Oh, He's a won-der-ful Sav-ior— Gen-tly He cares for His own:
Oh, He's a won-der-ful Sav-ior— Some day He's com-ing a-gain:

Go-ing to dark Cal-va-ry, Dy-ing our death on the tree;
Gra-cious-ly meets ev-'ry need, Lis-tens and heeds when we plead;
Com-ing His glo-ry to show, Rule all the na-tions be-low;

Oh, He's a won-der-ful Sav-ior— Won-der-ful Sav-ior is He!
Oh, He's a won-der-ful Sav-ior— Won-der-ful Sav-ior in-deed!
Oh, He's a won-der-ful Sav-ior— Won-der-ful Sav-ior to know!

42

All Hail the Power

CORONATION

EDWARD PERRONET, 1726-1792
Alt. by John Rippon, 1751-1836

OLIVER HOLDEN, 1765-1844

1. All hail the pow'r of Je-sus' name! Let an-gels pros-trate fall;
2. Ye cho-sen seed of Is-rael's race, Ye ran-somed from the fall,
3. Let ev-'ry kin-dred, ev-'ry tribe, On this ter-res-trial ball,
4. O that with yon-der sa-cred throng We at His feet may fall!

Bring forth the roy-al di-a-dem, And crown Him Lord of all;
Hail Him who saves you by His grace, And crown Him Lord of all;
To Him all maj-es-ty as-cribe, And crown Him Lord of all;
We'll join the ev-er-last-ing song, And crown Him Lord of all;

Bring forth the roy-al di-a-dem, And crown Him Lord of all!
Hail Him who saves you by His grace, And crown Him Lord of all!
To Him all maj-es-ty as-cribe, And crown Him Lord of all!
We'll join the ev-er-last-ing song, And crown Him Lord of all!

43

Alternate tune

MILES LANE

WILLIAM SHRUBSOLE, 1760-1806

1. All hail the pow'r of Je-sus' name! Let an-gels prostrate fall; Bring forth the royal

di-a-dem, And crown Him, crown Him, crown Him, Crown Him Lord of all!

And Can It Be That I Should Gain?   44

SAGINA

CHARLES WESLEY, 1707-1788   THOMAS CAMPBELL, 1777-1844

1. And can it be that I should gain An in - t'rest in the
2. He left His Fa - ther's throne a - bove, So free, so in - fi -
3. No con-dem - na - tion now I dread, I am my Lord's and

Sav - ior's blood? Died He for me, who caused His pain? For me, who
ite His grace! Empt-ied Him-self of all but love, And bled for
He is mine; A - live in Him, my liv - ing Head, And clothed in

CHORUS

Him to death pur - sued?
Ad - am's help-less race.   A - maz-ing love! How can it be
right - eous-ness di - vine.

That Thou, my God, shouldst die for me? A - maz - ing love!
A - maz - ing love!

rit.

How can it be That Thou, my God, shouldst die for me?
How can it be That Thou, my God,

45   Ye Servants of God, Your Master Proclaim

LYONS

CHARLES WESLEY, 1707-1788   Arr. from J. MICHAEL HAYDN, 1737-1806

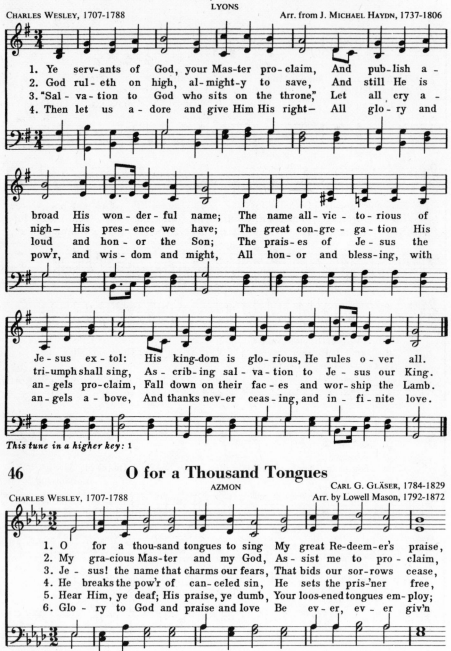

1. Ye serv-ants of God, your Mas-ter pro-claim, And pub-lish a-
2. God rul-eth on high, al-might-y to save, And still He is
3. "Sal-va-tion to God who sits on the throne," Let all cry a-
4. Then let us a-dore and give Him His right— All glo-ry and

broad His won-der-ful name; The name all-vic-to-rious of
nigh— His pres-ence we have; The great con-gre-ga-tion His
loud and hon-or the Son; The prais-es of Je-sus the
pow'r, and wis-dom and might, All hon-or and bless-ing, with

Je-sus ex-tol: His king-dom is glo-rious, He rules o-ver all.
tri-umph shall sing, As-crib-ing sal-va-tion to Je-sus our King.
an-gels pro-claim, Fall down on their fac-es and wor-ship the Lamb.
an-gels a-bove, And thanks nev-er ceas-ing, and in-fi-nite love.

This tune in a higher key: 1

46   O for a Thousand Tongues

AZMON

CHARLES WESLEY, 1707-1788   CARL G. GLÄSER, 1784-1829
      Arr. by Lowell Mason, 1792-1872

1. O for a thou-sand tongues to sing My great Re-deem-er's praise,
2. My gra-cious Mas-ter and my God, As-sist me to pro-claim,
3. Je-sus! the name that charms our fears, That bids our sor-rows cease,
4. He breaks the pow'r of can-celed sin, He sets the pris-'ner free,
5. Hear Him, ye deaf; His praise, ye dumb, Your loos-ened tongues em-ploy;
6. Glo-ry to God and praise and love Be ev-er, ev-er giv'n

O for a Thousand Tongues

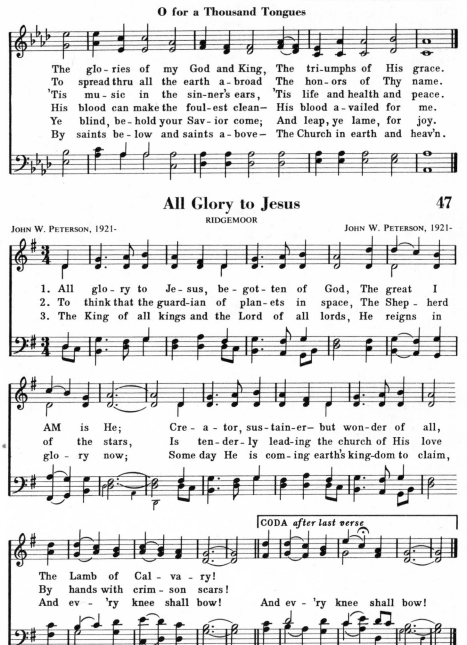

The glo - ries of my God and King, The tri-umphs of His grace.
To spread thru all the earth a - broad The hon - ors of Thy name.
'Tis mu - sic in the sin-ner's ears, 'Tis life and health and peace.
His blood can make the foul-est clean— His blood a - vailed for me.
Ye blind, be - hold your Sav - ior come; And leap, ye lame, for joy.
By saints be - low and saints a - bove— The Church in earth and heav'n.

All Glory to Jesus 47

RIDGEMOOR

JOHN W. PETERSON, 1921-   JOHN W. PETERSON, 1921-

1. All glo - ry to Je - sus, be - got - ten of God, The great I
2. To think that the guard-ian of plan-ets in space, The Shep - herd
3. The King of all kings and the Lord of all lords, He reigns in

AM is He; Cre - a - tor, sus - tain-er— but won-der of all,
of the stars, Is ten-der-ly lead-ing the church of His love
glo - ry now; Some day He is com-ing earth's king-dom to claim,

CODA after last verse

The Lamb of Cal - va - ry!
By hands with crim - son scars!
And ev - 'ry knee shall bow! And ev - 'ry knee shall bow!

48 His Matchless Worth

ARIEL

SAMUEL MEDLEY, 1738-1799

LOWELL MASON, 1792-1872
Possibly adapted from W. A. Mozart, 1756-1791

1. O could I speak the match-less worth, O could I
2. I'd sing the pre-cious blood He spilt, My ran-som
3. I'd sing the char-ac-ters He bears, And all the
4. Well, the de-light-ful day will come When my dear

sound the glo-ries forth Which in my Sav-ior shine, I'd
from the dread-ful guilt Of sin and wrath di-vine! I'd
forms of love He wears, Ex-alt-ed on His throne: In
Lord will bring me home And I shall see His face; Then

soar and touch the heav'n-ly strings, And vie with Ga-briel while he sings
sing His glo-rious right-eous-ness, In which all-per-fect heav'n-ly dress
loft-iest songs of sweet-est praise, I would to ev-er-last-ing days
with my Sav-ior, Broth-er, Friend, A blest e-ter-ni-ty I'll spend,

In notes al-most di-vine, In notes al-most di-vine.
My soul shall ev-er shine, My soul shall ev-er shine.
Make all His glo-ries known, Make all His glo-ries known.
Tri-um-phant in His grace, Tri-um-phant in His grace.

Our Great Savior

HYFRYDOL

J. WILBUR CHAPMAN, 1859-1918

ROWLAND W. PRICHARD, 1811-1887
Arr. by Robert Harkness, 1880-1961

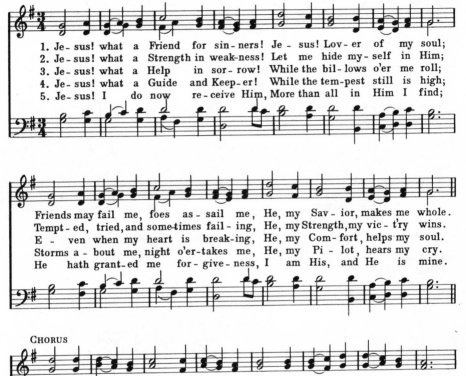

1. Je- sus! what a Friend for sin-ners! Je- sus! Lov- er of my soul;
2. Je- sus! what a Strength in weak-ness! Let me hide my- self in Him;
3. Je- sus! what a Help in sor- row! While the bil- lows o'er me roll;
4. Je- sus! what a Guide and Keep-er! While the tem-pest still is high;
5. Je- sus! I do now re- ceive Him, More than all in Him I find;

Friends may fail me, foes as - sail me, He, my Sav- ior, makes me whole.
Tempt- ed, tried, and some-times fail - ing, He, my Strength, my vic- t'ry wins.
E - ven when my heart is break-ing, He, my Com- fort, helps my soul.
Storms a - bout me, night o'er-takes me, He, my Pi - lot, hears my cry.
He hath grant-ed me for- give- ness, I am His, and He is mine.

CHORUS

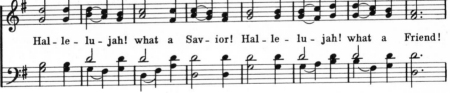

Hal - le - lu - jah! what a Sav - ior! Hal - le - lu - jah! what a Friend!

Sav - ing, help-ing, keep-ing, lov - ing, He is with me to the end.

50

Fairest Lord Jesus!

CRUSADERS' HYMN

From *Münster Gesangbuch*, 1677
4th vs. trans. by Joseph A. Seiss, 1823-1904

From *Schlesische Volkslieder*, 1842
Adapted by Richard S. Willis, 1819-1900

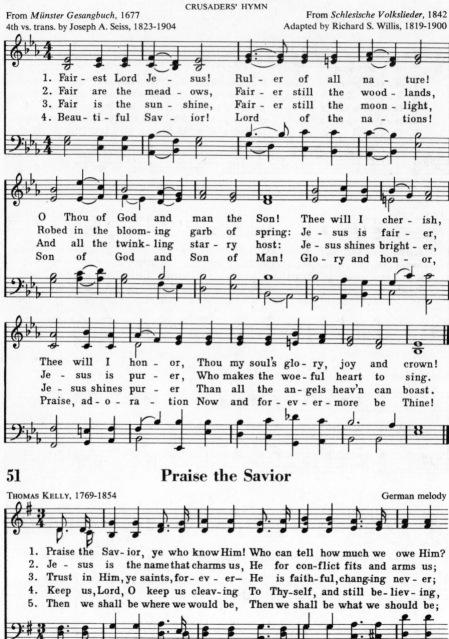

1. Fair - est Lord Je - sus! Rul - er of all na - ture!
2. Fair are the mead - ows, Fair - er still the wood - lands,
3. Fair is the sun - shine, Fair - er still the moon - light,
4. Beau - ti - ful Sav - ior! Lord of the na - tions!

O Thou of God and man the Son! Thee will I cher - ish,
Robed in the bloom - ing garb of spring: Je - sus is fair - er,
And all the twink - ling star - ry host: Je - sus shines bright - er,
Son of God and Son of Man! Glo - ry and hon - or,

Thee will I hon - or, Thou my soul's glo - ry, joy and crown!
Je - sus is pur - er, Who makes the woe - ful heart to sing.
Je - sus shines pur - er Than all the an - gels heav'n can boast.
Praise, ad - o - ra - tion Now and for - ev - er - more be Thine!

51

Praise the Savior

THOMAS KELLY, 1769-1854

German melody

1. Praise the Sav - ior, ye who know Him! Who can tell how much we owe Him?
2. Je - sus is the name that charms us, He for con - flict fits and arms us;
3. Trust in Him, ye saints, for - ev - er— He is faith - ful, chang - ing nev - er;
4. Keep us, Lord, O keep us cleav - ing To Thy - self, and still be - liev - ing,
5. Then we shall be where we would be, Then we shall be what we should be;

Praise the Savior

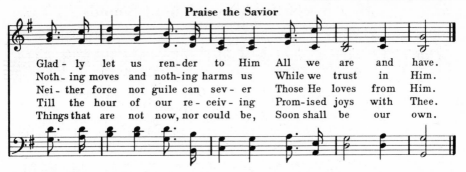

Glad - ly let us ren-der to Him All we are and have.
Noth _ ing moves and noth-ing harms us While we trust in Him.
Nei - ther force nor guile can sev - er Those He loves from Him.
Till the hour of our re - ceiv - ing Prom-ised joys with Thee.
Things that are not now, nor could be, Soon shall be our own.

Majestic Sweetness Sits Enthroned   52

ORTONVILLE

SAMUEL STENNETT, 1727-1795   THOMAS HASTINGS, 1784-1872

1. Ma - jes - tic sweet-ness sits en-throned Up - on the
2. No mor - tal can with Him com-pare A - mong the
3. He saw me plunged in deep dis - tress And flew to
4. To Him I owe my life and breath And all the

Sav - ior's brow; His head with ra - diant glo - ries crowned, His
sons of men; Fair - er is He than all the fair Who
my re - lief; For me He bore the shame-ful cross And
joys I have; He makes me tri - umph o - ver death And

lips with grace o'er - flow, His lips with grace o'er - flow.
fill the heav'n-ly train, Who fill the heav'n - ly train.
car - ried all my grief, And car - ried all my grief.
saves me from the grave, And saves me from the grave.

Another harmonization of this tune, in a lower key: 267

53   ## How Sweet the Name of Jesus Sounds

BRIDGEWATER

JOHN NEWTON, 1725-1807

JOHN W. PETERSON, 1921-

1. How sweet the name of Je - sus sounds In a be - liev - er's ear!
2. Dear name! the Rock on which I build, My Shield and Hid - ing - place,
3. Je - sus, my Shep-herd, Broth-er, Friend, My Proph-et, Priest and King,
4. Weak is the ef - fort of my heart, And cold my warm - est thought;
5. Till then I would Thy love pro - claim With ev - 'ry fleet - ing breath;

It soothes his sor - rows, heals his wounds, And drives a - way his fear.
My nev - er - fail - ing Treas-ury, filled With bound-less stores of grace.
My Lord, my Life, my Way, my End, Ac - cept the praise I bring.
But when I see Thee as Thou art, I'll praise Thee as I ought.
And may the mu - sic of Thy name Re - fresh my soul in death.

Alternate tunes: CAMPMEETING—273, ST. PETER—417

54   ## For the Beauty of the Earth

DIX

FOLLIOTT S. PIERPOINT, 1835-1917

CONRAD KOCHER, 1786-1872

1. For the beau - ty of the earth, For the glo - ry of the skies,
2. For the won - der of each hour Of the day and of the night,
3. For the joy of hu - man love, Broth-er, sis - ter, par - ent, child,
4. For Thy Church that ev - er - more Lift - eth ho - ly hands a - bove,

For the love which from our birth O - ver and a - round us lies:
Hill and vale and tree and flow'r, Sun and moon and stars of light:
Friends on earth and friends a - bove, For all gen - tle thoughts and mild:
Of - f'ring up on ev - 'ry shore Her pure sac - ri - fice of love:

This tune in a lower key: 96

For the Beauty of the Earth

Christ our God, to Thee we raise This our hymn of grate-ful praise.

Come, Christians, Join to Sing

MADRID

55

CHRISTIAN HENRY BATEMAN, 1813-1889

Source unknown
Arr. by Don Peterman, 1925-

1. Come, Chris-tians, join to sing— Al - le - lu - ia! A - men!
2. Come, lift your hearts on high— Al - le - lu - ia! A - men!
3. Praise yet our Christ a - gain— Al - le - lu - ia! A - men!

Loud praise to Christ our King— Al - le - lu - ia! A - men!
Let prais - es fill the sky— Al - le - lu - ia! A - men!
Life shall not end the strain— Al - le - lu - ia! A - men!

Let all, with heart and voice, Be - fore His throne re - joice;
He is our Guide and Friend, To us He'll con - de - scend;
On heav - en's bliss - ful shore His good-ness we'll a - dore,

Praise is His gra - cious choice: Al - le - lu - ia! A - men!
His love shall nev - er end: Al - le - lu - ia! A - men!
Sing - ing for - ev - er - more, "Al - le - lu - ia! A - men!"

56

I Am His and He Is Mine

EVERLASTING LOVE

WADE ROBINSON, 1838-1877

JAMES MOUNTAIN, 1844-1933

1. Loved with ev - er - last-ing love, Led by grace that love to know—
2. Heav'n a - bove is soft - er blue, Earth a - round is sweet - er green;
3. Things that once were wild a - larms Can - not now dis-turb my rest;
4. His for - ev - er, on - ly His— Who the Lord and me shall part?

Spir - it, breath-ing from a - bove, Thou hast taught me it is so!
Some-thing lives in ev - 'ry hue Christ-less eyes have nev - er seen!
Closed in ev - er - last - ing arms, Pil - lowed on the lov - ing breast!
Ah, with what a rest of bliss Christ can fill the lov - ing heart!

O this full and per-fect peace, O this trans-port all di - vine—
Birds with glad - der songs o'er - flow, Flow'rs with deep-er beau-ties shine,
O to lie for - ev - er here, Doubt and care and self re - sign,
Heav'n and earth may fade and flee, First-born light in gloom de - cline,

In a love which can-not cease, I am His and He is mine; He is mine.
Since I know, as now I know, I am His and He is mine; He is mine.
While He whis-pers in my ear— I am His and He is mine; He is mine.
But while God and I shall be, I am His and He is mine; He is mine.

Jesus, I Am Resting
TRANQUILLITY

JEAN SOPHIA PIGOTT, 1845-1882

JAMES MOUNTAIN, 1844-1933

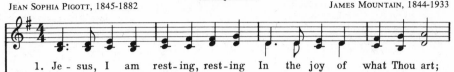

1. Je - sus, I am rest-ing, rest-ing In the joy of what Thou art;
2. Sim-ply trust-ing Thee, Lord Je-sus, I be-hold Thee as Thou art,
3. Ev- er lift Thy face up- on me As I work and wait for Thee;

CHORUS— *Je - sus, I am rest-ing, rest-ing In the joy of what Thou art;*

Fine

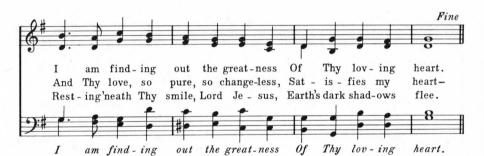

I am find - ing out the great-ness Of Thy lov - ing heart.
And Thy love, so pure, so change-less, Sat - is - fies my heart—
Rest - ing'neath Thy smile, Lord Je - sus, Earth's dark shad-ows flee.

I am find - ing out the great-ness Of Thy lov - ing heart.

Thou hast bid me gaze up - on Thee, And Thy beau-ty fills my soul,
Sat - is - fies its deep-est long-ings, Meets, sup-plies its ev - 'ry need,
Bright-ness of my Fa-ther's glo - ry, Sun-shine of my Fa-ther's face,

D. C.

For by Thy trans - form-ing pow-er Thou hast made me whole.
Com- pass-eth me round with bless-ings: Thine is love in - deed!
Keep me ev - er trust-ing, rest-ing, Fill me with Thy grace.

57

58 Jesus, the Very Thought of Thee

ST. AGNES

Attr. to Bernard of Clairvaux, 1091-1153
Trans. by Edward Caswall, 1814-1878

JOHN B. DYKES, 1823-1876

1. Je - sus, the ver - y thought of Thee With sweet-ness fills my breast;
2. Nor voice can sing, nor heart can frame, Nor can the mem - 'ry find
3. O hope of ev - 'ry con - trite heart, O joy of all the meek,
4. But what to those who find? Ah, this Nor tongue nor pen can show—
5. Je - sus, our on - ly joy be Thou, As Thou our prize wilt be;

But sweet - er far Thy face to see And in Thy pres - ence rest.
A sweet - er sound than Thy blest name, O Sav - ior of man - kind.
To those who fall how kind Thou art! How good to those who seek!
The love of Je - sus, what it is, None but His loved ones know.
Je - sus, be Thou our glo - ry now And thru e - ter - ni - ty.

This tune in a lower key: 158

59 The Great Physician

WILLIAM HUNTER, 1811-1877

JOHN H. STOCKTON, 1813-1877

1. The great Phy - si - cian now is near— The sym - pa - thiz - ing Je - sus;
2. Your man - y sins are all for-giv'n— O hear the voice of Je - sus;
3. All glo - ry to the dy - ing Lamb— I now be - lieve in Je - sus;
4. And when to that bright world a-bove We rise to be with Je - sus,

He speaks the droop-ing heart to cheer— O hear the voice of Je - sus!
Go on your way in peace to heav'n And wear a crown with Je - sus.
I love the bless - ed Sav-ior's name, I love the name of Je - sus.
We'll sing a - round the throne of love His name, the name of Je - sus.

The Great Physician

REFRAIN

Sweet-est note in ser-aph song, Sweet-est name on mor-tal tongue,

Sweet-est car-ol ev-er sung— Je-sus, bless-ed Je-sus!

Shepherd of Eager Youth 60

ITALIAN HYMN

CLEMENT OF ALEXANDRIA, c. 170 - c. 220
Trans. by Henry Martyn Dexter, 1821-1890

FELICE DE GIARDINI, 1716-1796
Arr. by Norman Johnson, 1928-

1. Shep-herd of ea-ger youth, Guid-ing in love and truth
2. Thou art our Ho-ly Lord, The all-sub-du-ing Word,
3. Ev-er be near our side, Our shep-herd and our guide,

Thru de-vious ways— Christ, our tri-um-phant King, We come Thy
Heal-er of strife; Thou didst Thy-self a-base That from sin's
Our staff and song; Je-sus, Thou Christ of God, By Thy en-

name to sing, Hith-er Thy chil-dren bring Trib-utes of praise.
deep dis-grace Thou might-est save our race And give us life.
dur-ing word Lead us where Thou hast trod, Make our faith strong.

Earliest known Christian hymn.
Another harmonization of this tune, in a higher key: 6
© 1966 by Singspiration, Inc. All rights reserved.

61 O the Deep, Deep Love of Jesus

EBENEZER

S. Trevor Francis, 1834-1925

Thomas J. Williams, 1869-1944

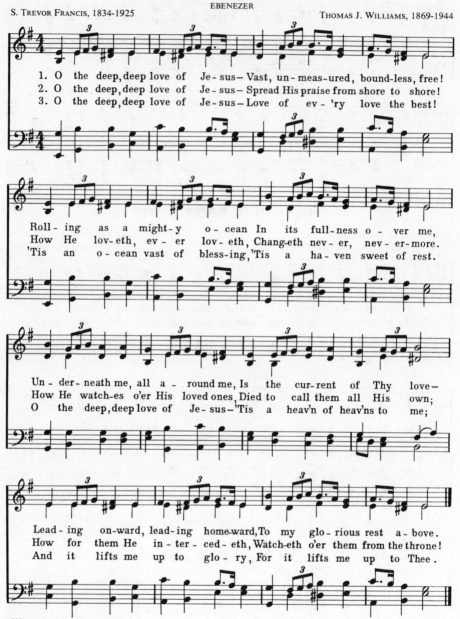

1. O the deep, deep love of Je-sus— Vast, un-meas-ured, bound-less, free!
2. O the deep, deep love of Je-sus— Spread His praise from shore to shore!
3. O the deep, deep love of Je-sus— Love of ev-'ry love the best!

Roll-ing as a might-y o-cean In its full-ness o-ver me,
How He lov-eth, ev-er lov-eth, Chang-eth nev-er, nev-er-more.
'Tis an o-cean vast of bless-ing, 'Tis a ha-ven sweet of rest.

Un-der-neath me, all a-round me, Is the cur-rent of Thy love—
How He watch-es o'er His loved ones, Died to call them all His own;
O the deep, deep love of Je-sus—'Tis a heav'n of heav'ns to me;

Lead-ing on-ward, lead-ing home-ward, To my glo-rious rest a-bove.
How for them He in-ter-ced-eth, Watch-eth o'er them from the throne!
And it lifts me up to glo-ry, For it lifts me up to Thee.

Alternate tunes: HOLY MANNA—15, HYFRYDOL—49, 84

Crown Him with Many Crowns

DIADEMATA

MATTHEW BRIDGES, 1800-1894
and GODFREY THRING, 1823-1903

GEORGE J. ELVEY, 1816-1893

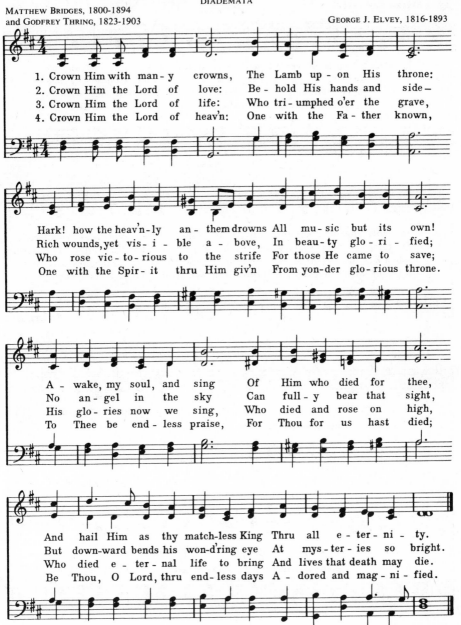

1. Crown Him with man - y crowns, The Lamb up - on His throne:
2. Crown Him the Lord of love: Be - hold His hands and side —
3. Crown Him the Lord of life: Who tri - umphed o'er the grave,
4. Crown Him the Lord of heav'n: One with the Fa - ther known,

Hark! how the heav'n-ly an - them drowns All mu - sic but its own!
Rich wounds, yet vis - i - ble a - bove, In beau - ty glo - ri - fied;
Who rose vic - to - rious to the strife For those He came to save;
One with the Spir - it thru Him giv'n From yon-der glo - rious throne.

A - wake, my soul, and sing Of Him who died for thee,
No an - gel in the sky Can full - y bear that sight,
His glo - ries now we sing, Who died and rose on high,
To Thee be end - less praise, For Thou for us hast died;

And hail Him as thy match-less King Thru all e - ter - ni - ty.
But down-ward bends his won-d'ring eye At mys - ter - ies so bright.
Who died e - ter - nal life to bring And lives that death may die.
Be Thou, O Lord, thru end - less days A - dored and mag - ni - fied.

This tune in a higher key: 403

63 Take the Name of Jesus with You

LYDIA BAXTER, 1809-1874

WILLIAM H. DOANE, 1832-1915

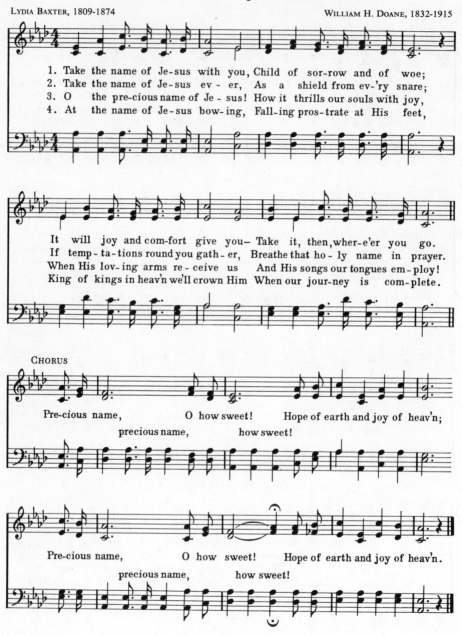

1. Take the name of Je-sus with you, Child of sor-row and of woe;
2. Take the name of Je-sus ev - er, As a shield from ev-'ry snare;
3. O the pre-cious name of Je - sus! How it thrills our souls with joy,
4. At the name of Je-sus bow-ing, Fall-ing pros-trate at His feet,

It will joy and com-fort give you— Take it, then, wher-e'er you go.
If temp-ta-tions round you gath-er, Breathe that ho - ly name in prayer.
When His lov-ing arms re - ceive us And His songs our tongues em-ploy!
King of kings in heav'n we'll crown Him When our jour-ney is com-plete.

CHORUS

Pre-cious name, O how sweet! Hope of earth and joy of heav'n;
precious name, how sweet!

Pre-cious name, O how sweet! Hope of earth and joy of heav'n.
precious name, how sweet!

The Name of Jesus

W. C. MARTIN, 19th century

EDMUND S. LORENZ, 1854-1942

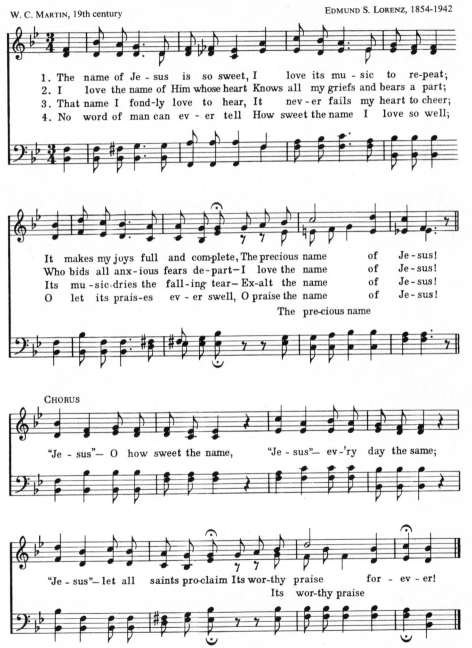

1. The name of Je - sus is so sweet, I love its mu - sic to re-peat;
2. I love the name of Him whose heart Knows all my griefs and bears a part;
3. That name I fond-ly love to hear, It nev - er fails my heart to cheer;
4. No word of man can ev - er tell How sweet the name I love so well;

It makes my joys full and com-plete, The precious name of Je - sus!
Who bids all anx-ious fears de-part—I love the name of Je - sus!
Its mu - sic dries the fall-ing tear—Ex-alt the name of Je - sus!
O let its prais-es ev - er swell, O praise the name of Je - sus!
The pre-cious name

CHORUS

"Je - sus"— O how sweet the name, "Je - sus"— ev - 'ry day the same;

"Je - sus"—let all saints pro-claim Its wor-thy praise for - ev - er!
Its wor-thy praise

65
Jesus! Jesus! Jesus!
LLANTHONY

Source unknown

From *Abbey Hymns*
Arr. by John W. Peterson, 1921-

1. Je - sus! Je - sus! Je - sus! Sing a - loud the name
2. Je - sus— name of cleans - ing, Wash - ing all our stains;
3. Je - sus— name of bold - ness, Mak - ing cow - ards brave;
4. Je - sus— name of beau - ty, Beau - ty far too bright
5. Je - sus— name of glad - ness Thru this vale of tears,

Till it soft - ly, slow - ly, Sets all hearts a - flame.
Je - sus— name of heal - ing, Balm for all our pains.
Name that in the bat - tle Cer - tain - ly must save.
For our earth-born fan - cy, For our mor - tal sight.
Till we reach the home - land And th' e - ter - nal years.

66
Jesus, Thou Joy of Loving Hearts
QUEBEC

Attr. to Bernard of Clairvaux, 1091-1153
Trans. by Ray Palmer, 1808-1887

HENRY BAKER, 1835-1910

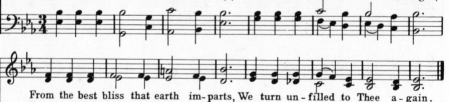

1. Je - sus, Thou Joy of lov - ing hearts, Thou Fount of life, Thou Light of men,
2. Thy truth un-changed hath ev - er stood, Thou sav-est those that on Thee call;
3. We taste Thee, O Thou liv - ing Bread, And long to feast up - on Thee still;
4. Our rest-less spir - its yearn for Thee, Where'er our changeful lot is cast:
5. O Je - sus, ev - er with us stay, Make all our mo-ments calm and bright;

From the best bliss that earth im-parts, We turn un-filled to Thee a - gain.
To them that seek Thee, Thou art good, To them that find Thee, all in all.
We drink of Thee, the Foun-tain-head, And thirst our souls from Thee to fill.
Glad when Thy gra - cious smile we see, Blest when our faith can hold Thee fast.
Chase the dark night of sin a - way, Shed o'er the world Thy ho - ly light.

How Can It Be?

AVIS B. CHRISTIANSEN, 1895-

JOHN W. PETERSON, 1921-

1. O Sav-ior, as my eyes be-hold The won-ders of Thy might un-told,
2. As at the cross I hum-bly bow And gaze up-on Thy thorn-crowned brow,
3. How can it be? How can it be? Was ev-er grace so full and free!

The heav'ns in glo-rious light ar-rayed, The vast cre-a-tion Thou hast made—
And view the pre-cious bleed-ing form By cru-el nails so bruised and torn,
From heights of bliss to depths of woe In lov-ing kind-ness Thou didst go,

And yet to think Thou lov-est me— My heart cries out, "How can it be?"
Know-ing Thy suf-f'ring was for me, In grief I cry, "How can it be?"
From sin and shame to res-cue me— O Love Di-vine, How can it be?

CHORUS

How can it be? How can it be? That

God should love a soul like me, O how can it be?

68 O Day of Rest and Gladness

MENDEBRAS

CHRISTOPHER WORDSWORTH, 1807-1885

German melody
Arr. by Lowell Mason, 1792-1872

1. O day of rest and glad-ness, O day of joy and light,
2. On thee, at the cre - a - tion, The light first had its birth;
3. To - day on wea - ry na - tions The heav'n-ly man-na falls;
4. New grac - es ev - er gain-ing From this our day of rest,

O balm of care and sad-ness, Most beau-ti - ful, most bright:
On thee, for our sal - va-tion, Christ rose from depths of earth;
To ho - ly con - vo - ca-tions The sil - ver trum-pet calls,
We reach the rest re - main-ing To spir-its of the blest.

On thee, the high and low-ly, Thru ag - es joined in tune,
On thee, our Lord, vic - to-rious, The Spir - it sent from heav'n;
Where Gos - pel light is glow-ing With pure and ra-diant beams,
To Ho - ly Ghost be prais-es, To Fa - ther, and to Son;

Sing "Ho - ly, Ho - ly, Ho - ly," To the great God Tri - une.
And thus on thee, most glo-rious, A tri - ple light was giv'n.
And liv - ing wa - ter flow-ing With soul-re - fresh-ing streams.
The Church her voice up - rais - es To Thee, blest Three in One.

Safely Through Another Week

SABBATH

JOHN NEWTON, 1725-1807 · LOWELL MASON, 1792-1872 · **69**

1. Safe-ly through an-oth-er week God has brought us on our way;
Let us now a bless-ing seek, Wait-ing in His courts to-day:
Day of all the week the best, Em-blem of e-ter-nal rest;
Day of all the week the best, Em-blem of e-ter-nal rest.

2. While we pray for par-d'ning grace Thru the dear Re-deem-er's name,
Show Thy rec-on-cil-ed face, Take a-way our sin and shame;
From our world-ly cares set free, May we rest this day in Thee;
From our world-ly cares set free, May we rest this day in Thee.

3. Here we come Thy name to praise— Let us feel Thy pres-ence near;
May Thy glo-ry meet our eyes While we in Thy house ap-pear:
Here af-ford us, Lord, a taste Of our ev-er-last-ing feast;
Here af-ford us, Lord, a taste Of our ev-er-last-ing feast.

4. May Thy gos-pel's joy-ful sound Con-quer sin-ners, com-fort saints;
May the fruits of grace a-bound, Bring re-lief for all com-plaints:
Thus may all our Sab-baths prove, Till we join the Church a-bove;
Thus may all our Sab-baths prove, Till we join the Church a-bove.

70

Holy, Holy, Holy

NICAEA

REGINALD HEBER, 1783-1826

JOHN B. DYKES, 1823-1876

1. Ho-ly, Ho-ly, Ho-ly, Lord God Al-might-y! Ear-ly in the
2. Ho-ly, Ho-ly, Ho-ly! All the saints a-dore Thee, Cast-ing down their
3. Ho-ly, Ho-ly, Ho-ly! Tho the dark-ness hide Thee, Tho the eye of
4. Ho-ly, Ho-ly, Ho-ly, Lord God Al-might-y! All Thy works shall

morn - ing our song shall rise to Thee; Ho-ly, Ho-ly, Ho - ly!
gold-en crowns a-round the glass-y sea; Cher-u-bim and ser-a-phim
sin-ful man Thy glo-ry may not see; On-ly Thou art ho-ly—
praise Thy name in earth and sky and sea; Ho-ly, Ho-ly, Ho - ly!

Mer - ci-ful and Might-y! God in Three Per-sons, bless-ed Trin-i-ty!
fall-ing down be-fore Thee, Which wert and art and ev-er-more shalt be.
there is none be-side Thee Per-fect in pow'r, in love and pur-i-ty.
Mer - ci-ful and Might-y! God in Three Per-sons, bless-ed Trin-i-ty!

71 Blessed Day of Rest and Cheer

SABBATSDAG

JOEL BLOMQVIST, 1840-1930
Trans. by Andrew L. Skoog, 1856-1934 — alt.

JOEL BLOMQVIST, 1840-1930
Arr. by Norman Johnson, 1928-

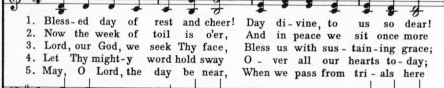

1. Bless-ed day of rest and cheer! Day di-vine, to us so dear!
2. Now the week of toil is o'er, And in peace we sit once more
3. Lord, our God, we seek Thy face, Bless us with sus-tain-ing grace;
4. Let Thy might-y word hold sway O-ver all our hearts to-day;
5. May, O Lord, the day be near, When we pass from tri-als here

Blessed Day of Rest and Cheer

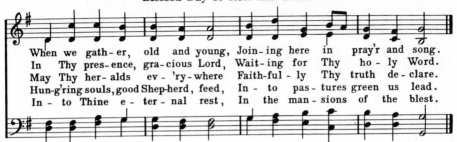

When we gath-er, old and young, Join-ing here in pray'r and song.
In Thy pres-ence, gra-cious Lord, Wait-ing for Thy ho-ly Word.
May Thy her-alds ev-'ry-where Faith-ful-ly Thy truth de-clare.
Hun-g'ring souls, good Shep-herd, feed, In-to pas-tures green us lead.
In-to Thine e-ter-nal rest, In the man-sions of the blest.

Still, Still with Thee 72

CONSOLATION

HARRIET B. STOWE, 1812-1896   FELIX MENDELSSOHN, 1809-1847

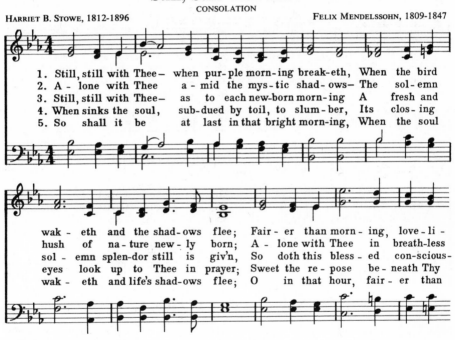

1. Still, still with Thee— when pur-ple morn-ing break-eth, When the bird
2. A-lone with Thee a-mid the mys-tic shad-ows— The sol-emn
3. Still, still with Thee— as to each new-born morn-ing A fresh and
4. When sinks the soul, sub-dued by toil, to slum-ber, Its clos-ing
5. So shall it be at last in that bright morn-ing, When the soul

wak-eth and the shad-ows flee; Fair-er than morn-ing, love-li-
hush of na-ture new-ly born; A-lone with Thee in breath-less
sol-emn splen-dor still is giv'n, So doth this bless-ed con-scious-
eyes look up to Thee in prayer; Sweet the re-pose be-neath Thy
wak-eth and life's shad-ows flee; O in that hour, fair-er than

er than day-light, Dawns the sweet con-scious-ness— I am with Thee!
ad-o-ra-tion, In the calm dew and fresh-ness of the morn!
ness, a-wak-ing, Breathe each day near-ness un-to Thee and heav'n!
wings o'er-shad-ing, But sweet-er still to wake and find Thee there!
day-light dawn-ing, Shall rise the glo-rious tho't— I am with Thee!

Alternate tune: O PERFECT LOVE—311

73 May Jesus Christ Be Praised

LAUDES DOMINI

German hymn, c. 1800
Trans. by Edward Caswall, 1814-1878

JOSEPH BARNBY, 1838-1896

1. When morn-ing gilds the skies, My heart a - wak - ing cries:
2. Does sad - ness fill my mind? A sol - ace here I find:
3. In heav'ns e - ter - nal bliss The love-liest strain is this:
4. Be this, while life is mine, My can - ti - cle di - vine:

May Je - sus Christ be praised! A - like at work and prayer
May Je - sus Christ be praised! Or fades my earth - ly bliss?
May Je - sus Christ be praised! The pow'rs of dark-ness fear
May Je - sus Christ be praised! Be this th'e - ter - nal song

To Je - sus I re - pair: May Je - sus Christ be praised!
My com - fort still is this: May Je - sus Christ be praised!
When this sweet chant they hear: May Je - sus Christ be praised!
Thru all the a - ges long: May Je - sus Christ be praised!

74 Now the Day Is Over

MERRIAL

SABINE BARING-GOULD, 1834-1924

JOSEPH BARNBY, 1838-1896

1. Now the day is o - ver, Night is draw - ing nigh;
2. Je - sus, give the wea - ry Calm and sweet re - pose;
3. Grant to lit - tle chil - dren Vi - sions bright of Thee;
4. Thru the long night-watch - es May Thine an - gels spread
5. When the morn - ing wak - ens, Then may I a - rise

Now the Day Is Over

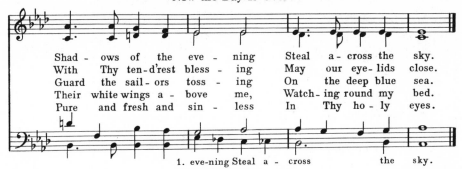

Shad - ows of the eve - ning Steal a - cross the sky.
With Thy ten-d'rest bless - ing May our eye- lids close.
Guard the sail- ors toss - ing On the deep blue sea.
Their white wings a - bove me, Watch- ing round my bed.
Pure and fresh and sin - less In Thy ho - ly eyes.

1. eve-ning Steal a - cross the sky.

Abide with Me
EVENTIDE

75

HENRY F. LYTE, 1793-1847

WILLIAM H. MONK, 1823-1889

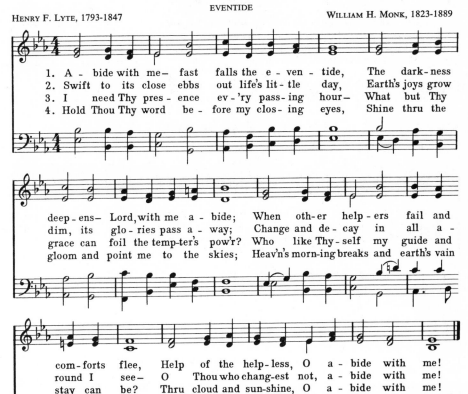

1. A - bide with me— fast falls the e - ven - tide, The dark-ness
2. Swift to its close ebbs out life's lit - tle day, Earth's joys grow
3. I need Thy pres - ence ev - 'ry pass - ing hour— What but Thy
4. Hold Thou Thy word be - fore my clos - ing eyes, Shine thru the

deep - ens— Lord, with me a - bide; When oth- er help - ers fail and
dim, its glo - ries pass a - way; Change and de - cay in all a -
grace can foil the temp-ter's pow'r? Who like Thy - self my guide and
gloom and point me to the skies; Heav'n's morn-ing breaks and earth's vain

com - forts flee, Help of the help- less, O a - bide with me!
round I see— O Thou who chang-est not, a - bide with me!
stay can be? Thru cloud and sun-shine, O a - bide with me!
shad - ows flee— In life, in death, O Lord, a - bide with me!

76 Savior, Breathe an Evening Blessing

EVENING PRAYER

JAMES EDMESTON, 1791-1867

GEORGE C. STEBBINS, 1846-1945

1. Sav - ior, breathe an eve-ning bless-ing Ere re-pose our spir-its seal:
2. Tho de - struc-tion walk a-round us, Tho the ar-rows past us fly,
3. Tho the night be dark and drear-y, Dark-ness can-not hide from Thee;
4. Should swift death this night o'er-take us And our couch be-come our tomb,

Sin and want we come con-fess-ing, Thou canst save, and Thou canst heal.
An-gel-guards from Thee sur-round us— We are safe if Thou art nigh.
Thou art He who, nev-er wea-ry, Watch-est where Thy peo-ple be.
May the morn in heav'n a-wake us, Clad in light and death-less bloom.

77 Sun of My Soul

HURSLEY

JOHN KEBLE, 1792-1866

From *Katholisches Gesangbuch,*
Vienna, c. 1774

1. Sun of my soul, Thou Sav-ior dear, It is not night if Thou be near;
2. When the soft dews of kind-ly sleep My wea-ry eye-lids gen-tly steep,
3. A - bide with me from morn till eve, For with-out Thee I can-not live;
4. Be near to bless me when I wake, Ere thru the world my way I take;

O may no earth-born cloud a - rise To hide Thee from Thy serv-ant's eyes!
Be my last thought, how sweet to rest For-ev-er on my Sav-ior's breast!
A-bide with me when night is nigh, For with-out Thee I dare not die.
A-bide with me till in Thy love I lose my-self in heav'n a-bove.

Day Is Dying in the West

78

CHAUTAUQUA

MARY A. LATHBURY, 1841-1913   WILLIAM F. SHERWIN, 1826-1888

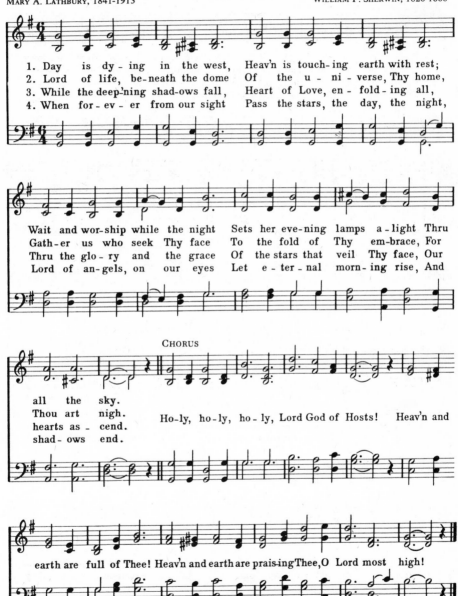

1. Day is dy-ing in the west, Heav'n is touch-ing earth with rest;
2. Lord of life, be-neath the dome Of the u-ni-verse, Thy home,
3. While the deep'-ning shad-ows fall, Heart of Love, en-fold-ing all,
4. When for-ev-er from our sight Pass the stars, the day, the night,

Wait and wor-ship while the night Sets her eve-ning lamps a-light Thru
Gath-er us who seek Thy face To the fold of Thy em-brace, For
Thru the glo-ry and the grace Of the stars that veil Thy face, Our
Lord of an-gels, on our eyes Let e-ter-nal morn-ing rise, And

CHORUS

all the sky.
Thou art nigh.
hearts as-cend.
shad-ows end.

Ho-ly, ho-ly, ho-ly, Lord God of Hosts! Heav'n and

earth are full of Thee! Heav'n and earth are prais-ing Thee, O Lord most high!

79 Softly Now the Light of Day

SEYMOUR

GEORGE W. DOANE, 1799-1859

CARL M. VON WEBER, 1786-1826

1. Soft - ly now the light of day Fades up - on my sight a - way;
2. Thou, whose all - per - vad - ing eye Naught es-capes—with-out, with- in,
3. Soon for me the light of day Shall for - ev - er pass a - way;
4. Thou who, sin - less, yet hast known All of man's in - firm - i - ty;

Free from care, from la - bor free, Lord, I would com-mune with Thee.
Par - don each in - firm - i - ty, O - pen fault and se - cret sin.
Then, from sin and sor - row free, Take me, Lord, to dwell with Thee.
Then, from Thine e - ter - nal throne, Je - sus, look with pity-ing eye.

Alternate tune: MERCY—165

80 Lord, Dismiss Us with Thy Blessing

SICILIAN MARINERS

Attr. to John Fawcett, 1740-1817 — alt.

From Tattersall's *Psalmody*, 1794

1. Lord, dis - miss us with Thy bless-ing, Fill our hearts with joy and peace;
2. Thanks we give and ad - o - ra - tion For Thy gos - pel's joy-ful sound;
3. So that when Thy love shall call us, Sav - ior, from the world a - way,

Let us each, Thy love pos - sess-ing, Tri - umph in re - deem-ing grace:
May the fruits of Thy sal - va - tion In our hearts and lives a - bound:
Fear of death shall not ap - pall us; Glad Thy sum-mons to o - bey,

This tune in a lower key: 152

Lord, Dismiss Us with Thy Blessing

O re - fresh us, O re - fresh us, Trav-'ling thru this wil - der - ness.
Ev - er faith-ful, ev - er faith-ful To the truth may we be found—
May we ev - er, may we ev - er Reign with Thee in end-less day.

Savior, Again to Thy Dear Name — 81

ELLERS

JOHN ELLERTON, 1826-1893

EDWARD J. HOPKINS, 1818-1901
Arr. by Eldon Burkwall, 1928-

1. Sav - ior, a - gain to Thy dear name we raise With one ac -
2. Grant us Thy peace up - on our home-ward way: With Thee be -
3. Grant us Thy peace, Lord, thru the com - ing night, Turn Thou for
4. Grant us Thy peace thru - out our earth-ly life, Our balm in

cord our part-ing hymn of praise; Once more we bless Thee ere our
gan, with Thee shall end the day; Guard Thou the lips from sin, the
us its dark-ness in - to light; From harm and dan - ger keep Thy
sor - row and our stay in strife; Then, when Thy voice shall bid our

wor - ship cease, Then, low- ly kneel-ing, wait Thy word of peace.
hearts from shame, That in this house have called up-on Thy name.
chil - dren free, For dark and light are both a - like to Thee.
con - flict cease, Call us, O Lord, to Thine e - ter - nal peace.

82 God Be with You

JEREMIAH E. RANKIN, 1828-1904

WILLIAM G. TOMER, 1833-1896

1. God be with you till we meet a-gain, By His coun-sels
2. God be with you till we meet a-gain, 'Neath His wings pro-
3. God be with you till we meet a-gain, When life's per-ils
4. God be with you till we meet a-gain, Keep love's ban-ner

guide, up-hold you, With His sheep se-cure-ly fold you—
tect-ing hide you, Dai-ly man-na still pro-vide you—
thick con-found you, Put His arms un-fail-ing round you—
float-ing o'er you; Smite death's threat'ning wave be-fore you—

CHORUS

God be with you till we meet a-gain. Till we meet, till we

meet, Till we meet at Je-sus' feet, till we meet, Till we

meet, till we meet— God be with you till we meet a-gain.

O Come, O Come, Emmanuel

VENI EMMANUEL

Latin hymn, 12th century
Trans. by John M. Neale, 1818-1866 — alt.

Plainsong, 13th century
Arr. by Eldon Burkwall, 1928-

Unison

1. O come, O come, Em - man - u - el, And ran-som cap - tive
2. O come, O come, Thou Lord of might, Who to Thy tribes, on
3. O come, Thou Rod of Jes - se, free Thine own from Sa - tan's
4. O come, Thou Day-spring, come and cheer Our spir - its by Thine
5. O come, Thou Key of Da - vid, come And o - pen wide our

Is - ra - el, That mourns in lone - ly ex - ile here
Si - nai's height, In an - cient times didst give the law
tyr - an - ny; From depths of hell Thy peo - ple save
ad - vent here; O drive a - way the shades of night
heav'n - ly home Where all Thy saints with Thee shall dwell—

REFRAIN
Parts

Un - til the Son of God ap - pear.
In cloud and maj - es - ty and awe.
And give them vic - t'ry o'er the grave.   Re - joice! re - joice!
And pierce the clouds and bring us light.
O come, O come, Em - man - u - el!

Em - man - u - el Shall come to thee, O Is - ra - el.

84 Come, Thou Long-Expected Jesus

HYFRYDOL

CHARLES WESLEY, 1707-1788

ROWLAND H. PRICHARD, 1811-1887
Arr. by Norman Johnson, 1928-

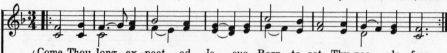

1. {Come, Thou long-ex-pect-ed Je-sus, Born to set Thy peo-ple free;
From our fears and sins re-lease us: Let us find our rest in Thee.

2. {Born Thy peo-ple to de-liv-er, Born a child and yet a King;
Born to reign in us for-ev-er; Now Thy gra-cious King-dom bring.

Is-rael's Strength and Con-so-la-tion, Hope of all the earth Thou art;
By Thine own e-ter-nal Spir-it Rule in all our hearts a-lone;

Dear De-sire of ev-'ry na-tion, Joy of ev-'ry long-ing heart.
By Thine all suf-fi-cient mer-it, Raise us to Thy glo-rious throne.

Another harmonization of this tune, in a higher key: 49

85 Silent Night! Holy Night!

STILLE NACHT

JOSEPH MOHR, 1792-1848
Trans. by John F. Young, 1820-1885

FRANZ GRÜBER, 1787-1863

1. Si-lent night! ho-ly night! All is calm, all is bright
2. Si-lent night! ho-ly night! Shep-herds quake at the sight;
3. Si-lent night! ho-ly night! Son of God, love's pure light

Silent Night! Holy Night!

Round yon vir - gin moth-er and Child, Ho - ly In - fant, so ten-der and mild —
Glo - ries stream from heav-en a - far, Heav'n-ly hosts sing al - le - lu - ia —
Ra - diant beams from Thy ho - ly face With the dawn of re - deem-ing grace —

Sleep in heav - en - ly peace, Sleep in heav - en - ly peace.
Christ the Sav - ior is born! Christ the Sav - ior is born!
Je - sus, Lord at Thy birth, Je - sus, Lord at Thy birth.

Away in a Manger 86

1-2 – Anonymous
3 – JOHN THOMAS McFARLAND, 1851-1913

JAMES R. MURRAY, 1841-1905
Arr. by Norman Johnson, 1928-

Unison

1. A - way in a man-ger, no crib for a bed, The lit - tle Lord
2. The cat - tle are low-ing, the Ba - by a - wakes, But lit - tle Lord
3. Be near me, Lord Je - sus, I ask Thee to stay Close by me for -

Je - sus laid down His sweet head; The stars in the sky looked
Je - sus, no cry - ing He makes; I love Thee, Lord Je - sus! look
ev - er, and love me, I pray; Bless all the dear chil - dren in

down where He lay, The lit - tle Lord Je - sus, a - sleep on the hay.
down from the sky, And stay by my cra - dle till morn - ing is nigh.
Thy ten - der care, And fit us for heav - en, to live with Thee there.

87

Joy to the World!

ANTIOCH

From Psalm 98
Isaac Watts, 1674-1748

Possibly adapted from G. F. Handel, 1685-1759
Arr. by Lowell Mason, 1792-1872

1. Joy to the world! the Lord is come! Let earth re-
2. Joy to the earth! the Sav-ior reigns! Let men their
3. No more let sins and sor-rows grow, Nor thorns in-
4. He rules the world with truth and grace, And makes the

ceive her King; Let ev-'ry heart pre-pare Him room,
songs em-ploy; While fields and floods, rocks, hills and plains
fest the ground; He comes to make His bless-ings flow
na-tions prove The glo-ries of His right-eous-ness,

And heav'n and na-ture sing, And heav'n and na-ture
Re-peat the sound-ing joy, Re-peat the sound-ing
Far as the curse is found, Far as the curse is
And won-ders of His love, And won-ders of His

1. And heav'n and na-ture sing, _____ And

sing, And heav'n, and heav'n and na-ture sing.
joy, Re-peat, re-peat the sound-ing joy.
found, Far as, far as the curse is found.
love, And won-ders, won-ders of His love.

heav'n and na-ture sing,

In a Cave

HAROLD B. FRANKLIN, 1889-1967

HAROLD B. FRANKLIN, 1889-1967

1. In a cave, a low-ly sta-ble, Christ our Lord was born;
2. Shep-herds heard the heav'n-ly cho-rus And were sore a-fraid;
3. "Born to you in Da-vid's cit-y Is your Lord and King—"
4. Leav-ing rest-ing flocks be-hind them, Sought they for the stall,
5. Let us, like the low-ly shep-herds, Seek the Lord this night,

From the heav-ens white-robed an-gels Sang that ho-ly morn.
But an an-gel spoke the ti-dings That all fears al-layed.
So an an-gel to the shep-herds Hope and joy did bring.
Where there lay, in swad-dling gar-ments, Christ, the hope of all.
That we may, by lives of serv-ice, Bring to all true light.

CHORUS

No - el, no - el! No - el, no - el! Rang through-out the sky;
star-lit sky;

No - el, no - el! No - el, no - el! Praise to God on high!

89

Angels We Have Heard on High

GLORIA

French carol, 18th century?

French melody, 18th century?
Arr. by John W. Peterson, 1921-

1. An-gels we have heard on high, Sweet-ly sing-ing o'er the plains,
2. Shep-herds, why this ju-bi-lee? Why your joy-ous strains pro-long?
3. Come to Beth-le-hem and see Him whose birth the an-gels sing;
4. See Him in a man-ger laid, Je-sus, Lord of heav'n and earth;

And the moun-tains, in re-ply, Ech-o-ing their joy-ous strains.
What the glad-some ti-dings be Which in-spire your heav'n-ly song?
Come, a-dore on bend-ed knee Christ the Lord, the new-born King.
Ma-ry, Jo-seph, lend your aid, With us sing our Sav-ior's birth.

REFRAIN

Glo - - - - - - - - - ri - a
in ex-cel-sis De - o! Glo - - - - -
- - - - - ri - a in ex-cel-sis De - o!

It Came upon the Midnight Clear

CAROL

EDMUND H. SEARS, 1810-1876

RICHARD S. WILLIS, 1819-1900

1. It came up-on the mid-night clear, That glo - rious song of old,
2. Still thru the clo - ven skies they come With peace-ful wings un - furled,
3. And ye, be-neath life's crush-ing load, Whose forms are bend - ing low,
4. For lo, the days are has-t'ning on, By proph- et bards fore - told,

From an-gels bend - ing near the earth To touch their harps of gold:
And still their heav'n - ly mu - sic floats O'er all the wea - ry world:
Who toil a - long the climb-ing way With pain- ful steps and slow,
When with the ev - er - cir-cling years Comes round the age of gold;

"Peace on the earth, good will to men, From heav'n's all gra - cious King!"
A - bove its sad and low-ly plains They bend on hov-'ring wing,
Look now! for glad and gold-en hours Come swift-ly on the wing:
When peace shall o - ver all the earth Its an - cient splen-dors fling,

The world in sol - emn still-ness lay To hear the an - gels sing.
And ev - er o'er its Ba-bel sounds The bless-ed an - gels sing.
O rest be - side the wea - ry road And hear the an - gels sing.
And the whole world give back the song Which now the an - gels sing.

91

The First Noel

English carol, before 1823

English melody
From Sandys' *Christmas Carols*, 1833

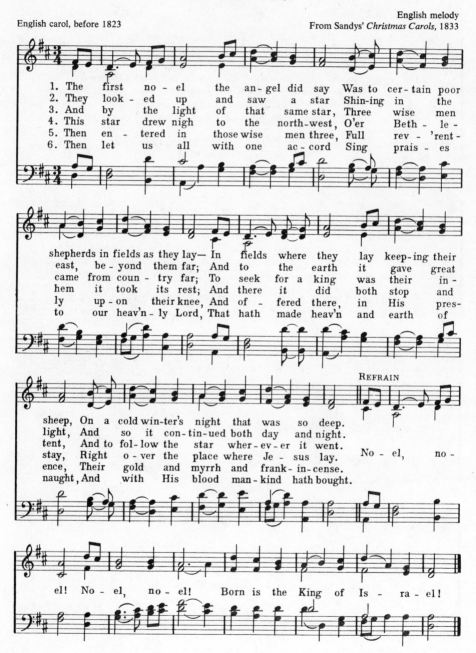

1. The first no - el the an - gel did say Was to cer - tain poor
2. They look - ed up and saw a star Shin-ing in the
3. And by the light of that same star, Three wise men
4. This star drew nigh to the north-west, O'er Beth - le -
5. Then en - tered in those wise men three, Full rev - 'rent -
6. Then let us all with one ac - cord Sing prais - es

shepherds in fields as they lay— In fields where they lay keep-ing their
east, be - yond them far; And to the earth it gave great
came from coun - try far; To seek for a king was their in -
hem it took its rest; And there it did both stop and
ly up - on their knee, And of - fered there, in His pres -
to our heav'n - ly Lord, That hath made heav'n and earth of

sheep, On a cold win-ter's night that was so deep.
light, And so it con-tin-ued both day and night.
tent, And to fol-low the star wher-ev-er it went.
stay, Right o - ver the place where Je - sus lay.
ence, Their gold and myrrh and frank - in-cense.
naught, And with His blood man - kind hath bought.

REFRAIN

No - el, no - el! No - el, no - el! Born is the King of Is - ra - el!

O Little Town of Bethlehem

ST. LOUIS

PHILLIPS BROOKS, 1835-1893

LEWIS H. REDNER, 1831-1908

1. O lit - tle town of Beth-le-hem, How still we see thee lie!
2. For Christ is born of Ma - ry— And gath-ered all a - bove,
3. How si - lent - ly, how si - lent - ly The won - drous gift is giv'n!
4. O ho - ly Child of Beth-le-hem, De - scend to us, we pray;

A - bove thy deep and dream-less sleep The si - lent stars go by;
While mor-tals sleep, the an - gels keep Their watch of won-d'ring love.
So God im - parts to hu-man hearts The bless - ings of His heav'n.
Cast out our sin and en - ter in— Be born in us to - day.

Yet in thy dark streets shin - eth The ev - er - last - ing Light—
O morn-ing stars, to - geth - er Pro-claim the ho - ly birth,
No ear may hear His com - ing, But, in this world of sin,
We hear the Christ-mas an - gels The great glad ti - dings tell;

The hopes and fears of all the years Are met in thee to - night.
And prais - es sing to God the King, And peace to men on earth.
Where meek souls will re - ceive Him still The dear Christ en - ters in.
O come to us, a - bide with us, Our Lord Em - man - u - el!

93 Hark! the Herald Angels Sing

MENDELSSOHN

CHARLES WESLEY, 1707-1788   FELIX MENDELSSOHN, 1809-1847

1. Hark! the her-ald an-gels sing, "Glo-ry to the new-born King;
2. Christ, by high-est heav'n a-dored, Christ, the ev-er-last-ing Lord:
3. Hail the heav'n-born Prince of Peace! Hail the Sun of Right-eous-ness!
4. Come, De-sire of Na-tions, come! Fix in us Thy hum-ble home:

Peace on earth, and mer-cy mild— God and sin-ners rec-on-ciled!"
Late in time be-hold Him come, Off-spring of a vir-gin's womb.
Light and life to all He brings, Ris'n with heal-ing in His wings.
Rise, the wom-an's con-q'ring seed, Bruise in us the ser-pent's head.

Joy-ful, all ye na-tions, rise, Join the tri-umph of the skies;
Veiled in flesh the God-head see, Hail th'in-car-nate De-i-ty!
Mild He lays His glo-ry by, Born that man no more may die;
Ad-am's like-ness now ef-face, Stamp Thine im-age in its place:

With th'an-gel-ic hosts pro-claim, "Christ is born in Beth-le-hem."
Pleased as man with men to dwell, Je-sus, our Em-man-u-el.
Born to raise the sons of earth, Born to give them sec-ond birth.
Sec-ond Ad-am from a-bove, Re-in-state us in Thy love.

Hark! the Herald Angels Sing

Hark! the her-ald an-gels sing, "Glo-ry to the new-born King!"

What Child Is This? 94
GREENSLEEVES

WILLIAM C. DIX, 1837-1898

English melody, before 1642

1. What Child is this, who, laid to rest, On Ma-ry's lap is sleep-ing?
2. Why lies He in such mean es-tate Where ox and ass are feed-ing?
3. So bring Him in-cense, gold and myrrh—Come, rich and poor, to own Him;

Whom an-gels greet with an-thems sweet, While shep-herds watch are keep-ing?
Good Christian, fear—for sin-ners here The si-lent Word is plead-ing.
The King of kings sal-va-tion brings—Let lov-ing hearts en-throne Him.

REFRAIN

This, this is Christ the King, Whom shep-herds guard and an-gels sing:

Haste, haste to bring Him laud—The Babe, the Son of Ma-ry.

95 ## While Shepherds Watched Their Flocks

CHRISTMAS

NAHUM TATE, 1652-1715

Arr. from George F. Handel, 1685-1759
in Weyman's *Melodia Sacra*, 1815

1. While shepherds watch'd their flocks by night, All seat-ed on the ground, The an-gel
2. "Fear not!" said he, for might-y dread Had seized their troubled mind; "Glad ti-dings
3. "To you in Da-vid's town this day Is born, of Da-vid's line, The Sav-ior
4. "The heav'n-ly Babe you there shall find To hu-man view dis-played, All mean-ly
5. "All glo-ry be to God on high, And to the earth be peace: Good will hence-

of the Lord came down, And glo-ry shone a-round, And glo-ry shone a-round.
of great joy I bring To you and all man-kind, To you and all man-kind.
who is Christ the Lord, And this shall be the sign— And this shall be the sign:
wrapt in swath-ing-bands And in a man-ger laid, And in a man-ger laid."
forth from heav'n to men Be-gin and nev-er cease! Be-gin and nev-er cease!"

96 ## As with Gladness Men of Old

DIX

WILLIAM C. DIX, 1837-1898

CONRAD KOCHER, 1786-1872

1. As with glad-ness men of old Did the guid-ing star be-hold
2. As with joy-ful steps they sped To that low-ly man-ger-bed,
3. As they of-fered gifts most rare At that man-ger rude and bare,
4. Ho-ly Je-sus, ev-'ry day Keep us in the nar-row way;

As with joy they hailed its light, Lead-ing on-ward, beam-ing bright—
There to bend the knee be-fore Him whom heav'n and earth a-dore,
So may we with ho-ly joy, Pure and free from sin's al-loy,
And, when earth-ly things are past, Bring our ran-somed souls at last

This tune in a higher key: 54

As with Gladness Men of Old

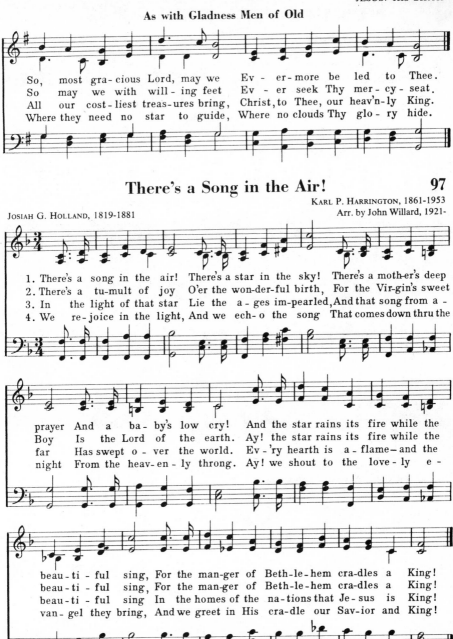

So, most gra-cious Lord, may we Ev-er-more be led to Thee.
So may we with will-ing feet Ev-er seek Thy mer-cy-seat.
All our cost-liest treas-ures bring, Christ, to Thee, our heav'n-ly King.
Where they need no star to guide, Where no clouds Thy glo-ry hide.

There's a Song in the Air! 97

KARL P. HARRINGTON, 1861-1953
Arr. by John Willard, 1921-

JOSIAH G. HOLLAND, 1819-1881

1. There's a song in the air! There's a star in the sky! There's a moth-er's deep
2. There's a tu-mult of joy O'er the won-der-ful birth, For the Vir-gin's sweet
3. In the light of that star Lie the a-ges im-pearled, And that song from a-
4. We re-joice in the light, And we ech-o the song That comes down thru the

prayer And a ba-by's low cry! And the star rains its fire while the
Boy Is the Lord of the earth. Ay! the star rains its fire while the
far Has swept o-ver the world. Ev-'ry hearth is a-flame—and the
night From the heav-en-ly throng. Ay! we shout to the love-ly e-

beau-ti-ful sing, For the man-ger of Beth-le-hem cra-dles a King!
beau-ti-ful sing, For the man-ger of Beth-le-hem cra-dles a King!
beau-ti-ful sing In the homes of the na-tions that Je-sus is King!
van-gel they bring, And we greet in His cra-dle our Sav-ior and King!

98 ## I Heard the Bells on Christmas Day

WALTHAM

HENRY W. LONGFELLOW, 1807-1882

J. BAPTISTE CALKIN, 1827-1905

1. I heard the bells on Christ-mas day Their old fa - mil - iar car - ols play,
2. I thought how, as the day had come, The bel-fries of all Chris-ten-dom
3. And in de-spair I bowed my head:"There is no peace on earth," I said,
4. Then pealed the bells more loud and deep:"God is not dead: nor doth He sleep;
5. Till ring - ing, sing-ing on its way The world re-volved from night to day—

And wild and sweet the words re-peat Of peace on earth, good-will to men.
Had rolled a - long th'un-bro - ken song Of peace on earth, good-will to men.
"For hate is strong, and mocks the song Of peace on earth, good-will to men."
The wrong shall fail, the right pre-vail, With peace on earth, good-will to men."
A voice, a chime, a chant sub-lime Of peace on earth, good-will to men!

99 ## Angels, from the Realms of Glory

REGENT SQUARE

JAMES MONTGOMERY, 1771-1854

HENRY SMART, 1813-1879

1. An - gels, from the realms of glo - ry, Wing your flight o'er all the earth;
2. Shep-herds, in the fields a - bid - ing, Watch-ing o'er your flocks by night,
3. Sag - es, leave your con-tem-pla - tions, Bright-er vi - sions beam a - far;
4. Saints be - fore the al - tar bend-ing, Watch-ing long in hope and fear,

Ye who sang cre - a - tion's sto - ry, Now pro-claim Mes - si - ah's birth;
God with man is now re - sid - ing, Yon-der shines the in-fant Light;
Seek the great De - sire of na - tions, Ye have seen His na - tal star:
Sud-den - ly the Lord, de-scend-ing, In His tem - ple shall ap - pear:

Alternate tune: KENT—7

Angels, from the Realms of Glory

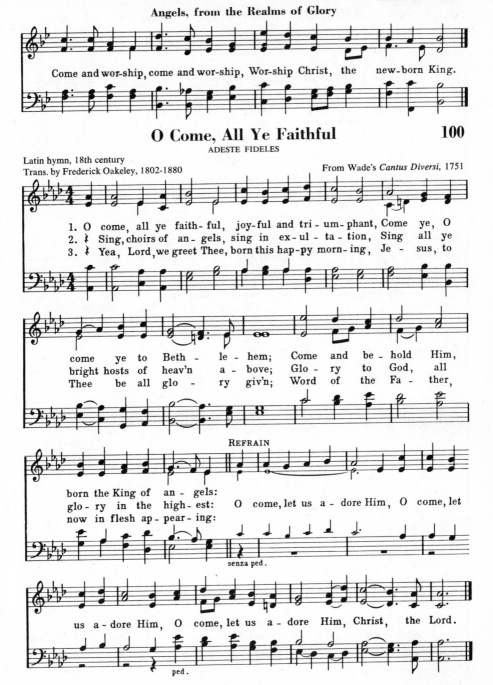

Come and wor-ship, come and wor-ship, Wor-ship Christ, the new-born King.

O Come, All Ye Faithful   **100**

ADESTE FIDELES

Latin hymn, 18th century
Trans. by Frederick Oakeley, 1802-1880

From Wade's *Cantus Diversi*, 1751

1. O come, all ye faith-ful, joy-ful and tri-um-phant, Come ye, O
2. Sing, choirs of an-gels, sing in ex-ul-ta-tion, Sing all ye
3. Yea, Lord, we greet Thee, born this hap-py morn-ing, Je-sus, to

come ye to Beth-le-hem; Come and be-hold Him,
bright hosts of heav'n a-bove; Glo-ry to God, all
Thee be all glo-ry giv'n; Word of the Fa-ther,

REFRAIN

born the King of an-gels:
glo-ry in the high-est: O come, let us a-dore Him, O come, let
now in flesh ap-pear-ing:

senza ped.

us a-dore Him, O come, let us a-dore Him, Christ, the Lord.

ped.

101 Thou Didst Leave Thy Throne

MARGARET

EMILY E. S. ELLIOTT, 1836-1897   TIMOTHY R. MATTHEWS, 1826-1910

1. Thou didst leave Thy throne And Thy king-ly crown When Thou
2. Heav-en's arch-es rang When the an-gels sang, Pro-
3. The fox-es found rest, And the birds their nest In the
4. Thou cam-est, O Lord, With the liv-ing word That should
5. When the heav-ens shall ring And the an-gels sing At Thy

cam-est to earth for me; But in Beth-le-hem's home
claim-ing Thy roy-al de-gree; But of low-ly birth
shade of the for-est tree; But Thy couch was the sod,
set Thy peo-ple free; But with mock-ing scorn
com-ing to vic-to-ry, Let Thy voice call me home,

Was there found no room For Thy ho-ly na-tiv-i-ty.
Didst Thou come to earth, And in great hu-mil-i-ty.
O Thou Son of God, In the des-erts of Gal-i-lee.
And with crown of thorn They bore Thee to Cal-va-ry.
Say-ing, "Yet there is room— There is room at My side for thee."

REFRAIN

1.–4. O come to my heart, Lord Je-sus—There is room in my heart for Thee!
5. My heart shall re-joice, Lord Je-sus, When Thou com-est and call-est for me!

Jesus, Wonderful Lord!

PAUL WHITE, 20th century   PAUL WHITE, 20th century

1. Born a-mong cat-tle, in pov-er-ty sore, Liv-ing in
2. Wea-ry— yet He is the world's on-ly rest, Hun-gry and
3. Friend of the friend-less— be-trayed and de-nied, Help of the

meek-ness by Gal-i-lee's shore, Dy-ing in shame as the
thirst-y— with plen-ty has blest, Tempt-ed— He prom-is-es
weak— in Geth-sem-a-ne cried, Light of the world— in gross

wick-ed ones swore: Je-sus, won-der-ful Lord!
grace for each test: Je-sus, won-der-ful Lord!
dark-ness He died: Je-sus, won-der-ful Lord!
won-der-ful Lord!

CHORUS

Won-der-ful, won-der-ful Je-sus! He is my friend, true to the end;

He gave Him-self to re-deem me— Je-sus, won-der-ful Lord!

103

One Day!

J. Wilbur Chapman, 1859-1918

Charles H. Marsh, 1886-1956

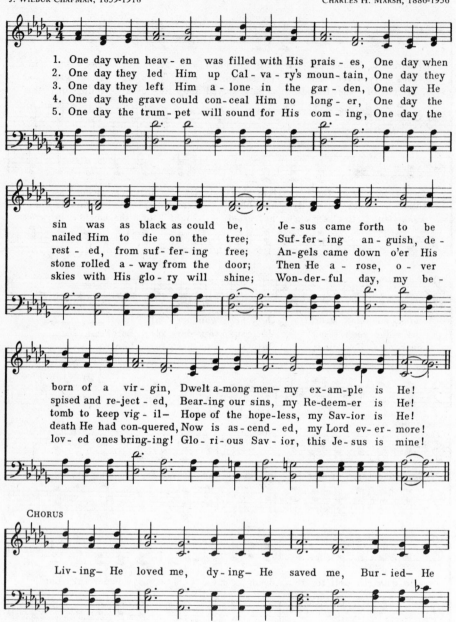

1. One day when heav-en was filled with His prais-es, One day when
2. One day they led Him up Cal-va-ry's moun-tain, One day they
3. One day they left Him a-lone in the gar-den, One day He
4. One day the grave could con-ceal Him no long-er, One day the
5. One day the trum-pet will sound for His com-ing, One day the

sin was as black as could be, Je-sus came forth to be
nailed Him to die on the tree; Suf-fer-ing an-guish, de-
rest-ed, from suf-fer-ing free; An-gels came down o'er His
stone rolled a-way from the door; Then He a-rose, o-ver
skies with His glo-ry will shine; Won-der-ful day, my be-

born of a vir-gin, Dwelt a-mong men— my ex-am-ple is He!
spised and re-ject-ed, Bear-ing our sins, my Re-deem-er is He!
tomb to keep vig-il— Hope of the hope-less, my Sav-ior is He!
death He had con-quered, Now is as-cend-ed, my Lord ev-er-more!
lov-ed ones bring-ing! Glo-ri-ous Sav-ior, this Je-sus is mine!

CHORUS

Liv-ing— He loved me, dy-ing— He saved me, Bur-ied— He

One Day!

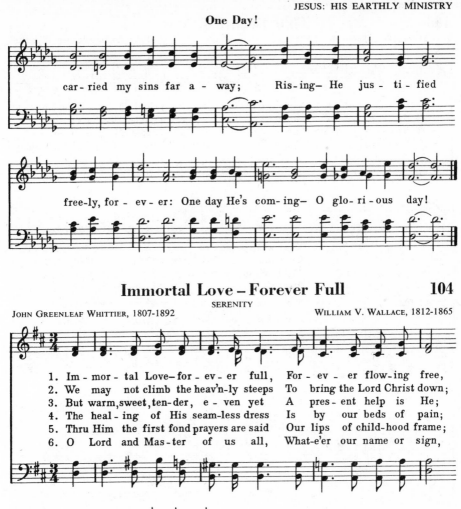

car - ried my sins far a - way; Ris-ing— He jus - ti - fied

free-ly, for - ev - er: One day He's com-ing— O glo - ri - ous day!

Immortal Love – Forever Full

104

SERENITY

JOHN GREENLEAF WHITTIER, 1807-1892 · WILLIAM V. WALLACE, 1812-1865

1. Im - mor - tal Love—for - ev - er full, For - ev - er flow-ing free,
2. We may not climb the heav'n-ly steeps To bring the Lord Christ down;
3. But warm, sweet, ten-der, e - ven yet A pres - ent help is He;
4. The heal - ing of His seam-less dress Is by our beds of pain;
5. Thru Him the first fond prayers are said Our lips of child-hood frame;
6. O Lord and Mas - ter of us all, What-e'er our name or sign,

For - ev - er shared, for - ev - er whole, A nev - er - ebb - ing sea!
In vain we search the low-est deeps, For Him no depths can drown.
And faith has still its Ol - i - vet, And love its Gal - i - lee.
We touch Him in life's throng and press, And we are whole a - gain.
The last low whis-pers of our dead Are bur - dened with His name.
We own Thy sway, we hear Thy call, We test our lives by Thine!

Alternate tunes: CAMPMEETING—273, MAITLAND—342

105 That Beautiful Name

Jean Perry, 1865-1935 — alt.

Mabel Johnston Camp, 1871-1937

1. I know of a Name, A beau-ti-ful Name, That an-gels brought
2. I know of a Name, A beau-ti-ful Name, That un-to a
3. The One of that Name My Sav-ior be-came, My Sav-ior of
4. I love that blest Name, That won-der-ful Name, Made high-er than

down to earth; They whis-pered it low, One night long a-go,
Babe was giv'n; The stars glit-tered bright Thru-out that glad night,
Cal-va-ry; My sins nailed Him there, My bur-dens He bare,
all in heav'n; 'Twas whis-pered, I know, In my heart long a-go—

To a maid-en of low-ly birth.
And an-gels praised God in heav'n.
He suf-fered all this for me.
To Je-sus my life I've giv'n.

CHORUS

That beau-ti-ful Name, That beau-ti-ful Name From sin has pow'r to free us! That beau-ti-ful Name, That won-der-ful Name, That match-less Name is Je - sus!

Tell Me the Story of Jesus

FANNY J. CROSBY, 1820-1915

JOHN R. SWENEY, 1837-1899

1. Tell me the sto - ry of Je - sus, Write on my heart ev-'ry word;
2. Fast-ing a - lone in the des - ert! Tell of the days that are past—
3. Tell of the cross where they nailed Him, Writh-ing in an-guish and pain;

CHORUS—*Tell me the sto - ry of Je - sus, Write on my heart ev-'ry word;*

Fine

Tell me the sto - ry most pre - cious, Sweet-est that ev - er was heard!
How for our sins He was tempt - ed, Yet was tri-um-phant at last.
Tell of the grave where they laid Him, Tell how He liv- eth a - gain!

Tell me the sto - ry most pre - cious, Sweet-est that ev - er was heard!

Tell how the an - gels, in cho - rus, Sang as they wel- comed His birth,
Tell of the years of His la - bor, Tell of the sor - row He bore—
Love, in that sto - ry so ten - der, Clear-er than ev - er I see:

D.C.

"Glo - ry to God in the high- est! Peace and good ti - dings to earth!"
He was de-spised and af - flict - ed, Home-less, re- ject- ed and poor.
Stay, let me weep while you whis- per, Love paid the ran - som for me!

107

Hosanna, Loud Hosanna

ELLACOMBE

JENNETTE THRELFALL, 1821-1880

From *Gesangbuch der Herzogl,*
Württemberg, 1784

1. Ho - san - na, loud ho - san - na, The lit - tle chil-dren sang;
2. From Ol - i - vet they fol - lowed 'Mid an ex - ult - ant crowd,
3. "Ho - san - na in the high - est!" That an - cient song we sing,

Thru pil - lared court and tem - ple The love - ly an - them rang;
The vic - tor palm branch wav - ing, And chant-ing clear and loud;
For Christ is our Re - deem - er, The Lord of heav'n, our King;

To Je - sus, who had blessed them Close fold - ed to His breast,
The Lord of men and an - gels Rode on in low - ly state,
O may we ev - er praise Him With heart and life and voice,

The chil - dren sang their prais - es, The sim - plest and the best.
Nor scorned that lit - tle chil - dren Should on His bid - ding wait.
And in His bliss - ful pres - ence E - ter - nal - ly re - joice!

Effective with other tunes in 76.76. D. meter.
This tune in a higher key: 27

All Glory, Laud and Honor 108

ST. THEODULPH

THEODULPH OF ORLEANS, 760-821
Trans. by John M. Neale, 1818-1866

MELCHIOR TESCHNER, 1584-1635

1. All glo - ry, laud and hon - or To Thee, Re - deem - er, King,
2. The com - pa - ny of an - gels Are prais - ing Thee on high,
3. To Thee, be - fore Thy pas - sion, They sang their hymns of praise;

To whom the lips of chil - dren Made sweet ho - san - nas ring:
And mor - tal men and all things Cre - at - ed make re - ply:
To Thee, now high ex - alt - ed, Our mel - o - dy we raise:

Thou art the King of Is - rael, Thou Da - vid's roy - al Son,
The peo - ple of the He - brews With palms be - fore Thee went;
Thou didst ac - cept their prais - es— Ac - cept the praise we bring,

Who in the Lord's name com - est, The King and bless - ed One!
Our praise and prayer and an - thems Be - fore Thee we pre - sent.
Who in all good de - light - est, Thou good and gra - cious King!

Alternate tunes: ELLACOMBE — 27 (107), LANCASHIRE — 407

109 Ride On! Ride On in Majesty!

ST. DROSTANE

JOHN B. DYKES, 1823-1876

HENRY HART MILMAN, 1791-1868

Arr. by Harold DeCou, 1932-

1. Ride on! ride on in maj - es - ty! Hark! all the tribes ho - san - na cry;
2. Ride on! ride on in maj - es - ty! In low - ly pomp ride on to die;
3. Ride on! ride on in maj - es - ty! The wing-ed squad-rons of the sky
4. Ride on! ride on in maj - es - ty! In low - ly pomp ride on to die;

O   Sav - ior meek, pur - sue Thy road With palms and scat-tered gar-ments strowed.
O   Christ, Thy tri - umphs now be - gin O'er   cap - tive death and con-quered sin.
Look down with sad and won-d'ring eyes To   see th'ap-proach-ing sac - ri - fice.
Bow Thy meek head to   mor - tal pain, Then take, O   God, Thy pow'r and reign.

Alternate tunes: OLD HUNDREDTH (original meter) — 8, WALTHAM — 98 (131)

110 Alas! and Did My Savior Bleed?

MARTYRDOM

ISAAC WATTS, 1674-1748

HUGH WILSON, 1766-1824

1. A - las! and did my Sav - ior bleed? And did my Sov - 'reign die?
2. Was it for crimes that I have done He groaned up - on the tree?
3. Well might the sun in dark-ness hide And shut his glo - ries in,
4. But drops of grief can ne'er re - pay The debt of love I owe;

Would He de - vote that sa - cred head For such a worm as I?
A - maz - ing pit - y! grace un-known! And love be - yond de - gree!
When Christ, the might - y Mak - er, died For man the crea - ture's sin.
Here, Lord, I give my - self a - way-'Tis all that I can do.

What Will You Do with Jesus?

111

ALBERT B. SIMPSON, 1843-1919　　　　　　　　　　　　MARY L. STOCKS, 1863-1934

1. Je - sus is stand-ing in　Pi - late's hall— Friendless, for-sak - en, be - trayed by all:
2. Je - sus is stand-ing on　tri - al still— You can be false to Him if you will,
3. Will you e - vade Him as　Pi - late tried? Or will you choose Him, what-e'er be - tide?
4. Will you, like Pe - ter, your Lord de - ny? Or will you scorn from His foes to fly,
5. "Je - sus, I give Thee my heart to - day! Je - sus, I'll fol - low Thee all the way,

Heark - en! what mean-eth the　sud - den call! What will you do with Je - sus?
You　can　be faith-ful thru good or ill: What will you do with Je - sus?
Vain - ly　you strug-gle from Him to hide: What will you do with Je - sus?
Dar - ing for Je - sus to　live or die? What will you do with Je - sus?
Glad - ly　o - bey - ing Thee!" will you say, "This will I do with Je - sus!"

CHORUS

What will you do　with　Je - sus? Neu-tral you can - not　be;

Some day your heart will be　ask - ing, "What will He do with me?"

112 Blessed Redeemer

Avis B. Christiansen, 1895-   Harry Dixon Loes, 1892-1965

1. Up Cal-v'ry's moun-tain, one dread-ful morn, Walked Christ my Sav-ior,
2. "Fa-ther, for-give them!" thus did He pray, E'en while His life-blood
3. O how I love Him, Sav-ior and Friend! How can my prais-es

wea-ry and worn; Fac-ing for sin-ners death on the cross,
flowed fast a-way; Pray-ing for sin-ners while in such woe—
ev-er find end! Thru years un-num-bered on heav-en's shore,

CHORUS

That He might save them from end-less loss.
No one but Je-sus ev-er loved so.   Bless-ed Re-deem-er, pre-cious Re-
My tongue shall praise Him for-ev-er-more.

deem-er! Seems now I see Him on Cal-va-ry's tree, Wound-ed and

bleed-ing, for sin-ners plead-ing—Blind and un-heed-ing— dy-ing for me!

The Old Rugged Cross

GEORGE BENNARD, 1873-1958   GEORGE BENNARD, 1873-1958

1. On a hill far a-way stood an old rug-ged cross, The em-blem of
2. O that old rug-ged cross, so de-spised by the world, Has a won-drous at-
3. In the old rug-ged cross, stained with blood so di-vine, A won-drous
4. To the old rug-ged cross I will ev-er be true, Its shame and re-

suf-f'ring and shame; And I love that old cross where the dear-est and best
trac-tion for me; For the dear Lamb of God left His glo-ry a-bove
beau-ty I see; For 'twas on that old cross Je-sus suf-fered and died
proach glad-ly bear; Then He'll call me some day to my home far a-way,

CHORUS

For a world of lost sin-ners was slain.
To bear it to dark Cal-va-ry.   So I'll cher-ish the old rug-ged
To par-don and sanc-ti-fy me.   cross, the
Where His glo-ry for-ev-er I'll share.

cross,   Till my tro-phies at last I lay down; I will cling to the
old rug-ged cross,

old rug-ged cross,   And ex-change it some day for a crown.
cross, the old rug-ged cross,

114 There Is a Green Hill Far Away

GREEN HILL

CECIL F. ALEXANDER, 1818-1895

GEORGE C. STEBBINS, 1846-1945

1. There is a green hill far a-way, With-out a cit-y wall,
2. We may not know, we can-not tell What pains He had to bear;
3. He died that we might be for-giv'n, He died to make us good,
4. There was no oth-er good e-nough To pay the price of sin;

Where the dear Lord was cru-ci-fied, Who died to save us all.
But we be-lieve it was for us He hung and suf-fered there.
That we might go at last to heav'n, Saved by His pre-cious blood.
He on-ly could un-lock the gate Of heav'n and let us in.

CHORUS

O dear-ly, dear-ly has He loved! And we must love Him too,

And trust in His re-deem-ing blood, And try His works to do.

Ivory Palaces

Henry Barraclough, 1891-
Arr. by Donald P. Hustad, 1918-

Henry Barraclough, 1891-

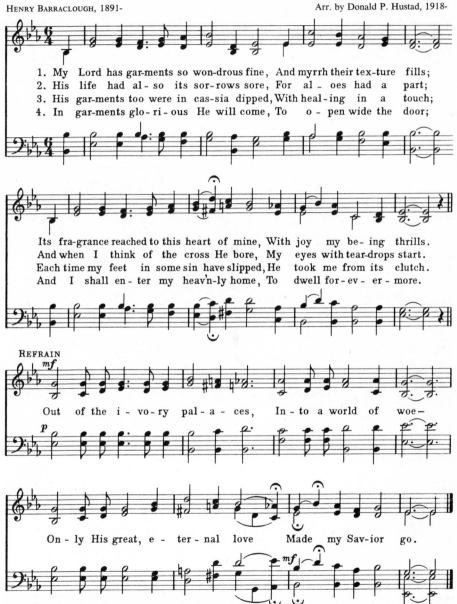

1. My Lord has gar-ments so won-drous fine, And myrrh their tex-ture fills;
2. His life had al-so its sor-rows sore, For al-oes had a part;
3. His gar-ments too were in cas-sia dipped, With heal-ing in a touch;
4. In gar-ments glo-ri-ous He will come, To o-pen wide the door;

Its fra-grance reached to this heart of mine, With joy my be-ing thrills.
And when I think of the cross He bore, My eyes with tear-drops start.
Each time my feet in some sin have slipped, He took me from its clutch.
And I shall en-ter my heav'n-ly home, To dwell for-ev-er-more.

REFRAIN

mf

Out of the i-vo-ry pal-a-ces, In-to a world of woe—

p

On-ly His great, e-ter-nal love Made my Sav-ior go.

116   O Sacred Head, Now Wounded

PASSION CHORALE

Attr. to Bernard of Clairvaux, 1091-1153

Trans. (into German) by Paul Gerhardt, 1607-1676   Hans Leo Hassler, 1564-1612

Trans. (from German) by James W. Alexander, 1804-1859   Har. by Johann Sebastian Bach, 1685-1750

1. O sa-cred Head, now wound-ed, With grief and shame weighed down,
2. What Thou, my Lord, hast suf-fered Was all for sin-ners' gain:
3. What lan-guage shall I bor-row To thank Thee, dear-est Friend,

Now scorn-ful-ly sur-round-ed With thorns Thy on-ly crown,
Mine, mine was the trans-gres-sion, But Thine the dead-ly pain.
For this Thy dy-ing sor-row, Thy pit-y with-out end?

How art Thou pale with an-guish, With sore a-buse and scorn!
Lo, here I fall, my Sav-ior! 'Tis I de-serve Thy place;
O make me Thine for-ev-er! And, should I faint-ing be,

How does that vis-age lan-guish Which once was bright as morn!
Look on me with Thy fa-vor, Vouch-safe to me Thy grace.
Lord, let me nev-er, nev-er Out-live my love to Thee!

Alternate tunes: ANGEL'S STORY—392, ST. HILDA—238

He Was Wounded for Our Transgressions 117

THOMAS O. CHISHOLM, 1866-1960   MERRILL DUNLOP, 1905-

1. He was wound-ed for our trans - gress - ions, He bore our
2. He was num - bered a - mong trans - gress - ors, We did es -
3. We had wan - dered, we all had wan - dered Far from the
4. Who can num - ber His gen - er - a - tion? Who shall de -

sins in His bod - y on the tree; For our guilt He
teem Him for - sak - en by His God; As our sac - ri -
fold of "the Shep-herd of the sheep;" But He sought us
clare all the tri - umphs of His cross? Mil - lions, dead, now

gave us peace, From our bon-dage gave re - lease, And with His stripes,
fice He died, That the law be sat - is - fied, And all our sin,
where we were, On the moun-tains bleak and bare, And brought us home,
live a - gain, Myr-iads fol - low in His train! Vic - to-rious Lord,

and with His stripes, And with His stripes our souls are healed.
and all our sin, And all our sin was laid on Him.
and brought us home, And brought us safe - ly home to God.
vic - to - rious Lord, Vic - to - rious Lord and com - ing King!

118 When I Survey the Wondrous Cross

HAMBURG

ISAAC WATTS, 1674-1748

From a Gregorian Chant
Arr. by Lowell Mason, 1792-1872

1. When I sur-vey the won-drous cross On which the Prince of glo-ry died,
2. For-bid it, Lord, that I should boast, Save in the death of Christ, my God;
3. See, from His head, His hands, His feet, Sor-row and love flow min-gled down;
4. Were the whole realm of na-ture mine, That were a pres-ent far too small:

My rich-est gain I count but loss, And pour con-tempt on all my pride.
All the vain things that charm me most—I sac-ri-fice them to His blood.
Did e'er such love and sor-row meet, Or thorns com-pose so rich a crown?
Love so a-maz-ing, so di-vine, De-mands my soul, my life, my all.

119 'Tis Midnight – and on Olive's Brow

OLIVE'S BROW

WILLIAM B. TAPPAN, 1794-1849

WILLIAM B. BRADBURY, 1816-1868

1. 'Tis mid-night—and on Ol-ive's brow The star is dimmed that late-ly shone:
2. 'Tis mid-night—and from all re-moved The Sav-ior wres-tles lone with fears;
3. 'Tis mid-night—and for oth-ers' guilt The Man of Sor-rows weeps in blood;
4. 'Tis mid-night—and from e-ther-plains Is borne the song that an-gels know;

'Tis mid-night— in the gar-den now The suf-fring Sav-ior prays a-lone.
E'en that dis-ci-ple whom He loved Heeds not His Mas-ter's grief and tears.
Yet He that hath in an-guish knelt Is not for-sak-en by His God.
Un-heard by mor-tals are the strains That sweet-ly soothe the Sav-ior's woe.

Opened for Me

120

MERRILL DUNLOP, 1905-

MERRILL DUNLOP, 1905-

1. There is a Foun-tain o-pened for my cleans-ing, Where sin's a-tone-ment by my Lord was made; He was the Lamb that was led to the slaugh-ter, His blood the foun-tain where my debt was paid.

2. There is a Rock that stands, by storms un-shak-en, Re-demp-tion's Au-thor the foun-da-tion laid; By faith my stand on His right-eous-ness I've tak-en, He will not fail— I shall not be dis-mayed.

3. There is a Book that points the path to glo-ry, E-ter-nal guide-post for the way-ward soul; On its fair pag-es is told the won-drous sto-ry Of life in Christ, the ev-er-last-ing goal.

4. There is a Hope, a won-drous con-so-la-tion, In a be-night-ed world a con-stant star; These eyes now dulled by the shad-ows that sur-round me My Sav-ior shall be-hold in realms a-far.

5. There is a Home my Sav-ior is pre-par-ing— I may not need to cross death's sul-len vale; Soon from earth's bond-age His com-ing will re-lease me To live where joys e-ter-nal shall pre-vail.

REFRAIN

O-pened for me, o-pened for me, The pre-cious, cleans-ing Fount was o-pened there for me.

121 — Blessed Calvary!

Avis B. Christiansen, 1895-   Lance B. Latham, 1894-

1. I look at the cross up-on Cal-va-ry, And O what a
2. I find at the cross bless-ed vic-to-ry, And grace for each
3. The cross is my hope for e-ter-ni-ty— No mer-it have

won-der di-vine! To think of the wealth it holds for me—
step of the way; The fount of God's love is flow-ing free,
I of my own; The shed blood of Christ my on-ly plea—

CHORUS

The rich-es of heav-en are mine.
And sweet-er it grows day by day. Bless-ed Cal-va-ry! Pre-cious
My trust is in Je-sus a-lone.

Cal-va-ry! 'Neath thy shad-ow I'll ev-er a-bide; Bless-ed Cal-va-

ry! Pre-cious Cal-va-ry! 'Twas there Je-sus suf-fered and died.

Why?

John M. Moore, 1925-

John M. Moore, 1925-

1. Why did they nail Him to Cal-va-ry's tree? Why? tell me, why was He there? Je-sus the Help-er, the Heal-er, the Friend— Why? tell me, why was He there?
2. Why should He love me, a sin-ner un-done? Why? tell me, why should He care? I do not mer-it the love He has shown— Why? tell me, why should He care?
3. Why should I lin-ger a-far from His love? Why? tell me, why should I fear? Some-how I know I should ven-ture and prove— Why? tell me, why should I fear?

CHORUS

All my in-i-qui-ties on Him were laid— He nailed them all to the tree. Je-sus the debt of my sin ful-ly paid— He paid the ran-som for me.

123 In the Cross of Christ I Glory

RATHBUN

JOHN BOWRING, 1792-1872

ITHAMAR CONKEY, 1815-1867

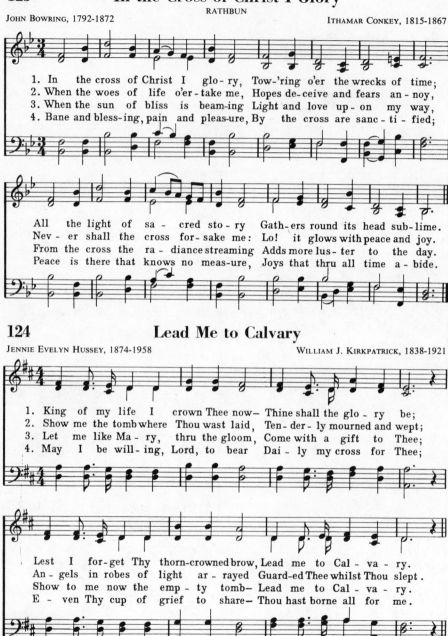

1. In the cross of Christ I glo-ry, Tow-'ring o'er the wrecks of time;
2. When the woes of life o'er-take me, Hopes de-ceive and fears an-noy,
3. When the sun of bliss is beam-ing Light and love up-on my way,
4. Bane and bless-ing, pain and pleas-ure, By the cross are sanc-ti-fied;

All the light of sa-cred sto-ry Gath-ers round its head sub-lime.
Nev-er shall the cross for-sake me: Lo! it glows with peace and joy.
From the cross the ra-diance streaming Adds more lus-ter to the day.
Peace is there that knows no meas-ure, Joys that thru all time a-bide.

124 Lead Me to Calvary

JENNIE EVELYN HUSSEY, 1874-1958

WILLIAM J. KIRKPATRICK, 1838-1921

1. King of my life I crown Thee now— Thine shall the glo-ry be;
2. Show me the tomb where Thou wast laid, Ten-der-ly mourned and wept;
3. Let me like Ma-ry, thru the gloom, Come with a gift to Thee;
4. May I be will-ing, Lord, to bear Dai-ly my cross for Thee;

Lest I for-get Thy thorn-crowned brow, Lead me to Cal-va-ry.
An-gels in robes of light ar-rayed Guard-ed Thee whilst Thou slept.
Show to me now the emp-ty tomb— Lead me to Cal-va-ry.
E-ven Thy cup of grief to share— Thou hast borne all for me.

Lead Me to Calvary

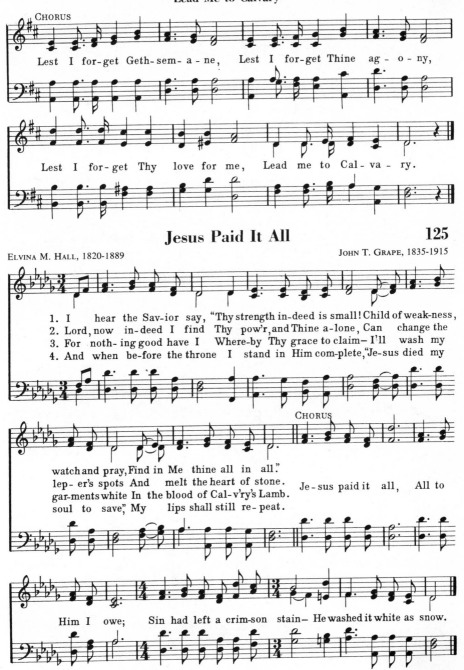

Lest I for-get Geth-sem-a-ne, Lest I for-get Thine ag-o-ny,

Lest I for-get Thy love for me, Lead me to Cal-va-ry.

Jesus Paid It All

125

ELVINA M. HALL, 1820-1889

JOHN T. GRAPE, 1835-1915

1. I hear the Sav-ior say, "Thy strength in-deed is small! Child of weak-ness,
2. Lord, now in-deed I find Thy pow'r, and Thine a-lone, Can change the
3. For noth-ing good have I Where-by Thy grace to claim— I'll wash my
4. And when be-fore the throne I stand in Him com-plete, "Je-sus died my

watch and pray, Find in Me thine all in all."
lep-er's spots And melt the heart of stone.
gar-ments white In the blood of Cal-v'ry's Lamb.
soul to save," My lips shall still re-peat.

CHORUS

Je-sus paid it all, All to

Him I owe; Sin had left a crim-son stain— He washed it white as snow.

126 Rock of Ages
TOPLADY

AUGUSTUS M. TOPLADY, 1740-1778

THOMAS HASTINGS, 1784-1872

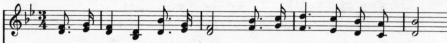

1. Rock of a - ges, cleft for me, Let me hide my-self in Thee;
2. Could my tears for - ev - er flow, Could my zeal no lan-guor know,
3. While I draw this fleet-ing breath, When my eyes shall close in death,

Let the wa - ter and the blood, From Thy wound-ed side which flowed,
These for sin could not a - tone— Thou must save, and Thou a - lone:
When I rise to worlds un-known And be-hold Thee on Thy throne,

Be of sin the dou-ble cure, Save from wrath and make me pure.
In my hand no price I bring, Sim - ply to Thy cross I cling.
Rock of A - ges, cleft for me, Let me hide my-self in Thee.

127 Hallelujah, What a Savior!
MAN OF SORROWS

PHILIP P. BLISS, 1838-1876

PHILIP P. BLISS, 1838-1876

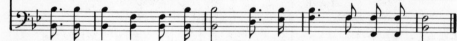

1. "Man of Sor-rows!" what a name For the Son of God,who came
2. Bear-ing shame and scoff-ing rude, In my place con-demned He stood—
3. Guilt-y, vile and help-less we, Spot-less Lamb of God was He;
4. Lift - ed up was He to die, "It is fin-ished," was His cry;
5. When He comes,our glo-rious King, All His ran-somed home to bring,

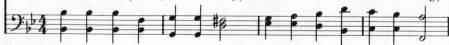

Hallelujah, What a Savior!

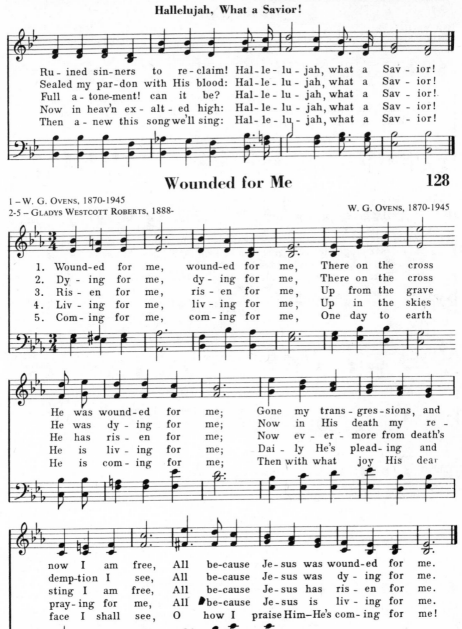

Ru - ined sin-ners to re-claim! Hal-le-lu-jah, what a Sav-ior!
Sealed my par-don with His blood: Hal-le-lu-jah, what a Sav-ior!
Full a-tone-ment! can it be? Hal-le-lu-jah, what a Sav-ior!
Now in heav'n ex-alt-ed high: Hal-le-lu-jah, what a Sav-ior!
Then a-new this song we'll sing: Hal-le-lu-jah, what a Sav-ior!

Wounded for Me   128

1 – W. G. Ovens, 1870-1945
2-5 – Gladys Westcott Roberts, 1888-

W. G. Ovens, 1870-1945

1. Wound-ed for me, wound-ed for me, There on the cross
2. Dy-ing for me, dy-ing for me, There on the cross
3. Ris-en for me, ris-en for me, Up from the grave
4. Liv-ing for me, liv-ing for me, Up in the skies
5. Com-ing for me, com-ing for me, One day to earth

He was wound-ed for me; Gone my trans-gres-sions, and
He was dy-ing for me; Now in His death my re-
He has ris-en for me; Now ev-er-more from death's
He is liv-ing for me; Dai-ly He's plead-ing and
He is com-ing for me; Then with what joy His dear

now I am free, All be-cause Je-sus was wound-ed for me.
demp-tion I see, All be-cause Je-sus was dy-ing for me.
sting I am free, All be-cause Je-sus has ris-en for me.
pray-ing for me, All be-cause Je-sus is liv-ing for me.
face I shall see, O how I praise Him—He's com-ing for me!

129 At the Cross

Isaac Watts, 1674-1748
Chorus — Ralph E. Hudson, 1843-1901

Ralph E. Hudson, 1843-1901

1. A - las! and did my Sav - ior bleed? And did my Sov-'reign die?
2. Was it for crimes that I have done He groaned up - on the tree?
3. Well might the sun in dark-ness hide And shut his glo - ries in,
4. But drops of grief can ne'er re - pay The debt of love I owe:

Would He de - vote that sa - cred head For such a worm as I?
A - maz - ing pit - y! grace un-known! And love be - yond de - gree!
When Christ, the might - y Mak - er, died For man the crea-ture's sin.
Here, Lord, I give my - self a - way— 'Tis all that I can do!

CHORUS

At the cross, at the cross where I first saw the light, And the

bur - den of my heart rolled a - way—
rolled a - way—
It was there by faith

I re - ceived my sight, And now I am hap-py all the day!

God Incarnate, Jesus Came   130

DOUGLAS

GEORGE SWEETING, 1924-
and JOHN W. PETERSON, 1921-

JOHN W. PETERSON, 1921-

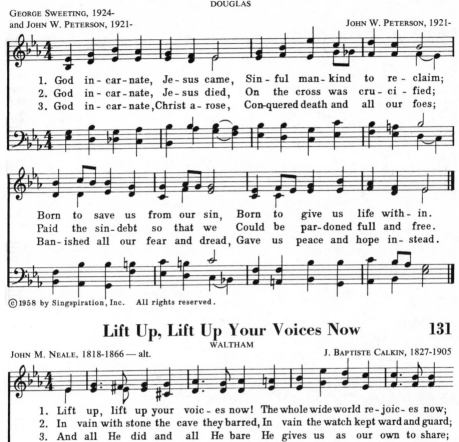

1. God in-car-nate, Je-sus came,   Sin-ful man-kind to re-claim;
2. God in-car-nate, Je-sus died,   On the cross was cru-ci-fied;
3. God in-car-nate, Christ a-rose, Con-quered death and all our foes;

Born to save us from our sin, Born to give us life with-in.
Paid the sin-debt so that we   Could be par-doned full and free.
Ban-ished all our fear and dread, Gave us peace and hope in-stead.

Lift Up, Lift Up Your Voices Now   131

WALTHAM

JOHN M. NEALE, 1818-1866 — alt.

J. BAPTISTE CALKIN, 1827-1905

1. Lift up, lift up your voic-es now! The whole wide world re-joic-es now;
2. In vain with stone the cave they barred, In vain the watch kept ward and guard;
3. And all He did and all He bare He gives us as our own to share;
4. O Vic-tor, aid us in the fight And lead thru death to realms of light;

The Lord hath tri-umphed glo-rious-ly, The Lord shall reign vic-to-rious-ly.
Ma-jes-tic, from the spoil-ed tomb, In pomp of tri-umph Christ is come.
And hope and joy and peace be-gin, For Christ has won, and man shall win.
We safe-ly pass where Thou hast trod, In Thee we die to rise to God.

132

He Lives

ALFRED H. ACKLEY, 1887-1960

ALFRED H. ACKLEY, 1887-1960

1. I serve a ris-en Sav-ior, He's in the world to-day; I know that He is liv-ing, what-ev-er men may say; I see His hand of mer-cy, I hear His voice of cheer, And just the time I need Him He's al-ways near.

2. In all the world a-round me I see His lov-ing care, And tho my heart grows wea-ry I nev-er will de-spair; I know that He is lead-ing thru all the storm-y blast, The day of His ap-pear-ing will come at last.

3. Re-joice, re-joice, O Chris-tian, lift up your voice and sing E-ter-nal hal-le-lu-jahs to Je-sus Christ the King! The hope of all who seek Him, the help of all who find, None oth-er is so lov-ing, so good and kind.

CHORUS

He lives, He lives, Christ Je-sus lives to-day! He walks with me and talks with me a-long life's nar-row way. He lives, He lives, sal-

He Lives

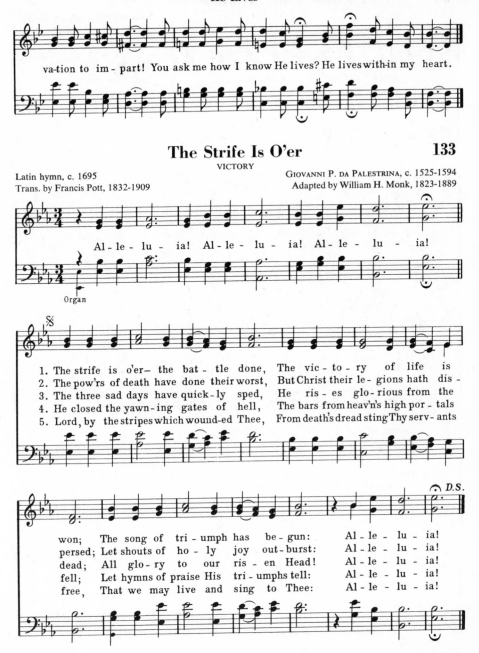

va-tion to im - part! You ask me how I know He lives? He lives with-in my heart.

The Strife Is O'er

VICTORY

133

Latin hymn, c. 1695
Trans. by Francis Pott, 1832-1909

Giovanni P. da Palestrina, c. 1525-1594
Adapted by William H. Monk, 1823-1889

Al - le - lu - ia! Al - le - lu - ia! Al - le - lu - ia!

Organ

1. The strife is o'er— the bat - tle done, The vic - to - ry of life is
2. The pow'rs of death have done their worst, But Christ their le - gions hath dis -
3. The three sad days have quick - ly sped, He ris - es glo - rious from the
4. He closed the yawn - ing gates of hell, The bars from heav'n's high por - tals
5. Lord, by the stripes which wound - ed Thee, From death's dread sting Thy serv - ants

D.S.

won; The song of tri - umph has be - gun: Al - le - lu - ia!
persed; Let shouts of ho - ly joy out - burst: Al - le - lu - ia!
dead; All glo - ry to our ris - en Head! Al - le - lu - ia!
fell; Let hymns of praise His tri - umphs tell: Al - le - lu - ia!
free, That we may live and sing to Thee: Al - le - lu - ia!

134 I Know That My Redeemer Liveth

JAMES H. FILLMORE, 1849-1936
Arr. by Jon Drevits, 1928-

JESSIE B. POUNDS, 1861-1921

1. I know that my Re-deem-er liv - eth And on the earth ____
2. I know His prom-ise nev-er fail - eth— The word He speaks, ____
3. I know my man-sion He pre-par - eth, That where He is ____

1. a -

____ a-gain shall stand; I know e-ter-nal life He giv - eth,
____ it can-not die; Tho cru-el death my flesh as-sail - eth,
____ there I may be; O won-drous tho't— for me He car - eth!

gain shall stand;

That grace and pow'r are in His hand.
Yet I shall see Him by and by.
And He at last will come for me.

1. are in His hand.

I know, I

CHORUS

know that Je-sus liv-eth, And on the earth

I know, I know

And on the earth

a-gain shall stand; I know, I know that life He

I know, I know

I Know That My Redeemer Liveth

giv - eth, That grace and pow'r are in His hand.

That grace and pow'r

The Day of Resurrection

135

JOHN OF DAMASCUS, early 8th century
Trans. by John M. Neale, 1818-1866

GREENLAND
Arr. from J. MICHAEL HAYDN, 1737-1806

1. The day of res - ur - rec - tion! Earth, tell it out a - broad—
2. Our hearts be pure from e - vil, That we may see a - right
3. Now let the heav'ns be joy - ful, Let earth her song be - gin,

The Pass - o - ver of glad - ness, The Pass - o - ver of God!
The Lord in rays e - ter - nal Of res - ur - rec - tion light;
Let the round world keep tri - umph And all that is there - in;

From death to life e - ter - nal, From this world to the sky,
And, lis - t'ning to His ac - cents, May hear, so calm and plain,
Let all things seen and un - seen Their notes in glad - ness blend,

Our Christ hath brought us o - ver With hymns of vic - to - ry!
His own "All hail!" and, hear - ing, May raise the vic - tor - strain.
For Christ the Lord hath ris - en, Our Joy that hath no end!

Alternate tunes: AURELIA—186, LANCASHIRE—407

136 Christ Is Risen from the Dead

FAIR OAKS

Thomas O. Chisholm, 1866-1960

Merrill Dunlop, 1905-

1. Christ is ris-en from the dead—He is ris-en as He said!
2. Gone the gar-den ag-o-ny, Dread-ful death of Cal-va-ry,
3. Chris-tian broth-ers, shout and sing— Death has lost its an-cient sting!
4. Heirs of glo-ry, thru His grace, Tears be dried from ev-'ry face!

Nev-er, since the heav-ens rang With the song the an-gels sang
Gone the hours of hope-less gloom While He lin-gered in the tomb;
Christ, the Cru-ci-fied be-fore, Is a-live for-ev-er-more!
Be your hearts no long-er sad, On this Eas-ter day be glad!

On the morn-ing of His birth, Had such glad-ness come to earth;
Like the wak-ing, did it seem, From a ter-ri-fy-ing dream—
Grave, where is thy vic-t'ry now? See the light up-on His brow!
Faith and hope are not in vain You are born to live a-gain!

Quick-ly were the ti-dings spread: Christ is ris-en from the dead!
Now what rap-t'rous joy in-stead: Christ is ris-en from the dead!
Emp-ty, see, the ston-y bed: Christ is ris-en from the dead!
Ev-'ry soul be com-fort-ed: Christ is ris-en from the dead!

Christ the Lord Is Risen Today

EASTER HYMN

CHARLES WESLEY, 1707-1788

From *Lyra Davidica*, 1708

1. Christ the Lord is ris'n to - day, Al - le - lu - ia!
2. Lives a - gain our glo - rious King, Al - le - lu - ia!
3. Love's re - deem - ing work is done, Al - le - lu - ia!
4. Soar we now where Christ has led, Al - le - lu - ia!

Sons of men and an - gels say: Al - le - lu - ia!
Where, O death, is now thy sting? Al - le - lu - ia!
Fought the fight, the bat - tle won, Al - le - lu - ia!
Fol - l'wing our ex - alt - ed Head, Al - le - lu - ia!

Raise your joys and tri - umphs high, Al - le - lu - ia!
Dy - ing once He all doth save, Al - le - lu - ia!
Death in vain for - bids Him rise, Al - le - lu - ia!
Made like Him, like Him we rise, Al - le - lu - ia!

Sing, ye heav'ns, and earth re - ply: Al - le - lu - ia!
Where thy vic - to - ry, O grave? Al - le - lu - ia!
Christ has o - pened Par - a - dise, Al - le - lu - ia!
Ours the cross, the grave, the skies, Al - le - lu - ia!

138

ROBERT LOWRY, 1826-1899

Christ Arose

ROBERT LOWRY, 1826-1899

1. Low in the grave He lay— Je - sus, my Sav-ior! Wait-ing the com-ing day—
2. Vain - ly they watch His bed— Je - sus, my Sav-ior! Vain-ly they seal the dead—
3. Death can-not keep his prey— Je - sus, my Sav-ior! He tore the bars a-way—

CHORUS *Faster*

Je - sus, my Lord!
Je - sus, my Lord! Up from the grave He a - rose, With a
Je - sus, my Lord! He a - rose,

might-y tri-umph o'er His foes; He a - rose a Vic-tor from the
He a - rose!

dark do-main, And He lives for - ev - er with His saints to reign: He a-

rose! He a - rose! Hal-le - lu-jah! Christ a - rose!
He a-rose! He a-rose!

Golden Harps Are Sounding

139

HERMAS

FRANCES R. HAVERGAL, 1836-1879   FRANCES R. HAVERGAL, 1836-1879

1. Gold-en harps are sounding, An-gel voic-es ring, Pearl-y gates are
2. He who came to save us, He who bled and died, Now is crowned with
3. Pray-ing for His chil-dren In that bless-ed place, Call-ing them to

o-pened, O-pened for the King: Christ,the King of glo-ry, Je-sus,
glo-ry At His Fa-ther's side: Nev-er-more to suf-fer, Nev-er-
glo-ry, Send-ing them His grace: His bright home pre-par-ing, Faith-ful

King of love, Is gone up in tri-umph To His throne a-bove.
more to die, Je-sus, King of glo-ry, Is gone up on high.
ones, for you; Je-sus ev-er liv-eth, Ev-er lov-eth too.

REFRAIN

All His work is end-ed, Joy-ful-ly we sing;

Je-sus hath as-cend-ed— Glo-ry to our King!

Alternate tunes: ARMAGEDDON — 372, ST. GERTRUDE — 181

140 Open Wide, Ye Doors

JOHN W. PETERSON, 1921-

JOHN W. PETERSON, 1921-

1. O - pen wide, ye ev-er-last-ing doors, Let the King of Glo - ry in;
2. Choir-ing an-gels, come and wait be-fore Him, He is wor-thy of thy praise;
3. And some day— O thrill-ing truth to pon- der—Christ is com-ing back a - gain!

D.C. 1.-2. O-pen wide, ye ev-er-last-ing doors, Let the King of Glo-ry in;
3. Glo-rious prom-ise that can-not be bro-ken, How it cheers the hearts of men!

Fine

Now re-turn-ing from His earth-ly wars, He the vic-to-ry did win.
With all heav-en wor-ship and a-dore Him, Ho-ly hymns and an-thems raise.
Break-ing thru the si-lent sky up yon-der, Ev-'ry eye shall see Him then.

Now re-turn-ing from His earth-ly wars, He the vic-to-ry did win!
Christ Him-self the bless-ed truth has spo-ken— He is com-ing back a-gain!

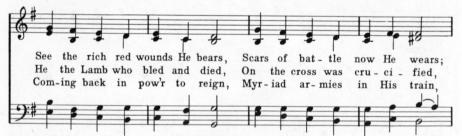

See the rich red wounds He bears, Scars of bat-tle now He wears;
He the Lamb who bled and died, On the cross was cru-ci-fied,
Com-ing back in pow'r to reign, Myr-iad ar-mies in His train,

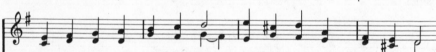

He has wrest-ed Sa-tan's throne— He must reign and He a-lone!
Tast-ing death for ev-'ry man: This the great re-demp-tive plan!
All the earth shall know His sway, Ev-'ry knee will bow that day;

Open Wide, Ye Doors

D.C.

Rise to meet and wel-come Him, Crown Him, saints and ser-a-phim.
Con-quer-or of death and hell, See— He lives and all is well!
E-ven so, come, Lord di-vine, Take the throne that's right-ly Thine.

Look, Ye Saints! the Sight Is Glorious   141

CORONAE

THOMAS KELLY, 1769-1854   WILLIAM H. MONK, 1823-1889

1. Look, ye saints! the sight is glo-rious: See the Man of Sor-rows now;
2. Crown the Sav-ior! an-gels, crown Him! Rich the tro-phies Je-sus brings;
3. Sin-ners in de-ri-sion crowned Him, Mock-ing thus the Sav-ior's claim;
4. Hark! those bursts of ac-cla-ma-tion! Hark! those loud tri-um-phant chords!

From the fight re-turned vic-to-rious, Ev-'ry knee to Him shall bow:
In the seat of pow'r en-throne Him, While the vault of heav-en rings:
Saints and an-gels crowd a-round Him, Own His ti-tle, praise His name:
Je-sus takes the high-est sta-tion— O what joy the sight af-fords!

Crown Him! crown Him! Crowns be-come the Vic-tor's brow.
Crown Him! crown Him! Crown the Sav-ior King of kings.
Crown Him! crown Him! Spread a-broad the Vic-tor's fame!
Crown Him! crown Him! King of kings and Lord of lords!

Alternate tunes: CWM RHONDDA—291, KENT—7 *(both require repetition of words, third score.)*

142

Jesus Shall Reign

DUKE STREET

ISAAC WATTS, 1674-1748

JOHN HATTON, c. 1710-1793

1. Je - sus shall reign wher-e'er the sun Does his suc-ces-sive jour-neys run,
2. From north to south the princ-es meet To pay their hom-age at His feet,
3. To Him shall end-less prayer be made And end-less prais-es crown His head;
4. Peo - ple and realms of ev - 'ry tongue Dwell on His love with sweet-est song,

His king-dom spread from shore to shore Till moons shall wax and wane no more.
While western em - pires own their Lord And sav-age tribes at-tend His word.
His name like sweet per-fume shall rise With ev-'ry morn-ing sac-ri-fice.
And in-fant voic-es shall pro-claim Their ear-ly bless-ings on His name.

143

Rejoice – the Lord Is King!

DARWALL

CHARLES WESLEY, 1707-1788

JOHN DARWALL, 1731-1789

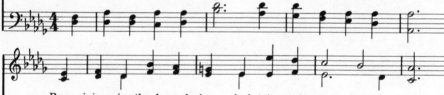

1. Re - joice—the Lord is King! Your Lord and King a - dore!
2. Je - sus the Sav-ior reigns, The God of truth and love;
3. His king-dom can-not fail— He rules o'er earth and heav'n;
4. Re - joice in glo-rious hope! Our Lord the Judge shall come

Re - joice, give thanks, and sing And tri-umph ev - er - more:
When He had purged our stains He took His seat a - bove:
The keys of death and hell Are to our Je - sus giv'n:
And take His ser - vants up To their e - ter - nal home:

Rejoice—the Lord Is King!

Lift up your heart, lift up your voice! Re-joice, a-gain I say, re-joice!

Hark! Ten Thousand Harps and Voices 144

HARWELL

THOMAS KELLY, 1769-1854

LOWELL MASON, 1792-1872

1. Hark! ten thou-sand harps and voic-es Sound the note of praise a-bove;
2. Je-sus, hail! whose glo-ry bright-ens All a-bove, and gives it worth;
3. King of glo-ry, reign for-ev-er— Thine an ev-er-last-ing crown;
4. Sav-ior, has-ten Thine ap-pear-ing— Bring, O bring the glo-rious day,

Je-sus reigns, and heav'n re-joic-es— Je-sus reigns, the God of love:
Lord of life, Thy smile en-light-ens, Cheers and charms Thy saints on earth:
Noth-ing from Thy love shall sev-er Those whom Thou hast made Thine own:
When, the aw-ful sum-mons hear-ing, Heav'n and earth shall pass a-way:

See, He sits on yon-der throne— Je-sus rules the world a-lone.
When we think of love like Thine, Lord, we own it love di-vine.
Hap-py ob-jects of Thy grace, Des-tined to be-hold Thy face.
Then with gold-en harps we'll sing, "Glo-ry, glo-ry to our King!"

Al-le-lu-ia! al-le-lu-ia! Al-le-lu-ia! A-men.

Alternate tunes: BEECHER—2, HYMN TO JOY—38

145 Hail, Thou Once-Despised Jesus!

AUTUMN

John Bakewell, 1721-1819

François H. Barthélémon, 1741-1808

1. Hail, Thou once-de-spis-ed Je-sus! Hail, Thou Gal-i-le-an King!
2. Pas-chal Lamb, by God ap-point-ed, All our sins on Thee were laid;
3. Je-sus, hail! en-throned in glo-ry, There for-ev-er to a-bide;
4. Wor-ship, hon-or, pow'r and bless-ing Thou art wor-thy to re-ceive;

Thou didst suf-fer to re-lease us; Thou didst free sal-va-tion bring.
By al-might-y love a-noint-ed, Thou hast full a-tone-ment made.
All the heav'n-ly hosts a-dore Thee, Seat-ed at Thy Fa-ther's side:
Loud-est prais-es, with-out ceas-ing, Meet it is for us to give.

Hail, Thou ag-o-niz-ing Sav-ior, Bear-er of our sin and shame!
All Thy peo-ple are for-giv-en Thru the vir-tue of Thy blood;
There for sin-ners Thou art plead-ing, There Thou dost our place pre-pare,
Help, ye bright an-gel-ic spir-its, Bring your sweet-est, no-blest lays;

By Thy mer-its we find fa-vor, Life is giv-en thru Thy name.
O-pened is the gate of heav-en, Peace is made 'twixt man and God.
Ev-er for us in-ter-ced-ing Till in glo-ry we ap-pear.
Help to sing our Sav-ior's mer-its, Help to chant Im-man-uel's praise!

Alternate tunes: BEECHER—2, ELLESDIE—324, 390

Sooner or Later

Lula W. Koch, 1892-

Wilbur E. Nelson, 20th century

1. Soon-er or lat-er the skies will be bright, Tears will be
2. Soon-er or lat-er, our Lord knows the hour, He'll send His
3. Soon-er or lat-er, yes, soon-er for some, Dark-ness will

all wiped a-way; (a-way;) Soon-er or lat-er, then com-eth the light,
be-lov-ed Son; (His Son;) Soon-er or lat-er, in His might and pow'r,
all then be past; (be past;) Soon-er or lat-er our Sav-ior will come—

CHORUS

Night will be turned in-to day. (glad day.) Soon-er or lat-er
Our bat-tles all will be won. (be won.)
With Him will your lot be cast? (be cast?)

cares will have flown, Sun-shine and glad-ness we'll see; _____ Soon-er or
we'll see;

lat-er God call-eth His own, With Him for-ev-er to be. _____
to be.

147 There'll Be No Dark Valley

WILLIAM O. CUSHING, 1823-1902

IRA D. SANKEY, 1840-1908

1. There'll be no dark val - ley when Je - sus comes, There'll be no dark
2. There'll be no more sor - row when Je - sus comes, There'll be no more
3. There'll be no more weep-ing when Je - sus comes, There'll be no more
4. There'll be songs of greet-ing when Je - sus comes, There'll be songs of

val - ley when Je-sus comes; There'll be no dark val - ley when Je - sus
sor - row when Je-sus comes; But a glo - rious mor-row when Je - sus
weep-ing when Je-sus comes; But a bless_ed reap-ing when Je - sus
greet-ing when Je-sus comes; And a joy - ful meet-ing when Je - sus

REFRAIN

comes To gath-er His loved ones home. To gath-er His loved ones

home, To gath-er His loved ones home; There'll be
safe home, safe home;

no dark val - ley when Je-sus comes To gath-er His loved ones home.

Will Jesus Find Us Watching?

148

FANNY J. CROSBY, 1820-1915

WILLIAM H. DOANE, 1832-1915

1. When Jesus comes to reward His servants, Whether it be noon or night, Faithful to Him will He find us watching, With our lamps all trimmed and bright?

2. If at the dawn of the early morning He shall call us one by one, When to the Lord we restore our talents, Will He answer thee—"Well done"?

3. Have we been true to the trust He left us? Do we seek to do our best? If in our hearts there is naught condemns us, We shall have a glorious rest.

4. Blessed are those whom the Lord finds watching, In His glory they shall share; If He shall come at the dawn or midnight, Will He find us watching there?

CHORUS

O can we say we are ready, brother? Ready for the soul's bright home? Say, will He find you and me still watching, Waiting, waiting when the Lord shall come?

149

When We See Christ

ESTHER KERR RUSTHOI, 1909-1962   ESTHER KERR RUSTHOI, 1909-1962

1. Oft-times the day seems long, our tri-als hard to bear, We're tempt-ed
2. Some-times the sky looks dark with not a ray of light, We're tossed and
3. Life's day will soon be o'er, all storms for-ev-er past, We'll cross the

to com-plain, to mur-mur and de-spair; But Christ will soon ap-pear
driv-en on, no hu-man help in sight; But there is one in heav'n
great di-vide to glo-ry, safe at last; We'll share the joys of heav'n—

to catch His Bride a-way, All tears for-ev-er o-ver in
who knows our deep-est care, Let Je-sus solve your prob-lem— just
a harp, a home, a crown, The tempt-er will be ban-ished, we'll

CHORUS

God's e-ter-nal day.
go to Him in pray'r. It will be worth it all when we see Je-sus,
lay our bur-den down.

Life's trials will seem so small when we see Christ; One glimpse of His dear face

When We See Christ

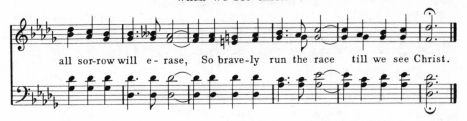

all sor-row will e-rase, So brave-ly run the race till we see Christ.

When He Cometh 150

WILLIAM O. CUSHING, 1823-1902

GEORGE F. ROOT, 1820-1895

1. When He com - eth, when He com - eth To make up His jew - els,
2. He will gath - er, He will gath - er The gems for His king - dom,
3. Lit - tle chil - dren, lit - tle chil - dren Who love their Re - deem - er

All His jew - els, pre-cious jew - els, His loved and His own:
All the pure ones, all the bright ones, His loved and His own:
Are the jew - els, pre-cious jew - els, His loved and His own:

REFRAIN

Like the stars of the morn - ing, His bright crown a - dorn - ing,

They shall shine in their beau - ty— Bright gems for His crown.

151
Jesus Is Coming Again

JOHN W. PETERSON, 1921-　　　　　　　　　　　　　　　　　JOHN W. PETERSON, 1921-

1. Mar-vel-ous mes-sage we bring,　Glo - ri-ous car - ol we　sing,
2. For - est and flow-er ex - claim,　Moun-tain and mead-ow the　same,
3. Stand-ing be-fore Him at　last,　Tri - al　and trou-ble all　past,

Won-der-ful word of the　King:　Je-sus is com-ing a - gain! (a-gain!)
All earth and heav-en pro - claim:　Je-sus is com-ing a - gain! (a-gain!)
Crowns at His feet we will　cast:　Je-sus is com-ing a - gain! (a-gain!)

CHORUS
Unison

Com - ing　a - gain,　Com - ing　a - gain;

May - be morn - ing, may - be noon,　May - be eve-ning and may-be soon!

Com - ing　a - gain,　Com - ing　a - gain;

Jesus Is Coming Again

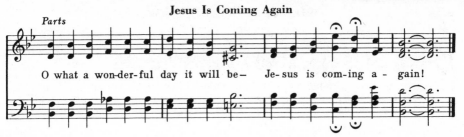

O what a won-der-ful day it will be— Je-sus is com-ing a - gain!

Lo! He Comes, with Clouds Descending 152

SICILIAN MARINERS

CHARLES WESLEY, 1707-1788 — alt. From Tattersall's *Psalmody*, 1794

1. Lo! He comes, with clouds de-scend-ing, Once for our sal - va - tion slain;
2. Ev - 'ry eye shall now be-hold Him, Robed in dread-ful maj - es - ty;
3. Yea, A - men! let all a - dore Thee, High on Thine e - ter - nal throne;

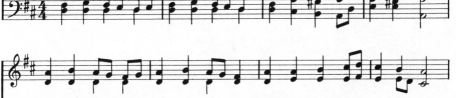

Thou-sand thou-sand saints at - tend-ing, Swell the tri - umph of His train:
Those who set at naught and sold Him, Pierced and nailed Him to the tree,
Sav - ior, take the pow'r and glo - ry, Claim the king - dom for Thine own:

Al - le - lu - ia! al - le - lu - ia! God ap - pears on earth to reign.
Deep - ly wail-ing, deep-ly wail-ing, Shall the true Mes - si - ah see.
O come quick-ly, O come quick-ly, Al - le - lu - ia! come, Lord, come!

This tune in a higher key: 80
Alternate tunes: KENT – 7, REGENT SQUARE – 99

153 **What If It Were Today?**

LELIA N. MORRIS, 1862-1929

LELIA N. MORRIS, 1862-1929

1. Je - sus is com-ing to earth a - gain— What if it were to - day?
2. Sa - tan's do-min-ion will then be o'er— O that it were to - day!
3. Faith-ful and true would He find us here If He should come to - day?

Com-ing in pow-er and love to reign— What if it were to - day?
Sor - row and sigh-ing shall be no more— O that it were to - day!
Watch-ing in glad-ness and not in fear, If He should come to - day?

Com-ing to claim His cho-sen Bride, All the re-deemed and pu-ri-fied,
Then shall the dead in Christ a-rise, Caught up to meet Him in the skies;
Signs of His com-ing mul-ti-ply, Morn-ing light breaks in east-ern sky;

rit. *a tempo*

O - ver this whole earth scat-tered wide— What if it were to - day?
When shall these glo-ries meet our eyes? What if it were to - day?
Watch, for the time is draw-ing nigh— What if it were to - day?

CHORUS *Unison* *Parts*

Glo - ry, glo - ry! Joy to my heart 'twill bring,
Joy to my heart 'twill bring,

What If It Were Today?

Glo - ry, glo - ry! When we shall crown Him King;
When we shall crown Him King;

Glo - ry, glo - ry! Haste to pre - pare the way—
Haste to pre - pare the way—

Glo - ry, glo - ry! Je - sus will come some day.

For God So Loved the World 154

Frances Townsend, 1906-

Alfred B. Smith, 1916-

For God so loved the world He gave His on - ly Son To die on Cal - v'ry's
Some day He's com - ing back—What glo - ry that will

tree, From sin to set me free; be! Won - der - ful His love to me.

155
He Is Coming Again

MABEL JOHNSTON CAMP, 1871-1937   MABEL JOHNSTON CAMP, 1871-1937

1. Lift up your heads, pil-grims a - wea-ry! See day's ap-proach now
2. Dark was the night— sin warred a-gainst us! Heav-y the load of
3. O bless-ed hope! O bliss-ful prom-ise! Fill-ing our hearts with
4. E - ven so, come, pre-cious Lord Je-sus! Cre-a-tion waits re -

crim-son the sky; Night shad-ows flee, and your Be-lov-ed, A -
sor-row we bore; But now we see signs of His com-ing— Our
rap-ture di-vine; O day of days! hail Thy ap-pear-ing! Thy
demp-tion to see; Caught up in clouds, soon we shall meet Thee— O

CHORUS

wait-ed with long-ing, at last draw-eth nigh.
hearts glow with-in us, joy's cup run-neth o'er! { He is com-ing a-
tran-scend-ent glo-ry for-ev-er shall shine! { He is com-ing a-
bless-ed as-sur-ance, for-ev-er with Thee!

1

gain, He is com-ing a-gain, The ver-y same Je-sus re-
gain, He is com-ing a-gain, With

2

ject-ed of men; pow'r and great glo-ry, He is com-ing a-gain!

Christ Returneth!

H. L. TURNER, 19th century

JAMES McGRANAHAN, 1840-1907

1. It may be at morn, when the day is a-wak-ing, When sun-light thru dark-ness and shad-ow is break-ing, That Je-sus will come in the full-ness of glo-ry To re-ceive from the world His own.

2. It may be at mid-day, it may be at twi-light, It may be, per-chance, that the black-ness of mid-night Will burst in-to light in the blaze of His glo-ry, When Je-sus re-ceives His own.

3. While hosts cry Ho-san-na, from heav-en de-scend-ing, With glo-ri-fied saints and the an-gels at-tend-ing, With grace on His brow, like a ha-lo of glo-ry, Will Je-sus re-ceive His own.

4. O joy! O de-light! should we go with-out dy-ing, No sick-ness, no sad-ness, no dread and no cry-ing, Caught up thru the clouds with our Lord in-to glo-ry, When Je-sus re-ceives His own.

CHORUS

O Lord Je-sus, how long, how long Ere we shout the glad song—Christ re-turn-eth! Hal-le-lu-jah! Hal-le-lu-jah! A-men, Hal-le-lu-jah! A-men.

157   What a Gathering!

FANNY J. CROSBY, 1820-1915

IRA D. SANKEY, 1840-1908

1. On that bright and gold-en morn-ing when the Son of man shall
2. When the blest who sleep in Je-sus at His bid-ding shall a -
3. When our eyes be-hold the cit-y with its man-y man-sions
4. O the King is sure-ly com-ing, and the time is draw-ing

come, And the ra-diance of His glo-ry we shall see,
rise From the si-lence of the grave and from the sea,
bright And its riv-er, calm and rest-ful, flow-ing free,
nigh When the bless-ed day of prom-ise we shall see;

When from ev-'ry clime and na-tion He shall call His peo-ple
And with bod-ies all ce-les-tial they shall meet Him in the
When the friends that death hath part-ed shall in bliss a-gain u-
Then the chang-ing "in a mo-ment, in the twin-kling of an

home, What a gath-'ring of the ran-somed that will be!
skies, What a gath-'ring and re-joic-ing there will be!
nite, What a gath-'ring and a greet-ing there will be!
eye," And for-ev-er in His pres-ence we shall be.

What a Gathering!

CHORUS

What a gath - 'ring, what a gath - 'ring, What a gath-'ring of the ran-somed in the sum-mer land of love! What a gath - 'ring, what a gath - 'ring Of the ran-somed in that hap- py home a - bove!

Come, Holy Spirit, Heavenly Dove   158

ST. AGNES

ISAAC WATTS, 1674-1748   JOHN B. DYKES, 1823-1876

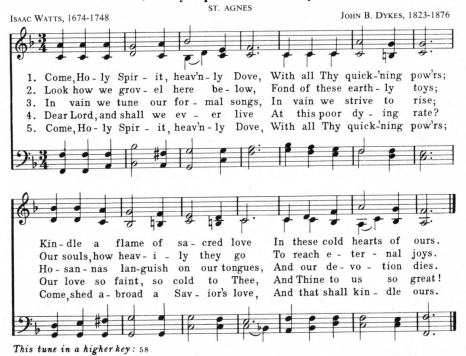

1. Come, Ho - ly Spir - it, heav'n - ly Dove, With all Thy quick-'ning pow'rs;
2. Look how we grov - el here be - low, Fond of these earth - ly toys;
3. In vain we tune our for - mal songs, In vain we strive to rise;
4. Dear Lord, and shall we ev - er live At this poor dy - ing rate?
5. Come, Ho - ly Spir - it, heav'n - ly Dove, With all Thy quick-'ning pow'rs;

Kin - dle a flame of sa - cred love In these cold hearts of ours.
Our souls, how heav - i - ly they go To reach e - ter - nal joys.
Ho - san - nas lan-guish on our tongues, And our de - vo - tion dies.
Our love so faint, so cold to Thee, And Thine to us so great!
Come, shed a - broad a Sav - ior's love, And that shall kin - dle ours.

This tune in a higher key: 58

Blessed Quietness

MANIE P. FERGUSON, 19th century

W. S. MARSHALL, 19th century
Adapted by James M. Kirk, 1854-1945

1. Joys are flow-ing like a riv-er Since the Com-fort-er has come;
2. Bring-ing life and health and glad-ness All a-round, this heav'n-ly Guest
3. Like the rain that falls from heav-en, Like the sun-light from the sky,
4. See, a fruit-ful field is grow-ing, Bless-ed fruit of right-eous-ness;
5. What a won-der-ful sal-va-tion, Where we al-ways see His face!

He a-bides with us for-ev-er, Makes the trust-ing heart His home.
Ban-ished un-be-lief and sad-ness, Chang'd our wea-ri-ness to rest.
So the Ho-ly Ghost is giv-en, Com-ing on us from on high.
And the streams of life are flow-ing In the lone-ly wil-der-ness.
What a per-fect hab-i-ta-tion, What a qui-et rest-ing place!

CHORUS

Bless-ed qui-et-ness, ho-ly qui-et-ness—What as-sur-ance in my soul!

On the storm-y sea He speaks peace to me— How the bil-lows cease to roll!

Channels Only

ADA ROSE GIBBS, 1865-1905
Arr. by Norman Johnson, 1928-

MARY E. MAXWELL, 20th century

1. How I praise Thee, pre-cious Sav-ior, That Thy love laid hold of me;
2. Emp-tied that Thou should-est fill me, A clean ves - sel in Thy hand,
3. Wit - ness - ing Thy pow'r to save me, Set - ting free from self and sin,
4. Je - sus, fill now with Thy Spir - it Hearts that full sur - ren-der know,

Thou hast saved and cleansed and filled me That I might Thy chan-nel be.
With no pow'r but as Thou giv-est Gra-cious-ly with each com-mand.
Thou who bought-est to pos-sess me, In Thy full-ness, Lord, come in.
That the streams of liv-ing wa-ter From our in-ner man may flow.

CHORUS

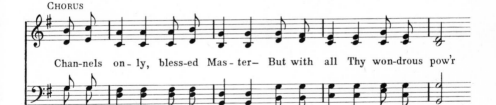

Chan-nels on-ly, bless-ed Mas-ter— But with all Thy won-drous pow'r

Flow-ing thru us, Thou canst use us Ev-'ry day and ev-'ry hour.

161 The Comforter Has Come

Frank Bottome, 1823-1894

William J. Kirkpatrick, 1838-1921

1. O spread the ti - dings 'round, wher - ev - er man is found, Wher-
ev - er hu-man hearts and hu-man woes a - bound; Let ev - 'ry Chris-tian
tongue pro-claim the joy-ful sound: The Com - fort - er has come!

2. The long, long night is past, the morn - ing breaks at last, And
hushed the dreadful wail and fu - ry of the blast, As o'er the gold - en
hills the day ad-vanc-es fast! The Com - fort - er has come!

3. Lo, the great King of kings, with heal - ing in His wings, To
ev - 'ry cap-tive soul a full de-liv-'rance brings; And thru the va - cant
cells the song of tri-umph rings: The Com - fort - er has come!

4. O bound-less love di - vine! how shall this tongue of mine To
won-d'ring mor-tals tell the match-less grace di-vine— That I, a child of
hell, should in His im - age shine! The Com - fort - er has come!

CHORUS

The Com - fort-er has come, the Com - fort-er has come! The
Ho - ly Ghost from heav'n—the Fa - ther's prom-ise giv'n; O spread the ti - dings

The Comforter Has Come

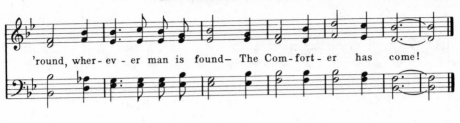

'round, wher - ev - er man is found— The Com - fort - er has come!

Fill Me Now

162

ELWOOD R. STOKES, 1815-1895

JOHN R. SWENEY, 1837-1899

1. Hov - er o'er me, Ho - ly Spir - it, Bathe my trem-bling heart and brow;
2. Thou canst fill me, gra - cious Spir - it, Tho I can - not tell Thee how;
3. I am weak-ness, full of weak-ness, At Thy sa - cred feet I bow;
4. Cleanse and com-fort, bless and save me, Bathe, O bathe my heart and brow;

Fill me with Thy hal - low'd pres-ence, Come, O come and fill me now.
But I need Thee, great - ly need Thee, Come, O come and fill me now.
Blest, di -vine, e - ter - nal Spir - it, Fill with pow'r, and fill me now.
Thou art com - fort - ing and sav - ing, Thou art sweet - ly fill - ing now.

CHORUS

Fill me now, fill me now, Je - sus, come and fill me now;

Fill me with Thy hal - low'd pres-ence—Come, O come and fill me now.

163 Open My Eyes, That I May See

CLARA H. SCOTT, 1841-1897

CLARA H. SCOTT, 1841-1897

1. O-pen my eyes, that I may see Glimpses of truth Thou hast for me;
2. O-pen my ears, that I may hear Voic-es of truth Thou send-est clear;
3. O-pen my mouth, and let me bear Glad-ly the warm truth ev-'ry-where;

Place in my hands the won-der-ful key That shall un-clasp and set me free.
And while the wave-notes fall on my ear, Ev - 'ry-thing false will dis-ap-pear.
O - pen my heart and let me pre-pare Love with Thy chil-dren thus to share.

Si - lent-ly now I wait for Thee, Read-y, my God, Thy will to see;
Si - lent-ly now I wait for Thee, Read-y, my God, Thy will to see;
Si - lent-ly now I wait for Thee, Read-y, my God, Thy will to see;

O - pen my eyes— il - lu - mine me, Spir - it di - vine!
O - pen my ears— il - lu - mine me, Spir - it di - vine!
O - pen my heart— il - lu - mine me, Spir - it di - vine!

Breathe on Me, Breath of God 164
TRENTHAM

EDWIN HATCH, 1835-1889

ROBERT JACKSON, 1842-1914

1. Breathe on me, Breath of God, Fill me with life a - new,
2. Breathe on me, Breath of God, Un - til my heart is pure,
3. Breathe on me, Breath of God, Till I am whol - ly Thine,
4. Breathe on me, Breath of God, So shall I nev - er die,

That I may love what Thou dost love And do what Thou wouldst do.
Un - til with Thee I will one will—To do and to en - dure.
Till all this earth-ly part of me Glows with Thy fire di - vine.
But live with Thee the per - fect life Of Thine e - ter - ni - ty.

Holy Ghost, with Light Divine 165
MERCY

LOUIS M. GOTTSCHALK, 1829-1869
Arr. by Edwin P. Parker, 1836-1925

ANDREW REED, 1787-1862

1. Ho - ly Ghost, with light di - vine, Shine up - on this heart of mine;
2. Ho - ly Ghost, with pow'r di - vine, Cleanse this guilt-y heart of mine;
3. Ho - ly Ghost, with joy di - vine, Cheer this sad-dened heart of mine;
4. Ho - ly Spir - it, all di - vine, Dwell with-in this heart of mine;

Chase the shades of night a - way, Turn my dark - ness in - to day.
Long hath sin with-out con - trol Held do - min - ion o'er my soul.
Bid my man - y woes de - part, Heal my wound-ed, bleed-ing heart.
Cast down ev - 'ry i - dol-throne, Reign su - preme and reign a - lone.

166
Cleanse Me
MAORI

J. Edwin Orr, 1912-

Maori melody
Arr. by Norman Johnson, 1928-

1. Search me, O God, and know my heart to - day; Try me, O
2. I praise Thee, Lord, for cleans-ing me from sin; Ful - fill Thy
3. Lord, take my life and make it whol - ly Thine; Fill my poor
4. O Ho - ly Ghost, re - viv - al comes from Thee; Send a re -

Sav - ior, know my thoughts, I pray. See if there be some wick - ed
Word and make me pure with - in. Fill me with fire where once I
heart with Thy great love di - vine. Take all my will, my pas - sion,
viv - al - start the work in me. Thy Word de - clares Thou wilt sup -

way in me; Cleanse me from ev - 'ry sin and set me free.
burned with shame; Grant my de - sire to mag - ni - fy Thy name.
self and pride; I now sur - ren - der, Lord - in me a - bide.
ply our need; For bless - ings now, O Lord, I hum - bly plead.

167
Holy Spirit, Now Outpoured
GLEN ECHO

John W. Peterson, 1921-

John W. Peterson, 1921-

1. Ho - ly Spir - it, now out-poured, Sent by our as - cend - ed Lord,
2. Fill each heart and reign a - lone, Break the i - dols we have known;
3. Guide in - to all truth, we plead, Light the Ho - ly Page we read;
4. May Thy quick'ning pow'r we feel— Hu - man doubt and weak-ness heal;

Holy Spirit, Now Outpoured

Bless our gath-'ring here to-day, Be our hal-lowed Guest, we pray.
Lead us to con-fes-sion true, Give us strength Thy will to do.
Write its pre-cepts deep with-in, Till we're kept from ev-'ry sin.
May Thy pres-ence, like a fire, Burn with-in— our zeal in-spire.

Even Me   168

ELIZABETH CODNER, 1824-1919

WILLIAM B. BRADBURY, 1816-1868

1. Lord, I hear of show'rs of bless-ing Thou art scat-t'ring full and free;
2. Pass me not, O ten-der Sav-ior! Let me love and cling to Thee;
3. Pass me not, O might-y Spir-it! Thou canst make the blind to see;
4. Love of God so pure and changeless, Blood of Christ so rich and free,
5. Pass me not! Thy lost one bring-ing, Bind my heart, O Lord, to Thee;

Show'rs the thirst-y land re-fresh-ing— Let some drops now fall on me.
I am long-ing for Thy fa-vor— Whilst Thou'rt call-ing, O call me.
Wit-ness-er of Je-sus' mer-it, Speak the word of pow'r to me.
Grace of God so strong and bound-less: Mag-ni-fy them all in me.
While the streams of life are spring-ing, Bless-ing oth-ers, O bless me.

REFRAIN

E-ven me, e-ven me, Let Thy bless-ing fall on me.

169

Holy Spirit, Faithful Guide

FAITHFUL GUIDE

MARCUS M. WELLS, 1815-1895   MARCUS M. WELLS, 1815-1895

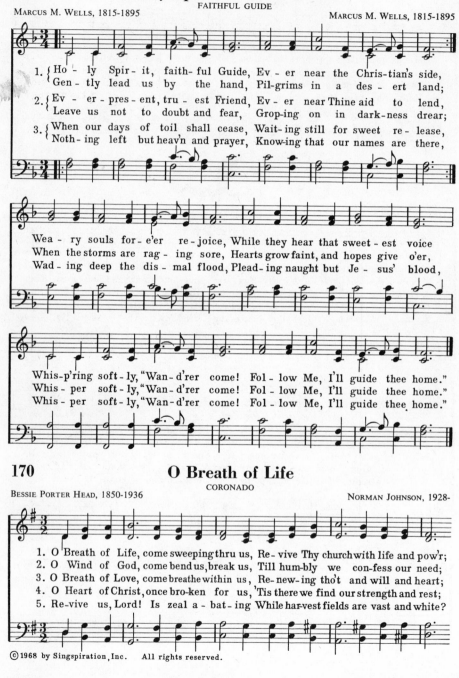

1. { Ho - ly Spir - it, faith- ful Guide, Ev - er near the Chris-tian's side,
   { Gen - tly lead us by the hand, Pil-grims in a des - ert land;

2. { Ev - er - pres - ent, tru - est Friend, Ev - er near Thine aid to lend,
   { Leave us not to doubt and fear, Grop-ing on in dark-ness drear;

3. { When our days of toil shall cease, Wait-ing still for sweet re - lease,
   { Noth - ing left but heav'n and prayer, Know-ing that our names are there,

Wea - ry souls for - e'er re - joice, While they hear that sweet - est voice
When the storms are rag - ing sore, Hearts grow faint, and hopes give o'er,
Wad - ing deep the dis - mal flood, Plead-ing naught but Je - sus' blood,

Whis-p'ring soft-ly, "Wan-d'rer come! Fol - low Me, I'll guide thee home."
Whis - per soft-ly, "Wan-d'rer come! Fol - low Me, I'll guide thee home."
Whis - per soft-ly, "Wan-d'rer come! Fol - low Me, I'll guide thee home."

170

O Breath of Life

CORONADO

BESSIE PORTER HEAD, 1850-1936   NORMAN JOHNSON, 1928-

1. O Breath of Life, come sweeping thru us, Re - vive Thy church with life and pow'r;
2. O Wind of God, come bend us, break us, Till hum-bly we con-fess our need;
3. O Breath of Love, come breathe within us, Re - new-ing tho't and will and heart;
4. O Heart of Christ, once bro-ken for us, 'Tis there we find our strength and rest;
5. Re - vive us, Lord! Is zeal a - bat-ing While har-vest fields are vast and white?

O Breath of Life

O Breath of Life, come, cleanse, re-new us, And fit Thy Church to meet this hour.
Then in Thy ten-der-ness re-make us, Re-vive, re-store— for this we plead.
Come, Love of Christ, a-fresh to win us, Re-vive Thy Church in ev-'ry part.
Our bro-ken con-trite hearts now sol-ace, And let Thy wait-ing Church be blest.
Re-vive us, Lord— the world is wait-ing! E-quip Thy Church to spread the light.

Spirit of God, Descend upon My Heart   171

MORECAMBE

GEORGE CROLY, 1780-1860   FREDERICK C. ATKINSON, 1841-1897

1. Spir-it of God, de-scend up-on my heart: Wean it from
2. Hast Thou not bid us love Thee, God and King? All, all Thine
3. Teach me to feel that Thou art al-ways nigh; Teach me the
4. Teach me to love Thee as Thine an-gels love, One ho-ly

earth, through all its puls-es move. Stoop to my weak-ness, might-y
own— soul, heart and strength and mind. I see Thy cross— there teach my
strug-gles of the soul to bear— To check the ris-ing doubt, the
pas-sion fill-ing all my frame: The bap-tism of the heav'n-de-

as Thou art, And make me love Thee as I ought to love.
heart to cling; O let me seek Thee, and O let me find.
reb-el sigh; Teach me the pa-tience of un-an-swered prayer.
scend-ed Dove— My heart an al-tar and Thy love the flame.

This tune in a lower key: 191

172 O Word of God Incarnate

MUNICH

WILLIAM W. HOW, 1823-1897

From *Meiningen Gesangbuch*, 1693
Har. by Felix Mendelssohn, 1809-1847

1. O Word of God in - car - nate, O Wis - dom from on high,
2. The Church from her dear Mas - ter Re-ceived the gift di - vine,
3. It float - eth like a ban - ner Be - fore God's host un - furled;
4. O make Thy Church, dear Sav - ior, A lamp of pur - est gold,

O Truth un-changed, un - chang - ing, O Light of our dark sky:
And still that light she lift - eth O'er all the earth to shine.
It shin - eth like a bea - con A - bove the dark - ling world.
To bear be - fore the na - tions Thy true light, as of old.

We praise Thee for the ra - diance That from the hal - lowed page,
It is the gold - en cas - ket Where gems of truth are stored;
It is the chart and com - pass That o'er life's surg - ing sea,
O teach Thy wan - d'ring pil - grims By this their path to trace,

A lan - tern to our foot - steps, Shines on from age to age.
It is the heav'n-drawn pic - ture Of Christ, the liv - ing Word.
'Mid mists and rocks and quick-sands, Still guides, O Christ, to Thee.
Till, clouds and dark - ness end - ed, They see Thee face to face.

Alternate tunes: AURELIA – 186, MENDEBRAS – 68

Thy Word Is Like a Garden, Lord

BETHLEHEM

EDWIN HODDER, 1837-1904   GOTTFRIED W. FINK, 1783-1846

1. Thy Word is like a gar - den, Lord, With flow-ers bright and fair;
2. Thy Word is like a star - ry host— A thou-sand rays of light
3. O may I love Thy pre - cious Word, May I ex - plore the mine;

And ev - 'ry-one who seeks may pluck A love - ly clus-ter there.
Are seen to guide the trav - el - er, And make his path-way bright.
May I its fra - grant flow - ers glean, May light up - on me shine.

Thy Word is like a deep, deep mine, And jew-els rich and rare
Thy Word is like an ar - mor - y Where sol-diers may re - pair
O may I find my ar - mor there, Thy Word my trust - y sword!

Are hid - den in its might - y depths For ev - 'ry search-er there.
And find, for life's long bat - tle-day, All need-ful weap-ons there.
I'll learn to fight with ev - 'ry foe The bat-tle of the Lord!

174   The Old Book and the Old Faith

GEORGE H. CARR, 20th century   GEORGE H. CARR, 20th century

1. 'Mid the storms of doubt and un-be-lief we fear, Stands a Book e -
2. 'Tis the Book that tells us of the Fa-ther's love, When He sent His
3. 'Tis the Book that tells us of the will of God And the Sav-ior's
4. 'Tis the Book that tells us of e-ter-nal life, Aft-er faith-ful

ter-nal that the world holds dear; Thru the rest-less a-ges it re-
Son to us from heav'n a-bove, Who by rich-est prom-ise cre-ates
teachings while the earth He trod— How He soothed earth's sor-rows and re-
serv-ice in a world of strife; And this glo-rious tri-umph o-ver

mains the same—'Tis the Book of God, and the Bi-ble is its name!
hope with-in, For 'tis thru His blood we are saved from ev-'ry sin!
lieved its woe, Thru whom strength is giv-en to con-quer ev-'ry foe!
death's dark fears Is the world's best gift in an age of count-less tears!

CHORUS

The old Book and the old Faith Are the Rock on which I stand!
The grand old Book and the dear old Faith   on which I stand!

The Old Book and the Old Faith

The old Book and the old Faith Are the bul-wark of the land!
The grand old Book and the dear old Faith

Thru storm and stress they stand the test, In ev-'ry clime and na-tion blest;

The old Book and the old Faith Are the hope of ev-'ry land!
The grand old Book and the dear old Faith

GRAND CHORUS AT CLOSE
(*May be omitted*)

O the grand old Book and the dear old Faith Are the Rock on which I stand!

O the grand old Book and the dear old Faith Are the hope of ev-'ry land!

175 Standing on the Promises

R. KELSO CARTER, 1849-1928   R. KELSO CARTER, 1849-1928

1. Stand-ing on the prom-is-es of Christ my King, Thru e-ter-nal
2. Stand-ing on the prom-is-es that can-not fail, When the howl-ing
3. Stand-ing on the prom-is-es of Christ the Lord, Bound to Him e-
4. Stand-ing on the prom-is-es I can-not fall, Lis-t'ning ev-'ry

a - ges let His prais-es ring; Glo-ry in the high-est I will
storms of doubt and fear as-sail, By the liv-ing word of God I
ter-nal-ly by love's strong cord, O-ver-com-ing dai-ly with the
mo-ment to the Spir-it's call, Rest-ing in my Sav-ior as my

CHORUS

shout and sing, Stand-ing on the prom-is-es of God. Stand - -
shall pre-vail, Stand-ing on the prom-is-es of God. Stand-ing on the
Spir-it's sword, Stand-ing on the prom-is-es of God. Stand-ing on the
all in all, Stand-ing on the prom-is-es of God.

ing, stand - - ing, Stand-ing on the
prom-is-es, stand-ing on the prom-is-es,

prom-is-es of God my Sav-ior; Stand - - ing,
Stand-ing on the prom-is-es,

Standing on the Promises

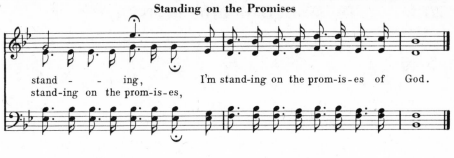

stand - - ing, I'm stand-ing on the prom-is-es of God.
stand-ing on the prom-is-es,

Break Thou the Bread of Life 176

BREAD OF LIFE

Mary Ann Lathbury, 1841-1913   William F. Sherwin, 1826-1888

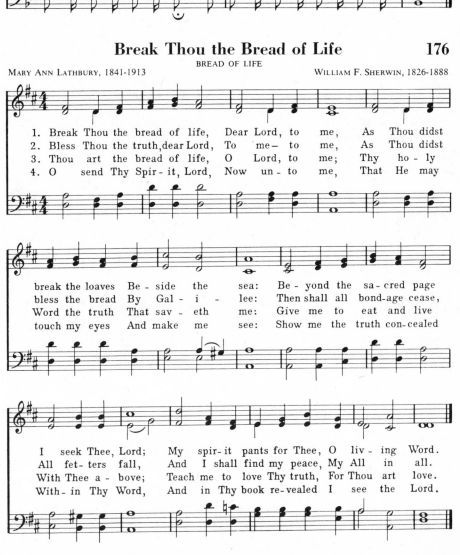

1. Break Thou the bread of life, Dear Lord, to me, As Thou didst
2. Bless Thou the truth, dear Lord, To me— to me, As Thou didst
3. Thou art the bread of life, O Lord, to me; Thy ho - ly
4. O send Thy Spir - it, Lord, Now un - to me, That He may

break the loaves Be - side the sea: Be - yond the sa - cred page
bless the bread By Gal - i - lee: Then shall all bond-age cease,
Word the truth That sav - eth me: Give me to eat and live
touch my eyes And make me see: Show me the truth con-cealed

I seek Thee, Lord; My spir-it pants for Thee, O liv - ing Word.
All fet - ters fall, And I shall find my peace, My All in all.
With Thee a - bove; Teach me to love Thy truth, For Thou art love.
With - in Thy Word, And in Thy book re-vealed I see the Lord.

177 Thy Word Have I Hid in My Heart

From Psalm 119
Adapted by Ernest O. Sellers, 1869-1952

ERNEST O. SELLERS, 1869-1952

1. Thy Word is a lamp to my feet, A light to my path al - way,
2. For - ev - er, O Lord, is Thy Word Es-tab-lished and fixed on high;
3. At morn-ing, at noon, and at night I ev - er will give Thee praise;
4. Thru Him whom Thy Word hath fore-told, The Sav-ior and Morn-ing Star,

To guide and to save me from sin And show me the heav'n-ly way.
Thy faith-ful-ness un - to all men A - bid-eth for - ev - er nigh.
For Thou art my por-tion, O Lord, And shall be thru all my days!
Sal - va - tion and peace have been brought To those who have strayed a - far.

CHORUS

Thy Word have I hid in my heart, (in my heart,) That I might not
sin a-gainst Thee; (a-gainst Thee;) That I might not sin, that
I might not sin, Thy Word have I hid in my heart.

The Bible Stands

Haldor Lillenas, 1885-1959   Haldor Lillenas, 1885-1959

1. The Bi-ble stands like a rock un-daunt-ed 'Mid the rag-ing
2. The Bi-ble stands like a moun-tain tow-'ring Far a-bove the
3. The Bi-ble stands, and it will for-ev-er When the world has
4. The Bi-ble stands ev-'ry test we give it For its Au-thor

storms of time; Its pag-es burn with the truth e-ter-nal, And they
works of men; Its truth by none ev-er was re-fut-ed, And de-
passed a-way; By in-spi-ra-tion it has been giv-en— All its
is di-vine; By grace a-lone I ex-pect to live it And to

CHORUS

glow with a light sub-lime.
stroy it they nev-er can.
pre-cepts I will o-bey.   The Bi-ble stands tho the hills may
prove it and make it mine.

tum-ble, It will firm-ly stand when the earth shall crum-ble; I will

plant my feet on its firm foun-da-tion, For the Bi-ble stands.

179 Holy Bible, Book Divine

ALETTA

JOHN BURTON, SR., 1773-1822

WILLIAM B. BRADBURY, 1816-1868

1. Ho - ly Bi - ble, Book di - vine, Pre - cious treas-ure, thou art mine:
2. Mine to chide me when I rove, Mine to show a Sav - ior's love;
3. Mine to com-fort in dis-tress— Suf-f'ring in this wil - der - ness;
4. Mine to tell of joys to come And the reb - el sin - ner's doom:

Mine to tell me whence I came, Mine to teach me what I am;
Mine thou art to guide and guard, Mine to pun - ish or re - ward;
Mine to show, by liv - ing faith, Man can tri - umph o - ver death;
O thou ho - ly Book di - vine, Pre - cious treas-ure, thou art mine.

180 Lord God, Our Thanks to Thee We Raise

BREWSTER

FREDERICK K. BREWSTER, 1884-1966

NORMAN JOHNSON, 1928-

1. Lord God, our thanks to Thee we raise For those who built this house of praise,
2. Here have our chil-dren known Thy care And raised their tho'ts to Thee in prayer;
3. Still thru the years be Thou our guide, Keep us from en - mi - ty and pride;
4. Be this our com-mon en - ter-prise: That truth be preach'd and pray'r a - rise,
5. Cre - ate in us the word, the deed, That ours may be a liv - ing creed;

Who long a - go to - geth - er stood To form a Chris-tian broth - er - hood.
Here have we shared the Wine, the Bread— Here have our liv - ing souls been fed.
Still help us choose the bet - ter part— A hum - ble and a thank-ful heart.
That each may seek the oth - er's good, And live and love as Je - sus would.
And cause Thy grace in us to dwell— A - bide with us, Im-man - u - el!

Alternate tunes: DUKE STREET—142, HURSLEY—77

Onward, Christian Soldiers

ST. GERTRUDE

SABINE BARING-GOULD, 1834-1924

ARTHUR S. SULLIVAN, 1842-1900

1. On-ward, Chris-tian sol - diers, March-ing as to war, With the cross of
2. At the sign of tri - umph Sa - tan's host doth flee; On, then, Chris-tian
3. Like a might-y ar - my Moves the Church of God; Broth-ers, we are
4. On-ward, then, ye peo - ple, Join our hap-py throng; Blend with ours your

Je - sus Go - ing on be - fore! Christ, the roy-al Mas - ter, Leads a -
sol - diers, On to vic-to-ry! Hell's foun-da-tions quiv-er At the
tread-ing Where the saints have trod. We are not di - vid - ed, All one
voic - es In the tri-umph song. Glo-ry, laud and hon - or Un - to

gainst the foe; For-ward in-to bat - tle See His ban-ner go!
shout of praise; Broth-ers, lift your voic - es, Loud your an-thems raise!
bod - y we— One in hope and doc - trine, One in char-i - ty.
Christ the King— This thru count-less a - ges Men and an-gels sing.

REFRAIN

On-ward, Chris-tian sol - diers, March-ing as to war,

With the cross of Je - sus Go - ing on be - fore!

182 O Where Are Kings and Empires Now

ST. ANNE

A. CLEVELAND COXE, 1818-1896

Attr. to William Croft, 1678-1727

1. O where are kings and em-pires now Of old that went and came?
2. We mark her good-ly bat-tle-ments And her foun-da-tions strong;
3. For not like king-doms of the world Thy ho-ly Church, O God;
4. Un-shak-en as e-ter-nal hills, Im-mov-a-ble she stands,

But, Lord, Thy Church is pray-ing yet, A thou-sand years the same.
We hear with-in the sol-emn voice Of her un-end-ing song.
Tho earth-quake shocks are threat'ning her, And tem-pests are a-broad:
A moun-tain that shall fill the earth, A house not made with hands.

183 Faith of Our Fathers

ST. CATHERINE

FREDERICK W. FABER, 1814-1863

HENRI F. HEMY, 1818-1888
Adapted by James G. Walton, 1821-1905

1. Faith of our fa-thers, liv-ing still In spite of dun-geon, fire and sword—
2. Our fa-thers, chained in pris-ons dark, Were still in heart and con-science free;
3. Faith of our fa-thers, we will love Both friend and foe in all our strife;

O how our hearts beat high with joy When-e'er we hear that glo-rious word!
How sweet would be their chil-dren's fate If they, like them, could die for thee!
And preach thee too, as love knows how, By kind-ly words and vir-tuous life.

Faith of Our Fathers

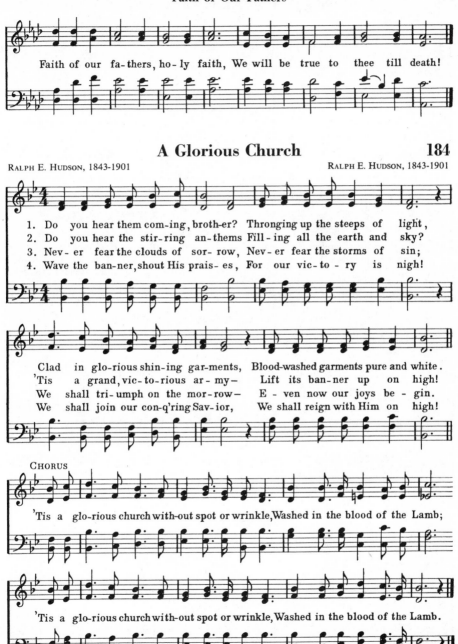

Faith of our fa-thers, ho-ly faith, We will be true to thee till death!

A Glorious Church 184

RALPH E. HUDSON, 1843-1901
RALPH E. HUDSON, 1843-1901

1. Do you hear them com-ing, broth-er? Thronging up the steeps of light,
2. Do you hear the stir-ring an-thems Fill-ing all the earth and sky?
3. Nev-er fear the clouds of sor-row, Nev-er fear the storms of sin;
4. Wave the ban-ner, shout His prais-es, For our vic-to-ry is nigh!

Clad in glo-rious shin-ing gar-ments, Blood-washed garments pure and white.
'Tis a grand, vic-to-rious ar-my— Lift its ban-ner up on high!
We shall tri-umph on the mor-row— E-ven now our joys be-gin.
We shall join our con-q'ring Sav-ior, We shall reign with Him on high!

CHORUS

'Tis a glo-rious church with-out spot or wrinkle, Washed in the blood of the Lamb;

'Tis a glo-rious church with-out spot or wrinkle, Washed in the blood of the Lamb.

185 Glorious Things of Thee Are Spoken

AUSTRIAN HYMN

JOHN NEWTON, 1725-1807

FRANZ JOSEPH HAYDN, 1732-1809

1. Glo - rious things of thee are spo - ken, Zi - on, cit - y of our God;
2. See, the streams of liv - ing wa - ters, Spring-ing from e - ter - nal love,
3. Round each hab - i - ta - tion hov-'ring, See the cloud and fire ap - pear

He whose word can - not be bro - ken Formed thee for His own a - bode:
Well sup - ply thy sons and daugh-ters And all fear of want re - move:
For a glo - ry and a cov - 'ring, Show - ing that the Lord is near!

On the Rock of A - ges found-ed, What can shake thy sure re - pose?
Who can faint while such a riv - er Ev - er flows their thirst to as - suage?
Glo-rious things of Thee are spo - ken, Zi - on, cit - y of our God;

With sal - va - tion's walls sur-round-ed, Thou mayst smile at all thy foes.
Grace which, like the Lord, the Giv - er, Nev - er fails from age to age.
He whose word can - not be bro - ken Formed thee for His own a - bode.

The Church's One Foundation

AURELIA

SAMUEL J. STONE, 1839-1900

SAMUEL S. WESLEY, 1810-1876

1. The Church-'s one foun-da-tion Is Je-sus Christ her Lord;
2. E-lect from ev-'ry na-tion, Yet one o'er all the earth,
3. 'Mid toil and trib-u-la-tion And tu-mult of her war,
4. Yet she on earth hath un-ion With God the Three in One,

She is His new cre-a-tion By wa-ter and the Word:
Her char-ter of sal-va-tion One Lord, one faith, one birth;
She waits the con-sum-ma-tion Of peace for-ev-er-more;
And mys-tic sweet com-mun-ion With those whose rest is won:

From heav'n He came and sought her To be His ho-ly bride;
One ho-ly name she bless-es, Par-takes one ho-ly food,
Till with the vi-sion glo-rious Her long-ing eyes are blest,
O hap-py ones and ho-ly! Lord, give us grace that we,

With His own blood He bought her, And for her life He died.
And to one hope she press-es, With ev-'ry grace en-dued.
And the great Church vic-to-rious Shall be the Church at rest.
Like them, the meek and low-ly, On high may dwell with Thee.

187
Blest Be the Tie That Binds

DENNIS

JOHN FAWCETT, 1740-1817

HANS G. NAEGELI, 1773-1836

1. Blest be the tie that binds Our hearts in Chris-tian love! The
2. Be - fore our Fa - ther's throne We pour our ar - dent prayers; Our
3. We share our mu - tual woes, Our mu - tual bur - dens bear; And
4. When we a - sun - der part It gives us in - ward pain; But

fel - low-ship of kin - dred minds Is like to that a - bove.
fears, our hopes, our aims are one, Our com - forts and our cares.
oft - en for each oth - er flows The sym - pa - thiz - ing tear.
we shall still be joined in heart, And hope to meet a - gain.

188
I Love Thy Kingdom, Lord!

ST. THOMAS

TIMOTHY DWIGHT, 1752-1817

AARON WILLIAMS, 1731-1776

1. I love Thy king - dom, Lord! The house of Thine a - bode—
2. I love Thy Church, O God! Her walls be - fore Thee stand,
3. For her my tears shall fall, For her my prayers as - cend—
4. Be - yond my high - est joy I prize her heav'n - ly ways—
5. Sure as Thy truth shall last, To Zi - on shall be giv'n

The Church our blest Re - deem-er saved With His own pre - cious blood.
Dear as the ap - ple of Thine eye And grav - en on Thy hand.
To her my cares and toils be giv'n Till toils and cares shall end.
Her sweet com-mun - ion, sol - emn vows, Her hymns of love and praise.
The bright-est glo - ries earth can yield, And bright - er bliss of heav'n.

This tune in a higher key: 23

In Jordan's Stream 189

BRIDGEWATER

JOHN W. PETERSON, 1921-　　　　　　　　　　　　　　　　　　JOHN W. PETERSON, 1921-

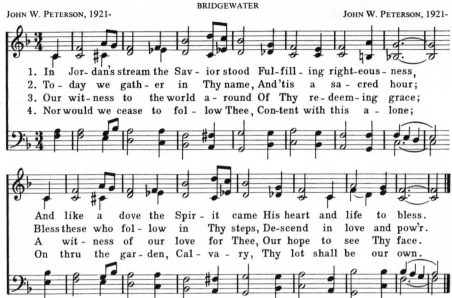

1. In Jor- dan's stream the Sav - ior stood Ful-fill - ing right-eous- ness,
2. To - day we gath- er in Thy name, And 'tis a sa - cred hour;
3. Our wit-ness to the world a - round Of Thy re-deem-ing grace;
4. Nor would we cease to fol - low Thee, Con-tent with this a - lone;

And like a dove the Spir - it came His heart and life to bless.
Bless these who fol - low in Thy steps, De-scend in love and pow'r.
A wit - ness of our love for Thee, Our hope to see Thy face.
On thru the gar - den, Cal - va - ry, Thy lot shall be our own.

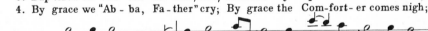

We Bless the Name of Christ, the Lord 190

RETREAT　　　　　　　THOMAS HASTINGS, 1784-1872

SAMUEL F. COFFMAN, 1872-1954　　　　　　　Arr. by John W. Peterson, 1921-

1. We bless the name of Christ, the Lord, We bless Him for His ho - ly Word,
2. We fol - low Him with pure de-light To sanc - ti - fy His sa-cred rite;
3. Bap-tized in God— the Fa - ther, Son, And Ho - ly Spir-it— Three in One,
4. By grace we "Ab - ba, Fa - ther" cry; By grace the Com-fort- er comes nigh;

Who loved to do His Fa - ther's will, And all His right-eous-ness ful - fill.
And thus our faith with wa - ter seal, To prove o - be - dience that we feel.
With con-science free, we rest in God, In love and peace, thru Je - sus' blood.
And for Thy grace our love shall be For - ev - er, on - ly, Lord, for Thee.

191   Here, O My Lord, I See Thee Face to Face

MORECAMBE

HORATIUS BONAR, 1808-1889   FREDERICK C. ATKINSON, 1841-1897

1. Here, O my Lord, I see Thee face to face, Here would I
2. Here would I feed up-on the bread of God, Here drink with
3. I have no help but Thine, nor do I need An-oth-er
4. Mine is the sin, but Thine the right-eous-ness, Mine is the

touch and han-dle things un-seen, Here grasp with firm-er hand e-
Thee the roy-al wine of heav'n, Here would I lay a-side each
arm save Thine to lean up-on; It is e-nough, my Lord, e-
guilt, but Thine the cleans-ing blood; Here is my robe, my ref-uge,

ter-nal grace, And all my wea-ri-ness up-on Thee lean.
earth-ly load, Here taste a-fresh the calm of sin for-giv'n.
nough in-deed— My strength is in Thy might, Thy might a-lone.
and my peace, Thy blood, Thy right-eous-ness, O Lord, my God.

This tune in a higher key: 171

192   According to Thy Gracious Word

JAMES MONTGOMERY, 1771-1854   MANOAH   From Greatorex's *Collection*, 1851

1. Ac-cord-ing to Thy gra-cious word, In meek hu-mil-i-ty,
2. Thy bod-y, bro-ken for my sake, My bread from heav'n shall be;
3. Geth-sem-a-ne can I for-get? Or there Thy con-flict see,
4. When to the cross I turn mine eyes And rest on Cal-va-ry,
5. Re-mem-ber Thee and all Thy pains And all Thy love to me;
6. And when these fail-ing lips grow dumb And mind and mem-'ry flee,

This tune in a higher key: 5

According to Thy Gracious Word

This will I do, my dy-ing Lord: I will re-mem-ber Thee.
Thy tes-ta-men-tal cup I take, And thus re-mem-ber Thee.
Thine ag-o-ny and blood-y sweat, And not re-mem-ber Thee?
O Lamb of God, my sac-ri-fice, I must re-mem-ber Thee—
Yea, while a breath, a pulse re-mains, Will I re-mem-ber Thee.
When Thou shalt in Thy king-dom come, Je-sus, re-mem-ber me!

No, Not Despairingly   193

KEDRON

HORATIUS BONAR, 1808-1889

ANN B. SPRATT, 1829-?
Arr. by John W. Peterson, 1921-

1. No, not de-spair-ing-ly Come I to Thee;
2. Ah! mine in-iq-ui-ty Crim-son hath been,
3. Lord, I con-fess to Thee Sad-ly my sin;
4. Faith-ful and just art Thou, For-giv-ing all;
5. Then all is peace and light This soul with-in;

No, not dis-trust-ing-ly Bend I the knee: Sin hath gone
In-fi-nite, in-fi-nite Sin up-on sin: Sin of not
All I am tell I Thee, All I have been: Purge Thou my
Lov-ing and kind art Thou When poor ones call: Lord, let the
Thus shall I walk with Thee, The loved Un-seen: Lean-ing on

o-ver me, Yet is this still my plea— Je-sus hath died.
lov-ing Thee, Sin of not trust-ing Thee, In-fi-nite sin.
sin a-way, Wash Thou my soul this day— Lord, make me clean.
cleans-ing blood, Blood of the Lamb of God, Pass o'er my soul.
Thee, my God, Guid-ed a-long the road— Noth-ing be-tween.

194 Ye Must Be Born Again

WILLIAM T. SLEEPER, 1819-1904

GEORGE C. STEBBINS, 1846-1945

1. A rul-er once came to Je-sus by night To ask Him the
2. Ye chil-dren of men, at-tend to the word So sol-emn-ly
3. O ye who would en-ter that glo-ri-ous rest And sing with the
4. A dear one in heav-en thy heart yearns to see, At the beau-ti-ful

way of sal-va-tion and light; The Mas-ter made an-swer in
ut-tered by Je-sus the Lord; And let not this mes-sage to
ran-somed the song of the blest, The life ev-er-last-ing if
gate may be watch-ing for thee; Then list to the note of this

CHORUS

words true and plain, "Ye must be born a-gain."
you be in vain, "Ye must be born a-gain."
ye would ob-tain, "Ye must be born a-gain."
sol-emn re-frain, "Ye must be born a-gain."

"Ye must be
a-gain."

born a-gain, Ye must be born a-gain; I ver-i-ly,
a-gain, a-gain;

ver-i-ly say un-to thee, "Ye must be born a-gain."
a-gain."

Look and Live

WILLIAM A. OGDEN, 1841-1897

WILLIAM A. OGDEN, 1841-1897

1. I've a mes-sage from the Lord, hal-le-lu-jah! The mes-sage un-to
2. I've a mes-sage full of love, hal-le-lu-jah! A mes-sage, O my
3. Life is of-fered un-to you, hal-le-lu-jah! E-ter-nal life thy
4. I will tell you how I came, hal-le-lu-jah! To Je-sus when He

you I'll give; 'Tis re-cord-ed in His Word, hal-le-lu-jah!
friend, for you; 'Tis a mes-sage from a-bove, hal-le-lu-jah!
soul shall have, If you'll on-ly look to Him, hal-le-lu-jah!
made me whole: 'Twas be-liev-ing on His name, hal-le-lu-jah!

CHORUS

It is on-ly that you "look and live."
Je-sus said it and I know 'tis true. Look and live, _____
Look to Je-sus who a-lone can save. Look and live,
I trust-ed and He saved my soul.

my broth-er, live! Look to Je-sus now and live; 'Tis re-
my broth-er, live, look and live!

cord-ed in His Word, hal-le-lu-jah! It is on-ly that you "look and live."

196

Blessed Be the Fountain

Eden R. Latta, 1839-?

Henry S. Perkins, 1833-1914

1. Bless-ed be the Foun-tain of blood, To a world of sin-ners re-vealed;
2. Thorn-y was the crown that He wore, And the cross His bod-y o'er-came;
3. Fa-ther, I have wan-dered from Thee, Oft-en has my heart gone a-stray;

Bless-ed be the dear Son of God— On-ly by His stripes we are healed.
Griev-ous were the sor-rows He bore, But He suf-fered thus not in vain.
Crim-son do my sins seem to me— Wa-ter can-not wash them a-way.

Tho I've wan-dered far from His fold, Bring-ing to my heart pain and woe,
May I to that Foun-tain be led, Made to cleanse my sins here be-low;
Je-sus, to that Foun-tain of Thine, Lean-ing on Thy prom-ise, I go;

Wash me in the blood of the Lamb, And I shall be whit-er than snow.
Wash me in the blood that He shed, And I shall be whit-er than snow.
Cleanse me by Thy wash-ing di-vine, And I shall be whit-er than snow.

CHORUS

Whit-er than the snow, Whit-er than the snow—
Whit-er than the snow, Whit-er than the snow—

Blessed Be the Fountain

Wash me in the blood of the Lamb, And I shall be whit-er than snow.

Hallelujah, 'Tis Done! 197

PHILIP P. BLISS, 1838-1876

PHILIP P. BLISS, 1838-1876

1. 'Tis the prom-ise of God, full 'sal-va-tion to give
2. Tho the path-way be lone-ly and dan-ger-ous too,
3. Man-y loved ones have I in yon heav-en-ly throng;
4. There's a part in that cho-rus for you and for me,

Un-to him who on Je-sus, His Son, will be-lieve.
Sure-ly Je-sus is a-ble to car-ry me through.
They are safe now in glo-ry, and this is their song:
And the theme of our prais-es for-ev-er will be:

CHORUS

Hal-le-lu-jah, 'tis done! I be-lieve on the Son; I am

1.
2.

saved by the blood of the Cru-ci-fied One; Cru-ci-fied One.

198 There Is Power in the Blood

LEWIS E. JONES, 1865-1936   LEWIS E. JONES, 1865-1936

1. Would you be free from the bur-den of sin? There's pow'r in the blood,
2. Would you be free from your pas-sion and pride? There's pow'r in the blood,
3. Would you be whit-er, much whit-er than snow? There's pow'r in the blood,
4. Would you do serv-ice for Je-sus your King? There's pow'r in the blood,

pow'r in the blood; Would you o'er e-vil a vic-to-ry win? There's
pow'r in the blood; Come for a cleans-ing to Cal-va-ry's tide— There's
pow'r in the blood; Sin-stains are lost in its life-giv-ing flow— There's
pow'r in the blood; Would you live dai-ly His prais-es to sing? There's

CHORUS

won-der-ful pow'r in the blood. There is pow'r, pow'r, won-der-
there is

work-ing pow'r In the blood of the Lamb; There is
In the blood of the Lamb;

pow'r, pow'r, won-der-working pow'r In the pre-cious blood of the Lamb.
there is

Christ Receiveth Sinful Men

ERDMANN NEUMEISTER, 1671-1756
Trans. by Emma F. Bevan, 1827-1909

JAMES McGRANAHAN, 1840-1907

1. Sin-ners Je-sus will re-ceive! Sound this word of grace to all
2. Come, and He will give you rest, Trust Him, for His word is plain;
3. Now my heart con-demns me not, Pure be-fore the law I stand;
4. Christ re-ceiv-eth sin-ful men, E-ven me with all my sin;

Who the heav'n-ly path-way leave, All who lin-ger, all who fall.
He will take the sin-ful-est, Christ re-ceiv-eth sin-ful men.
He who cleansed me from all spot Sat-is-fied its last de-mand.
Purged from ev-'ry spot and stain, Heav'n with Him I en-ter in.

CHORUS

Sing it o'er and o'er a-gain: Christ re-
Sing it o'er a-gain, Sing it o'er a-gain: Christ re-

ceiv - - - eth sin-ful men; Make the mes - -
ceiv-eth sin-ful men, Christ re-ceiv-eth sin-ful men; Make the mes-sage

- sage clear and plain: Christ re-ceiv-eth sin-ful men.
plain, Make the mes-sage plain:

200 My Sins Are Blotted Out, I Know!

Merrill Dunlop, 1905-

Merrill Dunlop, 1905-

1. What a won-drous mes-sage in God's Word! My sins are blot-ted out,
2. Once my heart was black, but now what joy, My sins are blot-ted out,
3. I shall stand some day be-fore my King, My sins all blot-ted out,

I know! If I trust in His re-deem-ing blood, My sins are
I know! I have peace that noth-ing can de-stroy, My sins are
I know! With the ran-somed host I then shall sing: "My sins are

CHORUS

blot-ted out, I know!
blot-ted out, I know! My sins are blot-ted out, I know!
blot-ted out, I know!" I know!

My sins are blot-ted out, I know! They are bur-ied in the
I know!

depths of the deep-est sea: My sins are blot-ted out, I know!
I know!

He Is Able to Deliver Thee

WILLIAM A. OGDEN, 1841-1897   WILLIAM A. OGDEN, 1841-1897

1. 'Tis the grand-est theme thru the a - ges rung, 'Tis the grand-est theme for a
2. 'Tis the grand-est theme in the earth or main, 'Tis the grand-est theme for a
3. 'Tis the grand-est theme, let the ti-dings roll, To the guilt-y heart, to the

mor-tal tongue; 'Tis the grand-est theme that the world e'er sung—"Our God is
mor-tal strain; 'Tis the grand-est theme, tell the world a - gain—"Our God is
sin - ful soul; Look to God in faith, He will make thee whole—"Our God is

CHORUS

a - ble to de - liv-er thee." He is a - - - ble to de - liv-er thee,
                                 He is a - ble, He is a - ble

He is a - - - ble to de - liv-er thee; Tho by sin op - prest,
He is a - ble, He is a - ble

Go to Him for rest: "Our God is a - ble to de - liv-er thee."

In Times Like These

RUTH CAYE JONES, 1902-

RUTH CAYE JONES, 1902-

1. In times like these you need a Sav-ior, In times like these you need an
2. In times like these you need the Bi - ble, In times like these O be not
3. In times like these I have a Sav-ior, In times like these I have an

an - chor; Be ver-y sure, be ver-y sure Your an-chor holds
i - dle; Be ver-y sure, be ver-y sure Your an-chor holds
an - chor; I'm ver-y sure, I'm ver-y sure My an-chor holds

REFRAIN

and grips the Sol- id Rock! This Rock is Je - sus, Yes, He's the

One; This Rock is Je - sus, The on - ly One! 1,2. Be ver - y sure,
3. I'm ver - y sure,

be ver-y sure Your an-chor holds and grips the Sol-id Rock!
I'm ver-y sure My an-chor holds and grips the Sol-id Rock!

Whosoever Will

PHILIP P. BLISS, 1838-1876   PHILIP P. BLISS, 1838-1876

1. "Who-so-ev-er hear-eth"— shout, shout the sound! Spread the blessed ti-dings
2. Who-so-ev-er com-eth need not de-lay, Now the door is o-pen—
3. "Who-so-ev-er will"— the prom-ise is se-cure, "Who-so-ev-er will" for-

all the world a-round; Tell the joy-ful news wher-ev-er man is found:
en-ter while you may; Je-sus is the true, the on-ly Liv-ing Way:
ev-er must en-dure; "Who-so-ev-er will"— 'tis life for-ev-er-more:

CHORUS

"Who-so-ev-er will may come". "Who-so-ev-er will, who-so-ev-er will!"

Send the proc-la-ma-tion o-ver vale and hill; 'Tis a lov-ing

Fa-ther calls the wan-d'rer home—"Who-so-ev-er will may come."

204 Turn Your Eyes upon Jesus

HELEN H. LEMMEL, 1864-1961   HELEN H. LEMMEL, 1864-1961

1. O soul, are you wea-ry and trou - bled? No light in the
2. Thru death in - to life ev - er - last - ing He passed, and we
3. His word shall not fail you— He prom - ised; Be - lieve Him, and

dark-ness you see? There's light for a look at the Sav - ior, And
fol - low Him there; O - ver us sin no more hath do - min - ion— For
all will be well: Then go to a world that is dy - ing, His

CHORUS

life more a - bun-dant and free!
more than con-q'rors we are! Turn your eyes up-on Je - sus,
per-fect sal - va-tion to tell!

Look full in His won-der-ful face, _____ And the things of
won - der - ful face,

earth will grow strange-ly dim In the light of His glo - ry and grace.

Once for All!

PHILIP P. BLISS, 1838-1876   PHILIP P. BLISS, 1838-1876

1. Free from the law— O hap-py con - di - tion! Je - sus hath bled,
2. Now are we free — there's no con-dem - na - tion! Je - sus pro - vides
3. Chil-dren of God— O glo-ri - ous call-ing! Sure-ly His grace

and there is re - mis - sion; Cursed by the law and bruised by the fall,
a per-fect sal - va - tion; "Come un - to Me—" O hear His sweet call!
will keep us from fall-ing; Pass-ing from death to life at His call,

CHORUS

Grace hath re-deemed us once for all.
Come— and He saves us once for all. Once for all— O sin-ner, re -
Bless-ed sal - va - tion— once for all.

ceive it! Once for all— O broth-er, be - lieve it! Cling to the

cross, the bur-den will fall— Christ hath re-deemed us once for all!

Swell 2,3,4   Great 1-5

206 Wonderful Grace of Jesus

HALDOR LILLENAS, 1885-1959   HALDOR LILLENAS, 1885-1959

1. Won-der-ful grace of Je - sus, Great-er than all my sin;
2. Won-der-ful grace of Je - sus, Reach-ing to all the lost,
3. Won-der-ful grace of Je - sus, Reach-ing the most de - filed,

How shall my tongue de-scribe it, Where shall its praise be - gin?
By it I have been par-doned, Saved to the ut-ter - most;
By its trans-form-ing pow - er Mak-ing him God's dear child,

Tak-ing a-way my bur - den, Set-ting my spir-it free,
Chains have been torn a - sun - der, Giv-ing me lib-er - ty,
Pur-chas-ing peace and heav-en For all e-ter-ni-ty—

For the won-der-ful grace of Je - sus reach-es me.
For the won-der-ful grace of Je - sus reach-es me.
And the won-der-ful grace of Je - sus reach-es me.

CHORUS

the match-less grace of Je - sus,
Won-der-ful the match-less grace of Je - - sus, Deep-er than the

Wonderful Grace of Jesus

the roll-ing sea; Won - der - ful
might-y roll-ing sea; High-er than the moun-tain,

grace, all suf - fi - - cient for
spark-ling like a foun-tain, All - suf - fi - cient grace for e - ven

me, for e - ven me; Broad-er than the scope of my trans -
me; trans -

gres - sions, Great-er far than all my sin and shame;
gres-sions, sing it! my sin and shame;

O mag-ni-fy the pre-cious name of Je - sus, Praise His name!

207

O Happy Day!

PHILIP DODDRIDGE, 1702-1751

EDWARD F. RIMBAULT, 1816-1876

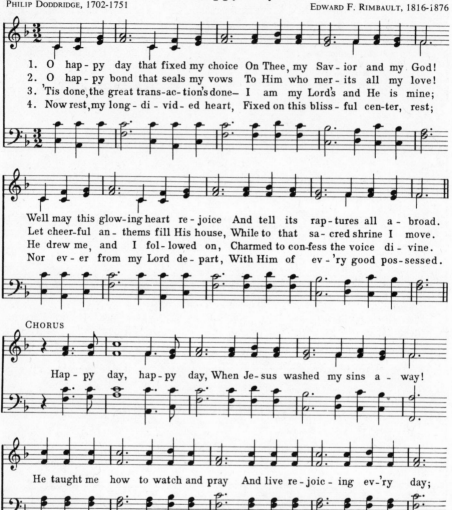

1. O hap-py day that fixed my choice On Thee, my Sav-ior and my God!
2. O hap-py bond that seals my vows To Him who mer-its all my love!
3. 'Tis done, the great trans-ac-tion's done— I am my Lord's and He is mine;
4. Now rest, my long-di-vid-ed heart, Fixed on this bliss-ful cen-ter, rest;

Well may this glow-ing heart re-joice And tell its rap-tures all a-broad.
Let cheer-ful an-thems fill His house, While to that sa-cred shrine I move.
He drew me, and I fol-lowed on, Charmed to con-fess the voice di-vine.
Nor ev-er from my Lord de-part, With Him of ev-'ry good pos-sessed.

CHORUS

Hap-py day, hap-py day, When Je-sus washed my sins a-way!

He taught me how to watch and pray And live re-joic-ing ev-'ry day;

Hap-py day, hap-py day, When Je-sus washed my sins a-way!

Are You Washed in the Blood?

Elisha A. Hoffman, 1839-1929   Elisha A. Hoffman, 1839-1929

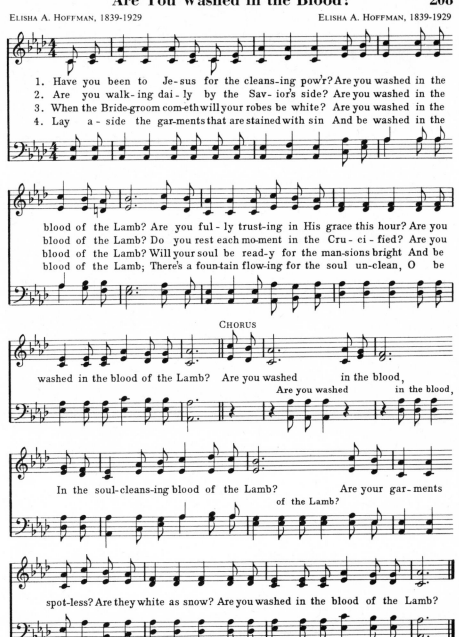

1. Have you been to Je-sus for the cleans-ing pow'r? Are you washed in the
2. Are you walk-ing dai-ly by the Sav-ior's side? Are you washed in the
3. When the Bride-groom com-eth will your robes be white? Are you washed in the
4. Lay a-side the gar-ments that are stained with sin And be washed in the

blood of the Lamb? Are you ful-ly trust-ing in His grace this hour? Are you
blood of the Lamb? Do you rest each mo-ment in the Cru-ci-fied? Are you
blood of the Lamb? Will your soul be read-y for the man-sions bright And be
blood of the Lamb; There's a foun-tain flow-ing for the soul un-clean, O be

CHORUS

washed in the blood of the Lamb? Are you washed in the blood,
Are you washed in the blood,

In the soul-cleans-ing blood of the Lamb? Are your gar-ments
of the Lamb?

spot-less? Are they white as snow? Are you washed in the blood of the Lamb?

209 Grace Greater Than Our Sin

JULIA H. JOHNSTON, 1849-1919

DANIEL B. TOWNER, 1850-1919

1. Mar - vel - ous grace of our lov - ing Lord, Grace that ex - ceeds our
2. Sin and de - spair, like the sea - waves cold, Threat - en the soul with
3. Dark is the stain that we can - not hide, What can a - vail to
4. Mar - vel - ous, in - fi - nite, match - less grace, Free - ly be - stowed on

sin and our guilt! Yon - der on Cal - va - ry's mount out - poured—
in - fi - nite loss; Grace that is great - er— yes, grace un - told—
wash it a - way? Look! there is flow - ing a crim - son tide—
all who be - lieve! You that are long - ing to see His face,

CHORUS

There where the blood of the Lamb was spilt. Grace, grace,
Points to the Ref - uge, the might - y Cross. Mar - vel - ous grace,
Whit - er than snow you may be to - day.
Will you this mo - ment His grace re - ceive?

God's grace, Grace that will par - don and cleanse with - in; Grace,
in - fi - nite grace, Mar - vel - ous

grace, God's grace, Grace that is great - er than all our sin!
grace, in - fi - nite grace,

Saved by the Blood

S. J. Henderson, 19th century

Daniel B. Towner, 1850-1919

1. Saved by the blood of the Cru-ci-fied One! Now ran-somed from
2. Saved by the blood of the Cru-ci-fied One! The an-gels re-
3. Saved by the blood of the Cru-ci-fied One! The Fa-ther He
4. Saved by the blood of the Cru-ci-fied One! All hail to the

sin and a new work be-gun; Sing praise to the Fa-ther and
joic-ing be-cause it is done; A child of the Fa-ther, joint-
spake, and His will it was done; Great price of my par-don, His
Fa-ther, all hail to the Son, All hail to the Spir-it, the

praise to the Son— Saved by the blood of the Cru-ci-fied One!
heir with the Son— Saved by the blood of the Cru-ci-fied One!
own pre-cious Son— Saved by the blood of the Cru-ci-fied One!
great Three in One! Saved by the blood of the Cru-ci-fied One!

CHORUS

Saved! _____ saved! _____ My sins are all par-doned, my
Glo-ry, I'm saved! glo-ry, I'm saved!

1

2

guilt is all gone! I'm saved by the blood of the Cru-ci-fied One!

211 Hallelujah for the Cross!

HORATIUS BONAR, 1808-1889 JAMES McGRANAHAN, 1840-1907

1. The cross, it stand-eth fast— Hal-le-lu-jah, hal-le-lu-jah!
2. It is the old cross still— Hal-le-lu-jah, hal-le-lu-jah!
3. 'Twas here the debt was paid— Hal-le-lu-jah, hal-le-lu-jah!

De-fy-ing ev-'ry blast— Hal-le-lu-jah, hal-le-lu-jah!
Its tri-umph let us tell— Hal-le-lu-jah, hal-le-lu-jah!
Our sins on Je-sus laid— Hal-le-lu-jah, hal-le-lu-jah!

The winds of hell have blown, The world its hate hath shown,
The grace of God here shone Thru Christ, the bless-ed Son,
So round the cross we sing Of Christ, our of-fer-ing,

Yet it is not o-ver-thrown— Hal-le-lu-jah for the cross!
Who did for sin a-tone— Hal-le-lu-jah for the cross!
Of Christ, our liv-ing King— Hal-le-lu-jah for the cross!

REFRAIN

Hal-le-lu-jah, hal-le-lu-jah, hal-le-lu-jah for the cross;

Hallelujah for the Cross!

Hal - le - lu - jah, hal - le - lu - jah, it shall nev - er suf - fer loss!

Nothing But the Blood   212

ROBERT LOWRY, 1826-1899   ROBERT LOWRY, 1826-1899

1. What can wash a - way my sin? Noth-ing but the blood of Je - sus;
2. For my par - don this I see— Noth-ing but the blood of Je - sus;
3. Noth-ing can for sin a - tone— Noth-ing but the blood of Je - sus;
4. This is all my hope and peace— Noth-ing but the blood of Je - sus;

What can make me whole a - gain? Noth-ing but the blood of Je - sus.
For my cleans-ing, this my plea— Noth-ing but the blood of Je - sus.
Naught of good that I have done— Noth-ing but the blood of Je - sus.
This is all my right-eous-ness— Noth-ing but the blood of Je - sus.

REFRAIN

Oh! pre - cious is the flow That makes me white as snow;

No oth - er fount I know, Noth-ing but the blood of Je - sus.

213 The Light of the World Is Jesus

PHILIP P. BLISS, 1838-1876   PHILIP P. BLISS, 1838-1876

1. The whole world was lost in the dark-ness of sin — The Light of the
2. No dark-ness have we who in Je - sus a - bide— The Light of the
3. Ye dwell-ers in dark-ness with sin-blind-ed eyes— The Light of the
4. No need of the sun-light in heav-en,we're told— The Light of that

world is Je - sus; Like sun-shine at noon-day His glo-ry shone in—
world is Je - sus; We walk in the Light when we fol-low our Guide—
world is Je - sus; Go wash at His bid-ding and light will a-rise—
world is Je - sus; The Lamb is the Light in the Cit-y of Gold—

CHORUS

The Light of the world is Je - sus.
The Light of the world is Je - sus.   Come to the Light, 'tis
The Light of the world is Je - sus.
The Light of that world is Je - sus.

shin-ing for thee! Sweet-ly the Light has dawned up-on me; Once I was

blind, but now I can see— The Light of the world is Je - sus.

Verily, Verily

JAMES McGRANAHAN, 1840-1907   JAMES McGRANAHAN, 1840-1907

1. O what a Sav-ior that He died for me! From con-dem-
2. All my in-iq-ui-ties on Him were laid, All my in-
3. Tho poor and need-y, I can trust my Lord, Tho weak and
4. Tho all un-wor-thy, yet I will not doubt, For him that

na-tion He hath made me free; "He that be-liev-eth on the
debt-ed-ness by Him was paid; All who be-lieve on Him, the
sin-ful I be-lieve His Word; O glad mes-sage! ev-'ry
com-eth He will not cast out; "He that be-liev-eth," O the

Son," saith He, "Hath ev-er-last-ing life."
Lord hath said, Have ev-er-last-ing life.
child of God "Hath ev-er-last-ing life."
good news shout, "Hath ev-er-last-ing life!"

CHORUS

"Ver-i-ly, ver-i-ly, I say un-to you— Ver-i-ly, ver-i-ly," mes-sage ev-er new;

"He that be-liev-eth on the Son," 'tis true, "Hath ev-er-last-ing life."

215 Nor Silver nor Gold

JAMES M. GRAY, 1851-1935

DANIEL B. TOWNER, 1850-1919

1. Nor sil-ver nor gold hath ob-tained my re-demp-tion, Nor rich-es of
2. Nor sil-ver nor gold hath ob-tained my re-demp-tion, The guilt on my
3. Nor sil-ver nor gold hath ob-tained my re-demp-tion, The ho-ly com-
4. Nor sil-ver nor gold hath ob-tained my re-demp-tion, The way in-to

earth could have saved my poor soul; The blood of the cross is my
con-science too heav-y had grown; The blood of the cross is my
mand-ment for-bade me draw near; The blood of the cross is my
heav-en could not thus be bought; The blood of the cross is my

on-ly foun-da-tion, The death of my Sav-ior now mak-eth me whole.
on-ly foun-da-tion, The death of my Sav-ior could on-ly a-tone.
on-ly foun-da-tion, The death of my Sav-ior re-mov-eth my fear.
on-ly foun-da-tion, The death of my Sav-ior re-demp-tion hath wrought.

CHORUS

I am re-deemed but not with sil-ver, I am
I am re-deemed, I'm re-deemed but not with sil-ver,

bought but not with gold, Bought with a price—
I am bought, I am bought but not with gold, Bought with a

Nor Silver nor Gold

the blood of Je - sus,   Pre-cious price of love un-told.
price—   the pre-cious blood of Je-sus,

Look to the Lamb of God   216

H. G. JACKSON, 19th century

JAMES M. BLACK, 1856-1938

1. If   you from sin   are long-ing to be   free,   Look to the Lamb of God;
2. When Sa-tan tempts, and doubts and fears as-sail,   Look to the Lamb of God;
3. Are   you a - wea - ry, does the way seem long?   Look to the Lamb of God;
4. Fear not when shad-ows on your path-way fall,   Look to the Lamb of God;

He,   to re - deem you, died on Cal-va-ry,   Look to the Lamb of God.
You in His strength shall o - ver all pre-vail,   Look to the Lamb of God.
His love will cheer and fill your heart with song, Look to the Lamb of God.
In   joy or sor - row Christ is all in all,   Look to the Lamb of God.

CHORUS

Look to the Lamb of God,   Look to the Lamb of God,
        the Lamb of God,   the Lamb of God,

For He a-lone is   a - ble to save you— Look to the Lamb of God.

217 Jesus, Thy Blood and Righteousness

GERMANY

Nicolaus L. von Zinzendorf, 1700-1760
Trans. by John Wesley, 1703-1791

From Gardiner's *Sacred Melodies,* 1815

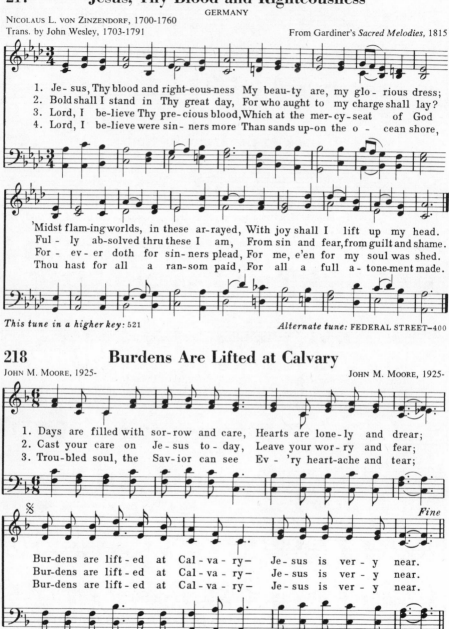

1. Je- sus, Thy blood and right-eous-ness My beau-ty are, my glo- rious dress;
2. Bold shall I stand in Thy great day, For who aught to my charge shall lay?
3. Lord, I be-lieve Thy pre-cious blood, Which at the mer-cy-seat of God
4. Lord, I be-lieve were sin- ners more Than sands up-on the o - cean shore,

'Midst flam-ing worlds, in these ar-rayed, With joy shall I lift up my head.
Ful - ly ab-solved thru these I am, From sin and fear, from guilt and shame.
For - ev - er doth for sin-ners plead, For me, e'en for my soul was shed.
Thou hast for all a ran-som paid, For all a full a - tone-ment made.

This tune in a higher key: 521   *Alternate tune:* FEDERAL STREET—400

218 Burdens Are Lifted at Calvary

John M. Moore, 1925-   John M. Moore, 1925-

1. Days are filled with sor-row and care, Hearts are lone-ly and drear;
2. Cast your care on Je-sus to-day, Leave your wor-ry and fear;
3. Trou-bled soul, the Sav-ior can see Ev - 'ry heart-ache and tear;

Fine

Bur-dens are lift-ed at Cal-va-ry— Je-sus is ver-y near.
Bur-dens are lift-ed at Cal-va-ry— Je-sus is ver-y near.
Bur-dens are lift-ed at Cal-va-ry— Je-sus is ver-y near.

D.S.— Bur-dens are lift-ed at Cal-va-ry— Je-sus is ver-y near.

Burdens Are Lifted at Calvary

CHORUS   *D. S.*

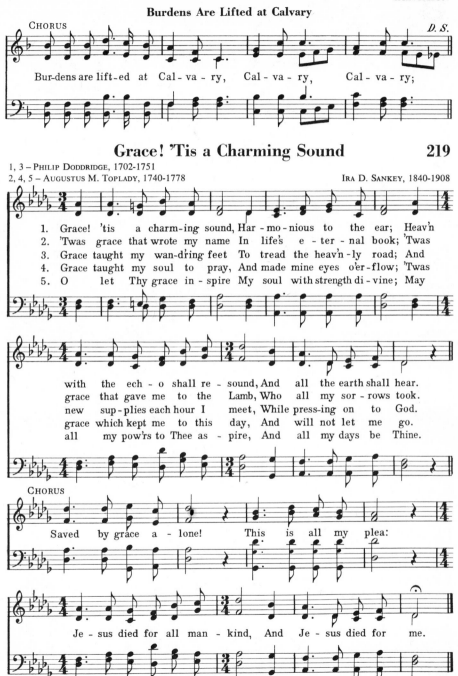

Bur-dens are lift-ed at Cal - va - ry, Cal - va - ry, Cal - va - ry;

Grace! 'Tis a Charming Sound   219

1, 3 – PHILIP DODDRIDGE, 1702-1751
2, 4, 5 – AUGUSTUS M. TOPLADY, 1740-1778   IRA D. SANKEY, 1840-1908

1. Grace! 'tis a charm-ing sound, Har - mo - nious to the ear; Heav'n
2. 'Twas grace that wrote my name In life's e - ter - nal book; 'Twas
3. Grace taught my wan-d'ring feet To tread the heav'n - ly road; And
4. Grace taught my soul to pray, And made mine eyes o'er - flow; 'Twas
5. O let Thy grace in - spire My soul with strength di - vine; May

with the ech - o shall re - sound, And all the earth shall hear.
grace that gave me to the Lamb, Who all my sor - rows took.
new sup - plies each hour I meet, While press-ing on to God.
grace which kept me to this day, And will not let me go.
all my pow'rs to Thee as - pire, And all my days be Thine.

CHORUS

Saved by grace a - lone! This is all my plea:

Je - sus died for all man - kind, And Je - sus died for me.

220 I'll Stand By Until the Morning

DANIEL W. WHITTLE, 1840-1901   JAMES McGRANAHAN, 1840-1907

1. Fierce and wild the storm is rag - ing   Round a help-less bark,
2. Wea - ry, help-less, hope-less sea - men,   Faint - ing on the deck,
3. On   a wild and storm-y   o - cean,   Sink - ing 'neath the wave,
4. Dar - ing death thy soul to   res - cue,   He   in love has come;

On   to doom 'tis swift-ly driv - ing,   O'er the wa - ters   dark!
With   what joy they hail their Sav - ior,   As   He hails their   wreck!
Souls   that per-ish heed the mes - sage—   Christ has come to   save!
Leave   the wreck and, in Him trust - ing,   Thou shalt reach thy   home!

CHORUS

Joy!   be-hold the Sav - ior!   Joy!   the mes-sage
Joy, O joy!   be - hold the Sav- ior!   Joy, O joy!   the

hear: "I'll stand by un - til the morn - ing— I've
mes - sage hear:

come to save you, do not fear;   Yes, I'll stand by un - til the

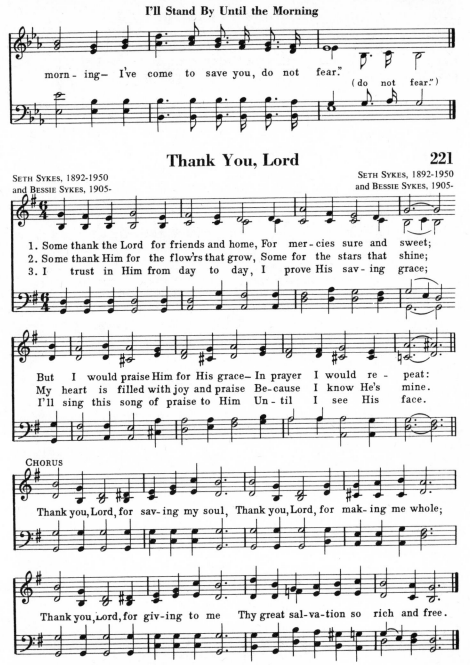

I'll Stand By Until the Morning

morn - ing— I've come to save you, do not fear." (do not fear.")

Thank You, Lord

221

SETH SYKES, 1892-1950
and BESSIE SYKES, 1905-

SETH SYKES, 1892-1950
and BESSIE SYKES, 1905-

1. Some thank the Lord for friends and home, For mer-cies sure and sweet;
2. Some thank Him for the flow'rs that grow, Some for the stars that shine;
3. I trust in Him from day to day, I prove His sav-ing grace;

But I would praise Him for His grace— In prayer I would re-peat:
My heart is filled with joy and praise Be-cause I know He's mine.
I'll sing this song of praise to Him Un-til I see His face.

CHORUS

Thank you, Lord, for sav-ing my soul, Thank you, Lord, for mak-ing me whole;

Thank you, Lord, for giv-ing to me Thy great sal-va-tion so rich and free.

There Is a Fountain

CLEANSING FOUNTAIN

WILLIAM COWPER, 1731-1800

American melody

1. There is a foun-tain filled with blood Drawn from Im-man-uel's veins,
2. The dy-ing thief re-joiced to see That foun-tain in his day,
3. Dear dy-ing Lamb, Thy pre-cious blood Shall nev-er lose its pow'r,
4. E'er since by faith I saw the stream Thy flow-ing wounds sup-ply,
5. When this poor lisp-ing, stam-m'ring tongue Lies si-lent in the grave,

And sin-ners plunged be-neath that flood Lose all their guilt-y stains:
And there may I, though vile as he, Wash all my sins a-way:
Till all the ran-somed Church of God Be saved to sin no more:
Re-deem-ing love has been my theme And shall be till I die:
Then in a no-bler, sweet-er song, I'll sing Thy pow'r to save:

Lose all their guilt-y stains, Lose all their guilt-y stains;
Wash all my sins a-way, Wash all my sins a-way;
Be saved to sin no more, Be saved to sin no more;
And shall be till I die, And shall be till I die;
I'll sing Thy pow'r to save, I'll sing Thy pow'r to save;

And sin-ners plunged be-neath that flood Lose all their guilt-y stains.
And there may I, though vile as he, Wash all my sins a-way.
Till all the ran-somed Church of God Be saved to sin no more.
Re-deem-ing love has been my theme And shall be till I die.
Then in a no-bler, sweet-er song, I'll sing Thy pow'r to save.

Arise, My Soul, Arise!

TOWNER

CHARLES WESLEY, 1707-1788

Source unknown
Harm. by J. W. P., and
Daniel B. Towner, 1850-1919

1. A - rise, my soul, a - rise! Shake off thy guilt - y fears;
2. He ev - er lives a - bove, For me to in - ter - cede;
3. Five bleed - ing wounds He bears, Re - ceived on Cal - va - ry;
4. The Fa - ther hears Him pray, His dear a - noint - ed one;
5. My God is rec - on - ciled, His par - d'ning voice I hear;

The bleed - ing Sac - ri - fice In my be - half ap - pears:
His all - re - deem - ing love, His pre - cious blood to plead:
They pour ef - fec - tual prayers, They strong - ly plead for me:
He can - not turn a - way The pres - ence of His Son:
He owns me for His child, I can no long - er fear:

Be - fore the throne my Sure - ty stands— My name is writ - ten
His blood a - toned for all our race, And sprin - kles now the
"For - give him, O for - give," they cry, "Nor let that ran - somed
His Spir - it an - swers to the blood, And tells me I am
With con - fi - dence I now draw nigh, And "Fa - ther, Ab - ba,

on His hands, My name is writ - ten on His hands.
throne of grace, And sprin - kles now the throne of grace.
sin - ner die! Nor let that ran - somed sin - ner die!"
born of God, And tells me I am born of God.
Fa - ther!" cry, And "Fa - ther, Ab - ba, Fa - ther" cry.

224 I Know Whom I Have Believed

DANIEL W. WHITTLE, 1840-1901   JAMES McGRANAHAN, 1840-1907

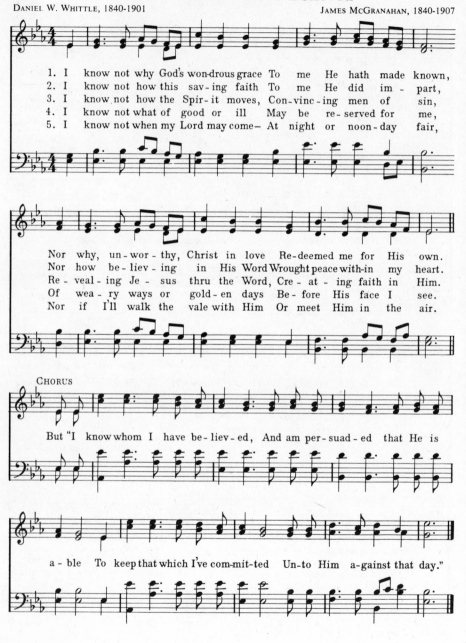

1. I know not why God's won-drous grace To me He hath made known,
2. I know not how this sav-ing faith To me He did im - part,
3. I know not how the Spir-it moves, Con-vinc-ing men of sin,
4. I know not what of good or ill May be re-served for me,
5. I know not when my Lord may come— At night or noon-day fair,

Nor why, un-wor-thy, Christ in love Re-deemed me for His own.
Nor how be-liev-ing in His Word Wrought peace with-in my heart.
Re-veal-ing Je-sus thru the Word, Cre-at-ing faith in Him.
Of wea-ry ways or gold-en days Be-fore His face I see.
Nor if I'll walk the vale with Him Or meet Him in the air.

CHORUS

But "I know whom I have be-liev-ed, And am per-suad-ed that He is

a-ble To keep that which I've com-mit-ted Un-to Him a-gainst that day."

I Heard the Voice of Jesus Say

VOX DILECTI

HORATIUS BONAR, 1808-1889   JOHN B. DYKES, 1823-1876

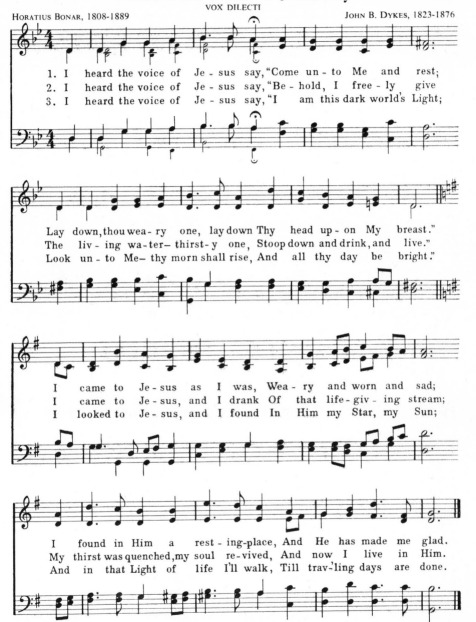

1. I heard the voice of Je - sus say, "Come un - to Me and rest;
2. I heard the voice of Je - sus say, "Be - hold, I free - ly give
3. I heard the voice of Je - sus say, "I am this dark world's Light;

Lay down, thou wea - ry one, lay down Thy head up - on My breast."
The liv - ing wa - ter— thirst - y one, Stoop down and drink, and live."
Look un - to Me— thy morn shall rise, And all thy day be bright."

I came to Je - sus as I was, Wea - ry and worn and sad;
I came to Je - sus, and I drank Of that life - giv - ing stream;
I looked to Je - sus, and I found In Him my Star, my Sun;

I found in Him a rest - ing-place, And He has made me glad.
My thirst was quenched, my soul re - vived, And now I live in Him.
And in that Light of life I'll walk, Till trav'-ling days are done.

Alternate tunes: GREEN HILL — 114, NO OTHER PLEA — 228

226 My Savior

GREENWELL

DORA GREENWELL, 1821-1882

WILLIAM J. KIRKPATRICK, 1838-1921

1. I am not skilled to un-der-stand What God hath willed, what God hath planned;
2. I take Him at His word in-deed—"Christ died for sin-ners," this I read—
3. That He should leave His place on high And come for sin-ful man to die,
4. And O that He ful-filled may see The trav-ail of His soul in me,
5. Yea, liv-ing, dy-ing, let me bring My strength, my sol-ace from this spring:

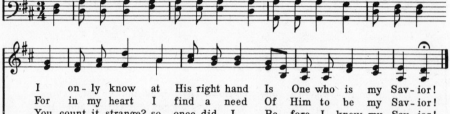

I on-ly know at His right hand Is One who is my Sav-ior!
For in my heart I find a need Of Him to be my Sav-ior!
You count it strange? so once did I, Be-fore I knew my Sav-ior!
And with His work con-tent-ed be, As I with my dear Sav-ior!
That He who lives to be my King Once died to be my Sav-ior!

227 The Cleansing Wave

PHOEBE P. KNAPP, 1839-1908

PHOEBE P. KNAPP, 1839-1908

1. O now I see the cleans-ing wave, The foun-tain deep and wide:
2. I rise to walk in heav'n's own light A-bove the world and sin,
3. A-maz-ing grace! 'tis heav'n be-low To feel the blood ap-plied,

Je-sus, my Lord, might-y to save, Points to His wound-ed side.
With heart made pure and gar-ments white, And Christ en-throned with-in.
And Je-sus, on-ly Je-sus know— My Je-sus cru-ci-fied.

The Cleansing Wave

CHORUS

The cleans-ing stream I see, I see! I plunge, and O it cleans-eth me!

O praise the Lord, it cleans-eth me! It cleans-eth me—yes, cleans-eth me.

My Faith Has Found a Resting Place   228

NO OTHER PLEA

LIDIE H. EDMUNDS, 19th century

Norwegian melody

1. My faith has found a rest-ing place— Not in de-vice nor creed:
2. E-nough for me that Je-sus saves— This ends my fear and doubt;
3. My heart is lean-ing on the Word— The writ-ten Word of God:
4. My great Phy-si-cian heals the sick, The lost He came to save;

I trust the Ev-er-liv-ing One— His wounds for me shall plead.
A sin-ful soul I come to Him— He'll nev-er cast me out.
Sal-va-tion by my Sav-ior's name— Sal-va-tion thru His blood.
For me His pre-cious blood He shed, For me His life He gave.

Fine

D.S.— is e-nough that Je-sus died, And that He died for me.

CHORUS

D.S.

I need no oth-er ar-gu-ment, I need no oth-er plea; It

229 Tell Me the Old, Old Story

A. Catherine Hankey, 1834-1911

William H. Doane, 1832-1915

1. Tell me the old, old sto-ry Of un-seen things a-bove, Of Je-sus
2. Tell me the sto-ry slow-ly, That I may take it in— That won-der-
3. Tell me the sto-ry soft-ly, With ear-nest tones and grave; Re-mem-ber,
4. Tell me the same old sto-ry When you have cause to fear That this world's

and His glo-ry, Of Je-sus and His love. Tell me the sto-ry
ful re-demp-tion, God's rem-e-dy for sin. Tell me the sto-ry
I'm the sin-ner Whom Je-sus came to save. Tell me the sto-ry
emp-ty glo-ry Is cost-ing me too dear. Yes, and when that world's

sim-ply, As to a lit-tle child, For I am weak and wea-ry,
oft-en, For I for-get so soon; The ear-ly dew of morn-ing
al-ways, If you would real-ly be, In an-y time of trou-ble,
glo-ry Is dawn-ing on my soul, Tell me the old, old sto-ry:

Chorus

And help-less and de-filed.
Has passed a-way at noon.
A com-fort-er to me. Tell me the old, old sto-ry, Tell me the
"Christ Je-sus makes thee whole."

old, old sto-ry, Tell me the old, old sto-ry Of Je-sus and His love.

Saved, Saved!

JACK P. SCHOLFIELD, 1882-

JACK P. SCHOLFIELD, 1882-
Arr. by Norman Johnson, 1928-

Unison

1. I've found a Friend who is all to me, His
2. He saves me from ev-'ry sin and harm, Se-
3. When poor and need-y and all a-lone, In

Play melody and bass in octaves.

love is ev-er true;_____ I love to tell how He
cures my soul each day;_____ I'm lean-ing strong on His
love He said to me,_____ "Come un-to me and I'll

lift-ed me And what His grace can do for you.
might-y arm— I know He'll guide me all the way.
lead you home To live with me e-ter-nal-ly."

CHORUS *Parts*

Saved ___ by His pow'r di-vine, Saved ___ to new life sub-lime!
I'm saved   I'm saved

Life now is sweet and my joy is com-plete, For I'm saved, saved, saved!

Jesus Saves!

PRISCILLA J. OWENS, 1829-1907   WILLIAM J. KIRKPATRICK, 1838-1921

1. We have heard the joy-ful sound— Je-sus saves! Je-sus saves!
2. Waft it on the roll-ing tide— Je-sus saves! Je-sus saves!
3. Sing a-bove the bat-tle strife— Je-sus saves! Je-sus saves!
4. Give the winds a might-y voice— Je-sus saves! Je-sus saves!

Spread the ti-dings all a-round— Je-sus saves! Je-sus saves!
Tell to sin-ners far and wide— Je-sus saves! Je-sus saves!
By His death and end-less life— Je-sus saves! Je-sus saves!
Let the na-tions now re-joice— Je-sus saves! Je-sus saves!

Bear the news to ev-'ry land, Climb the steeps and cross the waves;
Sing, ye is-lands of the sea! Ech-o back, ye o-cean caves!
Sing it soft-ly thru the gloom, When the heart for mer-cy craves;
Shout sal-va-tion full and free, High-est hills and deep-est caves;

On-ward! 'tis our Lord's com-mand— Je-sus saves! Je-sus saves!
Earth shall keep her ju-bi-lee— Je-sus saves! Je-sus saves!
Sing in tri-umph o'er the tomb— Je-sus saves! Je-sus saves!
This our song of vic-to-ry— Je-sus saves! Je-sus saves!

When I See the Blood

John Foote, 19th century

J. G. Foote, 19th century

1. Christ our Re-deem-er died on the cross, Died for the sin-ner, paid all his due; Sprin-kle your soul with the blood of the Lamb, And "I will pass, will pass o-ver you."
2. Chief-est of sin-ners Je-sus will save— All He has prom-ised, that He will do; Wash in the foun-tain o-pened for sin,
3. Judg-ment is com-ing, all will be there, Each one re-ceiv-ing just-ly his due; Hide in the sav-ing, sin-cleans-ing blood,
4. O great com-pas-sion! O bound-less love! O lov-ing kind-ness, faith-ful and true! Find peace and shel-ter un-der the blood,

Chorus

"When I see the blood, When I see the blood, When I see the blood, When I see the blood, I will pass, I will pass o-ver you."

233 Depth of Mercy

ALETTA

CHARLES WESLEY, 1707-1788

WILLIAM B. BRADBURY, 1816-1868

1. Depth of mer-cy! can there be Mer-cy still re-served for me?
2. I have long with-stood His grace, Long pro-voked Him to His face,
3. Now in-cline me to re-pent, Let me now my sins la-ment;
4. There for me my Sav-ior stands, Hold-ing forth His wound-ed hands;

Can my God His wrath for-bear— Me, the chief of sin-ners, spare?
Would not heark-en to His calls, Grieved Him by a thou-sand falls.
Now my foul re-volt de-plore, Weep, be-lieve, and sin no more.
God is love! I know, I feel, Je-sus weeps and loves me still.

Alternate tune: SEYMOUR—79

234 Wonderful Words of Life

PHILIP P. BLISS, 1838-1876

PHILIP P. BLISS, 1838-1876

1. Sing them o-ver a-gain to me— Won-der-ful words of Life;
2. Christ, the bless-ed One, gives to all Won-der-ful words of Life;
3. Sweet-ly ech-o the gos-pel call— Won-der-ful words of Life;

Let me more of their beau-ty see— Won-der-ful words of Life.
Sin-ner, list to the lov-ing call— Won-der-ful words of Life.
Of-fer par-don and peace to all— Won-der-ful words of Life.

Wonderful Words of Life

Words of life and beau - ty, Teach me faith and du - ty:
All so free - ly giv - en, Woo - ing us to heav - en:
Je - sus, on - ly Sav - ior, Sanc - ti - fy for - ev - er:

REFRAIN

Beau-ti-ful words, won-der-ful words, Won-der-ful words of Life; Life.

Pass Me Not

235

FANNY J. CROSBY, 1820-1915

WILLIAM H. DOANE, 1832-1915

1. Pass me not, O gen - tle Sav - ior— Hear my hum - ble cry!
2. Let me at a throne of mer - cy Find a sweet re - lief;
3. Trust - ing on - ly in Thy mer - it, Would I seek Thy face;
4. Thou the spring of all my com - fort, More than life to me!

While on oth - ers Thou art call - ing, Do not pass me by.
Kneel - ing there in deep con - tri - tion, Help my un - be - lief.
Heal my wound-ed, bro - ken spir - it, Save me by Thy grace.
Whom have I on earth be - side Thee? Whom in heav'n but Thee?

D.S.-While on oth-ers Thou art call - ing, Do not pass me by.

CHORUS

D.S.

Sav - ior, Sav - ior, Hear my hum - ble cry!

236 Amazing Grace

AMAZING GRACE

JOHN NEWTON, 1725-1807

American melody
From Carrell & Clayton's *Virginia Harmony*, 1831
Arr. by Norman Johnson, 1928-

1. A - maz - ing grace–how sweet the sound– That saved a wretch like me!
2. 'Twas grace that taught my heart to fear, And grace my fears re - lieved;
3. Thru man - y dan - gers, toils and snares I have al - read - y come;
4. When we've been there ten thou - sand years, Bright shin - ing as the sun,

I once was lost but now am found, Was blind but now I see.
How pre - cious did that grace ap - pear The hour I first be - lieved!
'Tis grace hath brought me safe thus far, And grace will lead me home.
We've no less days to sing God's praise Than when we'd first be - gun.

237 Why Do You Wait?

GEORGE F. ROOT, 1820-1895

GEORGE F. ROOT, 1820-1895

1. Why do you wait, dear broth - er, O why do you tar - ry so long?
2. What do you hope, dear broth - er, To gain by a fur - ther de - lay?
3. Do you not feel, dear broth - er, His Spir - it now striv - ing with - in?
4. Why do you wait, dear broth - er? The har - vest is pass - ing a - way;

Your Sav - ior is wait - ing to give you A place in His sanc - ti - fied throng.
There's no one to save you but Je - sus, There's no oth - er way but His way.
O why not ac - cept His sal - va - tion And throw off your bur - den of sin?
Your Sav - ior is long - ing to bless you, There's dan - ger and death in de - lay.

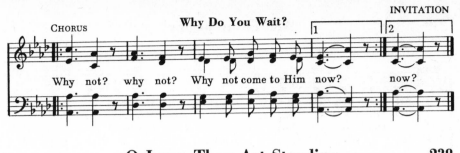

Why Do You Wait?

CHORUS

Why not? why not? Why not come to Him now? now?

O Jesus, Thou Art Standing 238

ST. HILDA

WILLIAM W. HOW, 1823-1897

JUSTIN H. KNECHT, 1752-1817
and EDWARD HUSBAND, 1843-1908

1. O Je - sus, Thou art stand-ing Out- side the fast-closed door,
2. O Je - sus, Thou art knock-ing— And lo! that hand is scarred,
3. O Je - sus, Thou art plead-ing In ac - cents meek and low,

In low - ly pa - tience wait - ing To pass the thresh-old o'er:
And thorns Thy brow en - cir - cle, And tears Thy face have marred:
"I died for you, My chil - dren, And will ye treat Me so?"

Shame on us, Chris-tian broth - ers, His Name and sign who bear,
O love that pass-eth knowl - edge, So pa - tient - ly to wait!
O Lord, with shame and sor - row We o - pen now the door;

O shame, thrice shame up - on us, To keep Him stand-ing there!
O sin that has no e - qual, So fast to bar the gate!
Dear Sav - ior, en - ter, en - ter, And leave us nev - er - more!

239 Art Thou Weary?

JOHN M. NEALE, 1818-1866   STEPHANOS
From the Greek of Stephen the Sabaite, 725-794
HENRY W. BAKER, 1821-1877

1. Art thou wea-ry, art thou lan-guid, Art thou sore dis-trest?
2. Hath He marks to lead me to Him, If He be my Guide?
3. Is there di-a-dem, as Mon-arch, That His brow a-dorns?
4. If I still hold close-ly to Him, What hath He at last?
5. If I ask Him to re-ceive me, Will He say me nay?
6. Find-ing, fol-l'wing, keep-ing, strug-gling, Is He sure to bless?

"Come to Me," saith One, "and, com-ing, Be at rest."
"In His feet and hands are wound-prints, And His side."
"Yea, a crown, in ver-y sure-ty, But of thorns."
"Sor-row van-quished, la-bor end-ed, Jor-dan passed."
"Not till earth and not till heav-en Pass a-way."
Saints, a-pos-tles, proph-ets, mar-tyrs An-swer, "Yes."

240 I Am Coming, Lord

LEWIS HARTSOUGH, 1828-1919   LEWIS HARTSOUGH, 1828-1919

1. I hear Thy wel-come voice That calls me, Lord, to Thee For cleans-ing in Thy
2. Tho com-ing weak and vile, Thou dost my strength as-sure; Thou dost my vile-ness
3. 'Tis Je-sus calls me on To per-fect faith and love, To per-fect hope and

CHORUS

pre-cious blood That flowed on Cal-va-ry.
ful-ly cleanse Till spot-less all and pure.   I am com-ing, Lord! Com-ing
peace and trust For earth and heav'n a-bove.

I Am Coming, Lord

now to Thee! Wash me, cleanse me in the blood That flowed on Cal-va-ry!

Have You Any Room for Jesus? 241

Source unknown, 19th century

C. C. WILLIAMS, ?-1882

1. Have you an-y room for Je - sus, He who bore your load of sin?
2. Room for pleas-ure, room for busi-ness— But, for Christ the Cru-ci - fied,
3. Have you an-y room for Je - sus, As in grace He calls a - gain?
4. Room and time now give to Je - sus, Soon will pass God's day of grace;

As He knocks and asks ad-mis - sion, Sin - ner, will you let Him in?
Not a place that He can en - ter, In the heart for which He died?
O to-day is time ac-cept-ed, To-mor-row you may call in vain.
Soon thy heart left cold and si - lent, And thy Sav-ior's plead-ing cease.

CHORUS

Room for Je-sus, King of glo - ry! Has-ten now, His word o - bey;

Swing the heart's door wide-ly o - pen, Bid Him en-ter while you may.

242 Jesus, I Come

WILLIAM T. SLEEPER, 1819-1904   GEORGE C. STEBBINS, 1846-1945

1. Out of my bond-age, sor-row and night, Je-sus, I come, Je-sus, I come;
2. Out of my shame-ful fail-ure and loss, Je-sus, I come, Je-sus, I come;
3. Out of un-rest and ar - ro-gant pride, Je-sus, I come, Je-sus, I come;
4. Out of the fear and dread of the tomb, Je-sus, I come, Je-sus, I come;

In - to Thy free-dom, glad-ness and light, Je-sus, I come to Thee.
In - to the glo-rious gain of Thy cross, Je-sus, I come to Thee.
In - to Thy bless-ed will to a - bide, Je-sus, I come to Thee.
In - to the joy and light of Thy home, Je-sus, I come to Thee.

Out of my sick-ness in-to Thy health, Out of my want and in-to Thy wealth,
Out of earth's sorrows in-to Thy balm, Out of life's storms and in-to Thy calm,
Out of my-self to dwell in Thy love, Out of de-spair in-to rap-tures a-bove,
Out of the depths of ru - in un-told, In - to the peace of Thy shel-ter-ing fold,

Out of my sin and in - to Thy-self, Je-sus, I come to Thee.
Out of dis-tress to ju - bi-lant psalm, Je-sus, I come to Thee.
Up-ward for aye on wings like a dove, Je-sus, I come to Thee.
Ev - er Thy glo-rious face to be-hold, Je-sus, I come to Thee.

Room at the Cross for You

IRA F. STANPHILL, 1914-   IRA F. STANPHILL, 1914-

1. The cross up-on which Je-sus died Is a shel-ter in
2. Tho mil-lions have found Him a friend And have turned from the
3. The hand of my Sav-ior is strong, And the love of my

which we can hide; And its grace so free is suf-
sins they have sinned, The Sav-ior still waits to
Sav-ior is long; Through sun-shine or rain, through

fi-cient for me, And deep is its foun-tain— as wide as the sea.
o-pen the gates And wel-come a sin-ner be-fore it's too late.
loss or in gain, The blood flows from Cal-v'ry to cleanse ev-'ry stain.

CHORUS

There's room at the cross for you, There's room at the cross for you; Tho

mil-lions have come, There's still room for one—Yes, there's room at the cross for you.

244 Let Jesus Come into Your Heart

Lelia N. Morris, 1862-1929

Lelia N. Morris, 1862-1929

1. If you are tired of the load of your sin, Let Je - sus come
2. If 'tis for pu - ri - ty now that you sigh, Let Je - sus come
3. If there's a tem-pest your voice can-not still, Let Je - sus come
4. If you would join the glad songs of the blest, Let Je - sus come

in - to your heart; If you de - sire a new life to be-gin,
in - to your heart; Foun-tains for cleans-ing are flow-ing near-by,
in - to your heart; If there's a void this world nev - er can fill,
in - to your heart; If you would en - ter the man-sions of rest,

Let Je - sus come in - to your heart.

CHORUS

Just now your doubt-ings give o'er, Just now re - ject Him no more; Just now throw o - pen the door— Let Je - sus come in - to your heart.

I Am Praying for You

IRA D. SANKEY, 1840-1908
Arr. by Eldon Burkwall, 1928-

S. O'MALLEY CLUFF, 1837-1910

1. I have a Sav-ior-He's plead-ing in glo-ry, A dear, lov-ing
2. I have a Fa-ther-to me He has giv-en A hope for e-
3. I have a robe-'tis re-splen-dent in white-ness-A-wait-ing in
4. When Christ has found you, tell oth-ers the sto-ry, That my lov-ing

Sav-ior, tho earth-friends be few; And now He is watch-ing in
ter-ni-ty, bless-ed and true; And soon He will call me to
glo-ry my won-der-ing view; O when I re-ceive it all
Sav-ior is your Sav-ior too; Then pray that your Sav-ior will

ten-der-ness o'er me-But O that my Sav-ior were your Sav-ior too.
meet Him in heav-en-But O that He'd let me bring you with me too!
shin-ing in bright-ness, Dear friend, could I see you re-ceiv-ing one too!
bring them to glo-ry, And prayer will be an-swered-'twas an-swered for you!

CHORUS

For you I am pray-ing, For you I am pray-ing,

For you I am pray-ing, I'm pray-ing for you.

246 Softly and Tenderly

WILL L. THOMPSON, 1847-1909

WILL L. THOMPSON, 1847-1909

1. Soft - ly and ten - der - ly Je - sus is call - ing, Call - ing for
2. Why should we tar - ry when Je - sus is plead - ing, Plead - ing for
3. Time is now fleet - ing, the mo - ments are pass - ing, Pass - ing from
4. O for the won - der - ful love He has prom - ised, Prom - ised for

you and for me; See, on the por - tals He's wait - ing and watch - ing,
you and for me? Why should we lin - ger and heed not His mer - cies,
you and from me; Shad - ows are gath - er - ing, death-beds are com - ing,
you and for me; Tho we have sinned He has mer - cy and par - don,

CHORUS

Watch - ing for you and for me.
Mer - cies for you and for me? Come home, come home,
Com - ing for you and for me.
Par - don for you and for me.

Ye who are wea - ry, come home; Ear - nest - ly,

ten - der - ly, Je - sus is call - ing— Call - ing, "O sin - ner, come home!"

Jesus Is Calling

FANNY J. CROSBY, 1820-1915

GEORGE C. STEBBINS, 1846-1945

1. Je-sus is ten-der-ly call-ing thee home— Call-ing to-day,
2. Je-sus is call-ing the wea-ry to rest— Call-ing to-day,
3. Je-sus is wait-ing, O come to Him now— Wait-ing to-day,
4. Je-sus is plead-ing, O list to His voice— Hear Him to-day,

call-ing to-day; Why from the sun-shine of love wilt thou roam
call-ing to-day; Bring Him thy bur-den and thou shalt be blest—
wait-ing to-day; Come with thy sins, at His feet low-ly bow—
hear Him to-day; They who be-lieve on His name shall re-joice—

REFRAIN

Far-ther and far-ther a-way?
He will not turn thee a-way.   Call - ing to-day,
Come, and no long-er de-lay.   Call-ing, call-ing to-day, to-day,
Quick-ly a-rise and a-way.

Call - ing to-day,   Je - - sus is
Call-ing, call-ing to-day, to-day;   Je-sus is ten-der-ly

call - - ing, Is ten-der-ly call-ing to-day.
call-ing to-day,

248

Why Not Now?

Daniel W. Whittle, 1840-1901

Charles C. Case, 1843-1918

1. While we pray and while we plead, While you see your soul's deep need,
2. You have wan-dered far a - way— Do not risk an - oth - er day;
3. In the world you've failed to find Aught of peace for trou-bled mind;
4. Come to Christ, con-fes-sion make— Come to Christ and par-don take;

While your Fa-ther calls you home, Will you not, my broth-er, come?
Do not turn from God your face, But to-day ac-cept His grace.
Come to Christ, on Him be-lieve— Peace and joy you shall re-ceive.
Trust in Him from day to day— He will keep you all the way.

CHORUS

|1 |2

Why not now? why not now? Why not come to Je-sus now? Je-sus now?
Why not now? why not now?

249

Just As I Am

WOODWORTH

Charlotte Elliott, 1789-1871

William B. Bradbury, 1816-1868

1. Just as I am, with-out one plea But that Thy blood was shed for me,
2. Just as I am, and wait-ing not To rid my soul of one dark blot,
3. Just as I am, tho tossed a-bout With man-y a con-flict, man-y a doubt,
4. Just as I am, poor, wretch-ed, blind— Sight, rich-es, heal-ing of the mind,
5. Just as I am, Thou wilt re-ceive, Wilt wel-come, par-don, cleanse, re-lieve;

Just As I Am

And that Thou bidd'st me come to Thee, O Lamb of God, I come! I come!
To Thee whose blood can cleanse each spot, O Lamb of God, I come! I come!
Fight-ings and fears with-in, with-out, O Lamb of God, I come! I come!
Yea, all I need in Thee to find— O Lamb of God, I come! I come!
Be - cause Thy prom-ise I be - lieve, O Lamb of God, I come! I come!

God's Final Call   250

JOHN W. PETERSON, 1921-

JOHN W. PETERSON, 1921-

1. Some day you'll hear God's fi - nal call to you   To take His
2. How can you live an - oth - er day in sin,   Think-ing some
3. If you re - ject God's fi - nal call of grace,   You'll have no

of - fer of sal - va - tion true—   This could be it, my friend, if
day with Christ you will be - gin?   O will you hear, a - bove the
chance your foot-steps to re - trace—   All hope will then be gone, and

you but knew: God's fi - nal call,   God's fi - nal call.
world's loud din, God's fi - nal call,   God's fi - nal call?
doom you'll face: O hear His call!   O hear His call!

251 Almost Persuaded

PHILIP P. BLISS, 1838-1876

PHILIP P. BLISS, 1838-1876

1. "Al - most per-suad-ed" now to be - lieve; "Al - most per-suad-ed"
2. "Al - most per-suad-ed," come, come to - day; "Al - most per-suad-ed,"
3. "Al - most per-suad-ed," har - vest is past! "Al - most per-suad-ed,"

Christ to re - ceive: Seems now some soul to say, "Go, Spir - it,
turn not a - way: Je - sus in - vites you here, An - gels are
doom comes at last! "Al - most" can - not a - vail, "Al - most" is

go Thy way, Some more con - ven-ient day On Thee I'll call."
lin-g'ring near, Prayers rise from hearts so dear, O wan-d'rer, come.
but to fail! Sad, sad, that bit - ter wail, "Al - most," but lost!

252 Only Trust Him

JOHN H. STOCKTON, 1813-1877

JOHN H. STOCKTON, 1813-1877

1. Come, ev - 'ry soul by sin op-pressed—There's mer-cy with the Lord,
2. For Je - sus shed His pre-cious blood Rich bless-ings to be - stow;
3. Yes, Je - sus is the Truth, the Way, That leads you in - to rest;

And He will sure - ly give you rest By trust-ing in His word.
Plunge now in - to the crim-son flood That wash-es white as snow.
Be - lieve in Him with - out de - lay And you are ful - ly blest.

Only Trust Him

CHORUS

On - ly trust Him, on - ly trust Him, On - ly trust Him now;
He will save you, He will save you, He will save you now.

May be sung one step lower.

Lord, I'm Coming Home

253

WILLIAM J. KIRKPATRICK, 1838-1921

WILLIAM J. KIRKPATRICK, 1838-1921

1. I've wan-dered far a - way from God— Now I'm com-ing home;
2. I've wast - ed man - y pre - cious years— Now I'm com-ing home;
3. I've tired of sin and stray - ing, Lord— Now I'm com-ing home;
4. My soul is sick, my heart is sore— Now I'm com-ing home;

The paths of sin too long I've trod— Lord, I'm com-ing home.
I now re-pent with bit - ter tears— Lord, I'm com-ing home.
I'll trust Thy love, be - lieve Thy word— Lord, I'm com-ing home.
My strength re-new, my hope re - store— Lord, I'm com-ing home.

CHORUS

Com-ing home, com - ing home, Nev - er - more to roam;

O - pen now Thine arms of love— Lord, I'm com-ing home.

254
Come to the Savior

GEORGE F. ROOT, 1820-1895   GEORGE F. ROOT, 1820-1895

1. Come to the Sav - ior, make no de - lay— Here in His Word He's
2. "Suf - fer the chil - dren!" O hear His voice, Let ev - 'ry heart leap
3. Think once a - gain, He's with us to - day— Heed now His blest com

shown us the way; Here in our midst He's stand - ing to - day,
forth and re - joice, And let us free - ly make Him our choice:
mands, and o - bey; Hear now His ac - cents ten - der - ly say,

CHORUS

Ten - der - ly say - ing, "Come!"
Do not de - lay, but come.   Joy - ful, joy - ful
"Will you, My chil - dren, come?"

will the meet-ing be, When from sin our hearts are pure and free,

And we shall gath-er, Sav - ior, with Thee In our e - ter - nal home.

Blessed Assurance

FANNY J. CROSBY, 1820-1915

PHOEBE P. KNAPP, 1839-1908

1. Bless-ed as-sur-ance, Je-sus is mine! O what a fore-taste of glo-ry di-vine! Heir of sal-va-tion, pur-chase of God, Born of His Spir-it, washed in His blood.

2. Per-fect sub-mis-sion, per-fect de-light! Vi-sions of rap-ture now burst on my sight; An-gels de-scend-ing bring from a-bove Ech-oes of mer-cy, whis-pers of love.

3. Per-fect sub-mis-sion—all is at rest, I in my Sav-ior am hap-py and blest; Watch-ing and wait-ing, look-ing a-bove, Filled with His good-ness, lost in His love.

CHORUS

This is my sto-ry, this is my song, Prais-ing my Sav-ior all the day long; This is my sto-ry, this is my song, Prais-ing my Sav-ior all the day long.

256 It Is Well with My Soul

HORATIO G. SPAFFORD, 1828-1888

PHILIP P. BLISS, 1838-1876

1. When peace, like a riv - er, at - tend - eth my way, When sor - rows like
2. Tho Sa - tan should buf - fet, tho tri - als should come, Let this blest as -
3. My sin— O the bliss of this glo - ri - ous tho't— My sin, not in
4. And, Lord, haste the day when my faith shall be sight, The clouds be rolled

sea - bil - lows roll— What - ev - er my lot, Thou hast taught me to say,
sur - ance con - trol, That Christ hath re - gard - ed my help - less es - tate,
part, but the whole, Is nailed to the cross, and I bear it no more:
back as a scroll: The trump shall re - sound and the Lord shall de - scend,

CHORUS

It is well, it is well with my soul.
And hath shed His own blood for my soul.   It is well
Praise the Lord, praise the Lord, O my soul!   It is well
"E - ven so"— it is well with my soul.

with my soul,
with my soul,   It is well, it is well with my soul.

'Tis So Sweet to Trust in Jesus

LOUISA M. R. STEAD, c. 1850-1917   WILLIAM J. KIRKPATRICK, 1838-1921

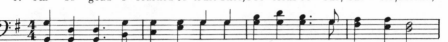

1. 'Tis   so   sweet to trust in Je - sus, Just to take Him at   His word,
2. O   how sweet to trust in Je - sus, Just to trust His cleans-ing blood,
3. Yes, 'tis sweet to trust in Je - sus, Just from sin and self   to cease,
4. I'm   so   glad I learned to trust Thee, Pre-cious Je - sus, Sav - ior, Friend;

Just to rest   up - on His prom - ise, Just   to know, "Thus saith the Lord."
Just in sim - ple faith to plunge me 'Neath the heal - ing, cleans-ing flood!
Just from Je - sus sim-ply tak - ing Life   and rest and joy and peace.
And I know that Thou art with me, Wilt   be with me to   the end.

CHORUS

Je - sus, Je - sus, how I trust Him! How I've proved Him o'er and o'er!

Je - sus, Je - sus, pre - cious Je - sus! O for grace to   trust Him more!

He Hideth My Soul

FANNY J. CROSBY, 1820-1915

WILLIAM J. KIRKPATRICK, 1838-1921

1. A won-der-ful Sav-ior is Je-sus my Lord, A won-der-ful
2. A won-der-ful Sav-ior is Je-sus my Lord— He tak-eth my
3. With num-ber-less bless-ings each mo-ment He crowns, And, filled with His
4. When clothed in His brightness trans-port-ed I rise To meet Him in

Sav-ior to me; He hid-eth my soul in the cleft of the rock, Where
bur-den a-way; He hold-eth me up and I shall not be moved, He
full-ness di-vine, I sing in my rap-ture, "O glo-ry to God For
clouds of the sky, His per-fect sal-va-tion, His won-der-ful love, I'll

CHORUS

riv-ers of pleas-ure I see.
giv-eth me strength as my day.
such a Re-deem-er as mine!"
shout with the mil-lions on high.

He hid-eth my soul in the cleft of the rock

That shadows a dry, thirsty land; He hid-eth my life in the depths of His love,

And cov-ers me there with His hand, And cov-ers me there with His hand.

The Rock That Is Higher Than I

259

Erastus Johnson, 1826-1909

William G. Fischer, 1835-1912

1. O some-times the shad-ows are deep, And rough seems the path to the goal;
2. O some-times how long seems the day, And some-times how wea-ry my feet;
3. O near to the Rock let me keep, If bless-ings or sor-rows pre-vail;

And sor-rows, some-times how they sweep Like tem-pests down o-ver the soul!
But toil-ing in life's dust-y way, The Rock's bless-ed shad-ow, how sweet!
Or climb-ing the moun-tain-way steep, Or walk-ing the shad-ow-y vale.

CHORUS

O then to the Rock let me fly,
let me fly,
To the

Rock that is high-er than I;
is high-er than I;
O then to the

Rock let me fly,
let me fly,
To the Rock that is high-er than I!

260 Is My Name Written There?

MARY A. KIDDER, 1820-1905

FRANK M. DAVIS, 1839-1896

1. Lord, I care not for rich-es, nei-ther sil-ver nor gold— I would
2. Lord, my sins they are man-y, like the sands of the sea, But Thy
3. O that beau-ti-ful cit-y with its man-sions of light, With its

make sure of heav-en, I would en-ter the fold. In the book of Thy
blood, O my Sav-ior, is suf-fi-cient for me; For Thy prom-ise is
glo-ri-fied be-ings in pure gar-ments of white; Where no e-vil thing

king-dom with its pa-ges so fair, Tell me, Je-sus, my Sav-ior, is my
writ-ten in bright let-ters that glow, "Tho your sins be as scar-let, I will
com-eth to de-spoil what is fair, Where the an-gels are watch-ing— yes, my

REFRAIN

name writ-ten there?
make them like snow." Is my name writ-ten there On the page white and
name's writ-ten there. 3. Yes, my name's writ-ten there On the page white and

fair? In the book of Thy king-dom, Is my name writ-ten there?
fair; In the book of Thy king-dom, Yes, my name's writ-ten there!

Trust and Obey

John H. Sammis, 1846-1919

Daniel B. Towner, 1850-1919

1. When we walk with the Lord In the light of His Word, What a glo-ry He
2. Not a shad-ow can rise, Not a cloud in the skies, But His smile quick-ly
3. Not a bur-den we bear, Not a sor-row we share, But our toil He doth
4. But we nev-er can prove The de-lights of His love Un-til all on the
5. Then in fel-low-ship sweet We will sit at His feet, Or we'll walk by His

sheds on our way! While we do His good will He a-bides with us still,
drives it a-way; Not a doubt nor a fear, Not a sigh nor a tear,
rich-ly re-pay; Not a grief nor a loss, Not a frown nor a cross,
al-tar we lay, For the fa-vor He shows And the joy He be-stows
side in the way; What He says we will do, Where He sends we will go—

Chorus

And with all who will trust and o-bey.
Can a-bide while we trust and o-bey.
But is blest if we trust and o-bey.   Trust and o-bey— For there's
Are for them who will trust and o-bey.
Nev-er fear, on-ly trust and o-bey.

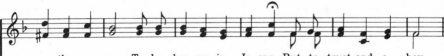

no oth-er way To be hap-py in Je-sus But to trust and o-bey.

262 Trusting Jesus

EDGAR PAGE STITES, 1836-1921

IRA D. SANKEY, 1840-1908

1. Sim - ply trust-ing ev - 'ry day, Trust-ing thru a storm-y way;
2. Bright-ly doth His Spir - it shine In - to this poor heart of mine;
3. Sing - ing if my way is clear, Pray-ing if the path be drear;
4. Trust-ing Him while life shall last, Trust-ing Him till earth be past;

E - ven when my faith is small, Trust-ing Je - sus— that is all.
While He leads I can-not fall, Trust-ing Je - sus— that is all.
If in dan - ger, for Him call, Trust-ing Je - sus— that is all.
Till with-in the jas - per wall, Trust-ing Je - sus— that is all.

CHORUS

Trust-ing as the mo - ments fly, Trust-ing as the days go by;

Trust-ing Him what - e'er be - fall, Trust-ing Je - sus— that is all.

A Shelter in the Time of Storm

263

Vernon J. Charlesworth, 1838-? — alt.

Ira D. Sankey, 1840-1908

1. The Lord's our Rock, in Him we hide— A shel-ter in the time of storm;
2. A shade by day, de-fense by night— A shel-ter in the time of storm;
3. The rag-ing storms may round us beat— A shel-ter in the time of storm;
4. O Rock di-vine, O Ref-uge dear— A shel-ter in the time of storm;

Se - cure what-ev - er ill be-tide— A shel-ter in the time of storm.
No fears a-larm, no foes af-fright— A shel-ter in the time of storm.
We'll nev-er leave our safe re-treat— A shel-ter in the time of storm.
Be Thou our help-er ev - er near— A shel-ter in the time of storm.

CHORUS

O Je-sus is a Rock in a wea-ry land, A wea-ry land, a wea-ry land;

O Je-sus is a Rock in a wea-ry land— A shel-ter in the time of storm.

264   In the Garden

C. AUSTIN MILES, 1868-1946   C. AUSTIN MILES, 1868-1946

1. I come to the gar-den a - lone, While the dew is
2. He speaks, and the sound of His voice Is so sweet the
3. I'd stay in the gar-den with Him Tho the night a -

still on the ros - es; And the voice I hear, fall-ing on my ear,
birds hush their sing - ing; And the mel - o - dy that He gave to me
round me be fall - ing; But He bids me go— thru the voice of woe,

REFRAIN

The Son of God dis - clos - es.
With - in my heart is ring - ing. And He walks with me, and He
His voice to me is call - ing.

talks with me, And He tells me I am His own, And the joy we

share as we tar - ry there, None oth-er has ev - er known.

We Have an Anchor

PRISCILLA J. OWENS, 1829-1907

WILLIAM J. KIRKPATRICK, 1838-1921

1. Will your an-chor hold   in the storms of life, When the clouds un - fold
2. It   is   safe-ly moored,'twill the storm with-stand, For 'tis   well   se - cured
3. When our eyes be-hold   thru the gath-'ring night The   cit - y of gold,

their   wings of strife? When the strong tides lift   and the   ca - bles strain,
by the Sav-ior's hand; Tho the   tem - pest rage and the wild winds blow,
our   har- bor bright, We shall an-chor fast   by the heav'n-ly shore,

CHORUS

Will your an-chor drift   or   firm re-main?
Not an an-gry wave shall our bark o'er-flow.   We have an an-chor that
With the storms all   past   for - ev - er-more.

keeps the soul Stead-fast and sure while the bil-lows roll, Fast-ened to the

Rock which can-not move, Grounded firm and deep   in the Sav-ior's love.

266 Fade, Fade, Each Earthly Joy

LUNDIE

JANE C. BONAR, 1821-1884

THEODORE E. PERKINS, 1831-1912

1. Fade, fade, each earth-ly joy— Je - sus is mine; Break, ev -'ry
2. Tempt not my soul a - way— Je - sus is mine; Here would I
3. Fare - well, ye dreams of night— Je - sus is mine; Lost in this
4. Fare - well, mor - tal - i - ty— Je - sus is mine; Wel - come, e -

ten - der tie— Je - sus is mine. Dark is the wil - der - ness,
ev - er stay— Je - sus is mine. Per - ish - ing things of clay,
dawn-ing bright— Je - sus is mine. All that my soul has tried
ter - ni - ty— Je - sus is mine. Wel - come, O loved and blest,

Earth has no rest-ing place; Je - sus a - lone can bless— Je - sus is mine.
Born but for one brief day, Pass from my heart a - way— Je - sus is mine.
Left but a dis-mal void; Je - sus has sat-is-fied— Je - sus is mine.
Wel-come, sweet scenes of rest; Wel-come, my Sav-ior's breast— Je - sus is mine.

267 All Things Work Out for Good

ORTONVILLE

THOMAS HASTINGS, 1784-1872

JOHN W. PETERSON, 1921-

Arr. by John W. Peterson, 1921-

1. All things work out for good, we know—Such is God's great de - sign; He or - ders
2. This is the faith that keeps me still, No mat-ter what the test, And lets me
3. So now the fu - ture holds no fear, God guards the work be - gun; And mor-tals
4. Some day the path He chose for me Will all be un - der - stood; In heav - en's

Another harmonization of this tune, in a higher key: 52

© 1961 by Singspiration, Inc. All rights reserved.

All Things Work Out for Good

all our steps be-low For pur-pos-es di - vine, For pur-pos-es di - vine.
glo - ry in His will— For well I know 'tis best, For well I know 'tis best.
are im-mor-tal here Un - til their work is done, Un - til their work is done.
clear-er light I'll see All things work'd out for good, All things work'd out for good.

How Firm a Foundation   268

FOUNDATION

"K" — in Rippon's *Selection of Hymns*, 1787

American melody
From Caldwell's *Union Harmony*, 1837

1. How   firm a foun-da-tion, ye saints of the Lord, Is   laid for your
2. "Fear   not, I am with thee— O   be   not dis-mayed, For   I   am thy
3. "When thru the deep wa-ters I   call thee to   go, The   riv-ers of
4. "When thru fi - ery tri - als thy path-way shall lie, My   grace, all-suf-
5. "The   soul that on Je - sus hath leaned for re-pose, I   will not, I

faith   in His   ex - cel-lent Word! What more   can He   say   than to
God,   I   will still give thee   aid; I'll strength-en thee, help   thee, and
woe   shall not thee   o - ver - flow; For   I   will be with thee thy
fi - cient, shall be   thy sup - ply; The flame shall not hurt thee— I
will   not de - sert   to his foes; That soul, tho all hell should en-

you   He hath said— To   you, who for ref - uge to   Je - sus have fled?
cause thee to stand, Up - held   by my gra - cious, om - nip - o - tent hand.
trou - bles to bless, And sanc - ti - fy to   thee thy deep-est dis - tress.
on - ly de - sign Thy dross to con-sume and thy gold to   re - fine.
deav - or to shake, I'll   nev - er— no, nev - er— no, nev - er for - sake!"

Alternate tunes: ADESTE FIDELES — 100, ST. DENIO — 34

269 Under His Wings

WILLIAM O. CUSHING, 1823-1902

IRA D. SANKEY, 1840-1908

1. Un-der His wings I am safe - ly a - bid-ing, Tho the night
2. Un-der His wings, what a ref - uge in sor-row! How the heart
3. Un-der His wings, O what pre-cious en - joy-ment! There will I

deep - ens and tem-pests are wild; Still I can trust Him— I
yearn-ing - ly turns to His rest! Oft - en when earth has no
hide till life's tri - als are o'er; Shel-tered, pro - tect - ed, no

know He will keep me, He has re-deemed me and I am His child.
balm for my heal-ing, There I find com - fort and there I am blest.
e - vil can harm me, Rest - ing in Je - sus I'm safe ev - er - more.

CHORUS

Un-der His wings, un-der His wings, Who from His love can sev-er?

Un-der His wings my soul shall a-bide, Safe-ly a - bide for - ev - er.

The Haven of Rest

270

GEORGE D. MOORE, 19th century
Arr. by Don Peterman, 1925-

HENRY L. GILMOUR, 1836-1920

1. My soul in sad ex-ile was out on life's sea, So bur-dened with
2. I yield-ed my-self to His ten-der em-brace, And, faith tak-ing
3. The song of my soul, since the Lord made me whole, Has been the old
4. O come to the Sav-ior—He pa-tient-ly waits To save by His

sin, and dis-trest, Till I heard a sweet voice say-ing, "Make me your choice!"
hold of the Word, My fet-ters fell off, and I an-chored my soul—
sto-ry so blest Of Je-sus, who'll save who-so-ev-er will have
pow-er di-vine; Come, an-chor your soul in the Ha-ven of Rest,

CHORUS

And I en-tered the Ha-ven of Rest.
The "Ha-ven of Rest" is my Lord.
A home in the Ha-ven of Rest!
And say, "My Be-lov-ed is mine."

I've an-chored my soul in the

Ha-ven of Rest, I'll sail the wide seas no more; The tem-pest may

sweep o'er the wild, storm-y deep— In Je-sus I'm safe ev-er-more.

271 My Anchor Holds

W. C. Martin, 19th century

Daniel B. Towner, 1850-1919

1. Tho the an-gry sur-ges roll On my tem-pest-driv-en soul,
2. Might-y tides a-bout me sweep, Per-ils lurk with-in the deep,
3. I can feel the an-chor fast As I meet each sud-den blast,
4. Trou-bles al-most 'whelm the soul, Griefs like bil-lows o'er me roll,

I am peace-ful, for I know, Wild-ly tho the winds may blow,
An-gry clouds o'er-shade the sky And the tem-pest ris-es high;
And the ca-ble, tho un-seen, Bears the heav-y strain be-tween;
Temp-ters seek to lure a-stray, Storms ob-scure the light of day:

I've an an-chor safe and sure That can ev-er-more en-dure.
Still I stand the tem-pest's shock, For my an-chor grips the Rock.
Thru the storm I safe-ly ride Till the turn-ing of the tide.
But in Christ I can be bold— I've an an-chor that shall hold.

CHORUS

And it holds, my an-chor holds! Blow your wild-est, then, O
And it holds, my an-chor holds! Blow your wild - - - est,

gale, On my bark so small and frail: By His grace I shall not
then, O gale,

My Anchor Holds

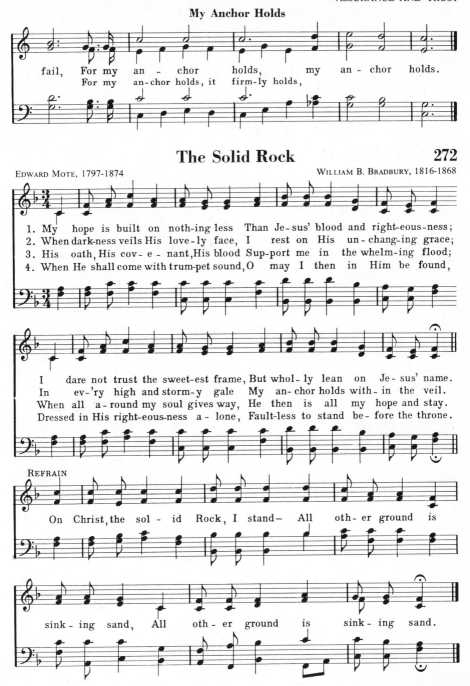

fail,   For my   an - chor   holds,   my   an - chor   holds.
For my   an-chor holds, it   firm-ly holds,

The Solid Rock

272

Edward Mote, 1797-1874

William B. Bradbury, 1816-1868

1. My   hope is built on noth-ing less   Than Je-sus' blood and right-eous-ness;
2. When dark-ness veils His love-ly face, I   rest on His   un-chang-ing grace;
3. His   oath, His cov-e-nant, His blood Sup-port me in   the whelm-ing flood;
4. When He shall come with trum-pet sound, O   may I then in   Him be found,

I   dare not trust the sweet-est frame, But whol-ly lean   on   Je-sus' name.
In   ev-'ry high and storm-y gale   My an-chor holds with-in the veil.
When all a-round my soul gives way, He then is   all   my hope and stay.
Dressed in His right-eous-ness a-lone, Fault-less to stand be-fore the throne.

Refrain

On Christ, the sol - id Rock, I stand— All   oth-er ground is

sink-ing sand,   All   oth-er   ground   is   sink-ing sand.

273

Walk in the Light

CAMPMEETING

American melody
Arr. by John W. Peterson, 1921-

BERNARD BARTON, 1784-1849

1. Walk in the light! so shalt thou know That fel-low-ship of love
2. Walk in the light! and thou shalt find Thy heart made tru-ly His,
3. Walk in the light! and thou shalt own Thy dark-ness passed a-way,
4. Walk in the light! and e'en the tomb No fear-ful shade shall wear;
5. Walk in the light! thy path shall be A path, tho thorn-y, bright;

His Spir-it on-ly can be-stow Who reigns in light a-bove.
Who dwells in cloud-less light en-shrined, In whom no dark-ness is.
Be-cause that light hath on thee shone In which is per-fect day.
Glo-ry shall chase a-way its gloom, For Christ hath con-quered there.
For God, by grace, shall dwell in thee, And God Him-self is light.

Alternate tune: MANOAH—5 (192)

274

Jesus Never Fails

ARTHUR A. LUTHER, 1891-1960

ARTHUR A. LUTHER, 1891-1960

1. Earth-ly friends may prove un-true, Doubts and fears as-sail; One still loves and
2. Tho the sky be dark and drear, Fierce and strong the gale, Just re-mem-ber
3. In life's dark and bit-ter hour Love will still pre-vail; Trust His ev-er-

CHORUS

cares for you, One who will not fail.
He is near, And He will not fail. Je-sus nev-er fails, Je-sus
last-ing pow'r— Je-sus will not fail.

Jesus Never Fails

nev-er fails; Heav'n and earth may pass a-way, But Je-sus nev-er fails.

I Belong to the King

275

J. Lincoln Hall, 1866-1930
Arr. by Jon Drevits, 1928-

Ida Reed Smith, 1865-1951

1. I be-long to the King— I'm a child of His love, I shall dwell in His
2. I be-long to the King— and He loves me I know, For His mer-cy and
3. I be-long to the King— and His prom-ise is sure, That we all shall be

pal-ace so fair, For He tells of its bliss in yon heav-en a-bove,
kind-ness, so free, Are un-ceas-ing-ly mine where-so-ev-er I go,
gath-ered at last In His king-dom a-bove, by life's wa-ters so pure,

D.S.- call me some day to His pal-ace a-bove—

Fine CHORUS

And His chil-dren its splen-dors shall share.
And my ref-uge un-fail-ing is He. I be-long to the King—
When this life with its tri-als is past.

I shall dwell by His glo-ri-fied throne.

D.S.

I'm a child of His love, And He nev-er for-sak-eth His own; He will

276
In the Hour of Trial

PENITENCE

James Montgomery, 1771-1854 — alt.

Spencer Lane, 1843-1903

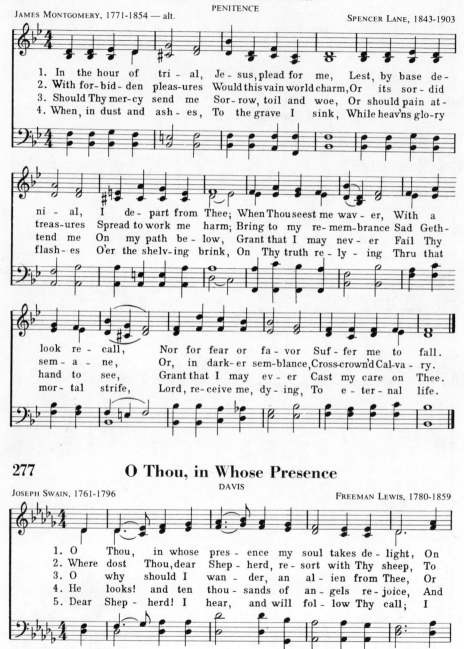

1. In the hour of trial, Je-sus, plead for me, Lest, by base de-
2. With for-bid-den pleas-ures Would this vain world charm, Or its sor-did
3. Should Thy mer-cy send me Sor-row, toil and woe, Or should pain at-
4. When, in dust and ash-es, To the grave I sink, While heav'ns glo-ry

ni - al, I de-part from Thee; When Thou seest me wav-er, With a
treas-ures Spread to work me harm; Bring to my re-mem-brance Sad Geth-
tend me On my path be-low, Grant that I may nev-er Fail Thy
flash-es O'er the shelv-ing brink, On Thy truth re-ly-ing Thru that

look re - call, Nor for fear or fa-vor Suf-fer me to fall.
sem - a - ne, Or, in dark-er sem-blance, Cross-crown'd Cal-va-ry.
hand to see, Grant that I may ev-er Cast my care on Thee.
mor - tal strife, Lord, re-ceive me, dy-ing, To e-ter-nal life.

277
O Thou, in Whose Presence

DAVIS

Joseph Swain, 1761-1796

Freeman Lewis, 1780-1859

1. O Thou, in whose pres-ence my soul takes de-light, On
2. Where dost Thou, dear Shep-herd, re-sort with Thy sheep, To
3. O why should I wan-der, an al-ien from Thee, Or
4. He looks! and ten thou-sands of an-gels re-joice, And
5. Dear Shep-herd! I hear, and will fol-low Thy call; I

O Thou, in Whose Presence

whom in af-flic-tion I call, My com-fort by day and my
feed them in pas-tures of love? Say, why in the val-ley of
cry in the des-ert for bread? Thy foes will re-joice when my
myr-i-ads wait for His word; He speaks! and e-ter-ni-ty,
know the sweet sound of Thy voice; Re-store and de-fend me, for

song in the night, My hope, my sal-va-tion, my all:
death should I weep, Or a-lone in this wil-der-ness rove?
sor-rows they see, And smile at the tears I have shed.
filled with His voice, Re-ech-oes the praise of the Lord.
Thou art my all, And in Thee I will ev-er re-joice.

I Am Trusting Thee, Lord Jesus 278

BULLINGER

Frances R. Havergal, 1836-1879   Ethelbert W. Bullinger, 1837-1913

1. I am trust-ing Thee, Lord Je-sus— Trust-ing on-ly Thee;
2. I am trust-ing Thee to guide me— Thou a-lone shalt lead,
3. I am trust-ing Thee for pow-er— Thine can nev-er fail;
4. I am trust-ing Thee, Lord Je-sus— Nev-er let me fall;

Trust-ing Thee for full sal-va-tion, Great and free.
Ev-'ry day and hour sup-ply-ing All my need.
Words which Thou Thy-self shalt give me Must pre-vail.
I am trust-ing Thee for-ev-er, And for all.

279 A Child of the King!

HARRIETT E. BUELL, 1834-1910   JOHN B. SUMNER, 1838-1918

1. My Fa-ther is rich in hous-es and lands, He hold-eth the
2. My Fa-ther's own Son, the Sav-ior of men, Once wan-dered o'er
3. I once was an out-cast stran-ger on earth, A sin-ner by
4. A tent or a cot-tage, why should I care? They're build-ing a

wealth of the world in His hands! Of ru-bies and dia-monds, of
earth as the poor-est of them; But now He is reign-ing for-
choice and an al-ien by birth; But I've been a-dopt-ed, my
pal-ace for me o-ver there! Tho ex-iled from home, yet

sil-ver and gold, His cof-fers are full— He has rich-es un-told.
ev-er on high, And will give me a home in heav'n by and by.
name's writ-ten down— An heir to a man-sion, a robe, and a crown.
still I may sing: All glo-ry to God, I'm a child of the King!

CHORUS

I'm a child of the King, A child of the King!

With Je-sus, my Sav-ior, I'm a child of the King!

Moment by Moment

DANIEL W. WHITTLE, 1840-1901

MAY WHITTLE MOODY, 1870-1963

1. Dy-ing with Je-sus by death reck-oned mine, Liv-ing with Je-sus a
2. Nev-er a tri-al that He is not there, Nev-er a bur-den that
3. Nev-er a heart-ache and nev-er a groan, Nev-er a tear-drop and
4. Nev-er a weak-ness that He doth not feel, Nev-er a sick-ness that

new life di-vine, Look-ing to Je-sus till glo-ry doth shine—
He doth not bear; Nev-er a sor-row that He doth not share—
nev-er a moan, Nev-er a dan-ger but there on the throne,
He can-not heal; Mo-ment by mo-ment, in woe or in weal,

CHORUS

Mo-ment by mo-ment, O Lord, I am Thine.
Mo-ment by mo-ment, I'm un-der His care.
Mo-ment by mo-ment, He thinks of His own. Mo-ment by mo-ment I'm
Je-sus, my Sav-ior, a-bides with me still.

kept in His love, Mo-ment by mo-ment I've life from a-bove; Look-ing to

Je-sus till glo-ry doth shine, Mo-ment by mo-ment, O Lord, I am Thine.

281
Never Alone

Source unknown, 19th century

Source unknown, 19th century
Arr. by Eldon Burkwall, 1928-

1. I've seen the light-ning flash-ing And heard the thun-der roll,
2. The world's fierce winds are blow-ing— Temp-ta-tion's sharp and keen;
3. When in af-flic-tion's val-ley I tread the road of care,
4. He died on Cal-v'ry's moun-tain, For me they pierced His side,

CHORUS No,— nev-er a-lone, No,— nev-er a-lone—

I've felt sin's break-ers dash-ing, Which tried to con-quer my soul;
I have a peace in know-ing My Sav-ior stands be-tween;
My Sav-ior helps me car-ry The cross so heav-y to bear;
For me He o-pened that foun-tain, The crim-son, cleans-ing tide;

He prom-ised nev-er to leave me, Nev-er to leave me a-lone;

I've heard the voice of my Sav-ior, He bid me still fight on—
He stands to shield me from dan-ger When all my friends are gone—
Tho all a-round me is dark-ness And earth-ly joys are flown,
For me He's wait-ing in glo-ry Up-on His heav'n-ly throne—

No,— nev-er a-lone, No,— nev-er a-lone—

D.C.

He prom-ised nev-er to leave me, Nev-er to leave me a-lone.
He prom-ised nev-er to leave me, Nev-er to leave me a-lone.
My Sav-ior whis-pers His prom-ise— Nev-er to leave me a-lone.
He prom-ised nev-er to leave me, Nev-er to leave me a-lone.

He prom-ised nev-er to leave me, Nev-er to leave me a-lone.

Hiding in Thee

WILLIAM O. CUSHING, 1823-1902

IRA D. SANKEY, 1840-1908

1. O safe to the Rock that is high - er than I My
2. In the calm of the noon-tide, in sor - row's lone hour, In
3. How oft in the con - flict, when pressed by the foe, I have

soul in its con - flicts and sor - rows would fly; So sin - ful, so
times when temp-ta - tion casts o'er me its pow'r, In the tem - pests of
fled to my Ref - uge and breathed out my woe; How oft - en, when

wea - ry—Thine, Thine would I be: Thou blest "Rock of
life, on its wide, heav - ing sea, Thou blest "Rock of
tri - als like sea - bil - lows roll, Have I hid - den in

CHORUS

A - ges," I'm hid - ing in Thee.
A - ges," I'm hid - ing in Thee. Hid - ing in Thee,
Thee, O Thou Rock of my soul.

Hid - ing in Thee, Thou blest "Rock of A - ges," I'm hid - ing in Thee.

283 Yesterday, Today, Forever

ALBERT B. SIMPSON, 1843-1919

JAMES H. BURKE, 19th century

1. O how sweet the glo-rious mes-sage Sim-ple faith may claim: Yes-ter-
2. He who par-doned err-ing Pe-ter Nev-er need'st thou fear, He who
3. He who 'mid the rag-ing bil-lows Walked up-on the sea Still can
4. As of old He walked to Em-ma-us, With them to a-bide, So thru

day, to-day, for-ev-er, Je-sus is the same! Still He loves to
came to faith-less Tho-mas All thy doubt will clear; He who let the
hush our wild-est tem-pest, As on Gal-i-lee; He who wept and
all life's way He walk-eth, Ev-er near our side; Soon a-gain shall

save the sin-ful, Heal the sick and lame, Cheer the mourn-er, calm the
loved dis-ci-ple On His bos-om rest Bids thee still, with love as
prayed in an-guish In Geth-sem-a-ne Drinks with us each cup of
we be-hold Him— Has-ten, Lord, the day! But 'twill still be "this same

CHORUS

tem-pest—Glo-ry to His name!
ten-der, Lean up-on His breast. {Yes-ter-day, to-day, for-ev-er,
trem-bling, In our ag-o-ny. All may change, but Je-sus nev-er—
Je-sus," As He went a-way.

|1
Je-sus is the same;

|2
Glo-ry to His name! Glo-ry to His name,

Yesterday, Today, Forever

Glo-ry to His name; All may change, but Je-sus nev-er— Glo-ry to His name!

Sweet Peace, the Gift of God's Love 284

PETER P. BILHORN, 1865-1936

PETER P. BILHORN, 1865-1936

1. There comes to my heart one sweet strain, A glad and a joy-ous re - frain;
2. Thru Christ on the cross peace was made, My debt by His death was all paid;
3. When Je - sus as Lord I had crowned, My heart with this peace did a - bound;
4. In Je - sus for peace I a - bide, And as I keep close to His side,

I sing it a - gain and a - gain— Sweet peace, the gift of God's love.
No oth - er foun-da-tion is laid For peace, the gift of God's love.
In Him the rich bless-ing I found— Sweet peace, the gift of God's love.
There's noth-ing but peace doth be - tide— Sweet peace, the gift of God's love.

CHORUS

Peace, peace, sweet peace! Won-der-ful gift from a - bove! (a-bove!) O

won-der-ful, won-der-ful peace! Sweet peace, the gift of God's love!

285
Peace, Perfect Peace
PAX TECUM

EDWARD H. BICKERSTETH, 1825-1906

GEORGE T. CALDBECK, 1852-1918
Arr. by Don Peterman, 1925-

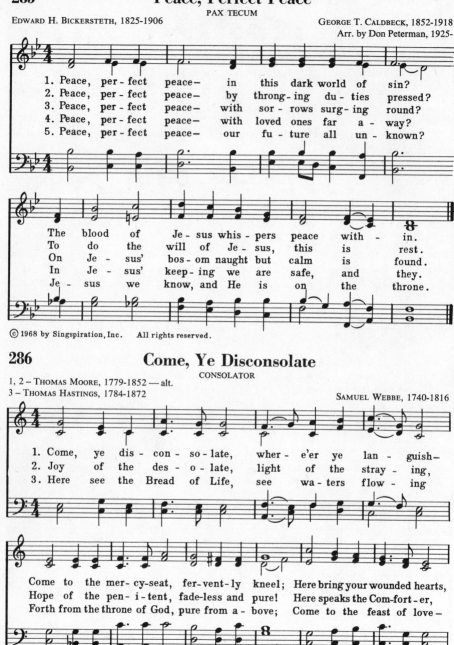

1. Peace, per-fect peace— in this dark world of sin?
2. Peace, per-fect peace— by throng-ing du-ties pressed?
3. Peace, per-fect peace— with sor-rows surg-ing round?
4. Peace, per-fect peace— with loved ones far a-way?
5. Peace, per-fect peace— our fu-ture all un-known?

The blood of Je-sus whis-pers peace with-in.
To do the will of Je-sus, this is rest.
On Je-sus' bos-om naught but calm is found.
In Je-sus' keep-ing we are safe, and they.
Je-sus we know, and He is on the throne.

286
Come, Ye Disconsolate
CONSOLATOR

1, 2 – THOMAS MOORE, 1779-1852 — alt.
3 – THOMAS HASTINGS, 1784-1872

SAMUEL WEBBE, 1740-1816

1. Come, ye dis-con-so-late, wher-e'er ye lan-guish—
2. Joy of the des-o-late, light of the stray-ing,
3. Here see the Bread of Life, see wa-ters flow-ing

Come to the mer-cy-seat, fer-vent-ly kneel; Here bring your wounded hearts,
Hope of the pen-i-tent, fade-less and pure! Here speaks the Com-fort-er,
Forth from the throne of God, pure from a-bove; Come to the feast of love—

Come, Ye Disconsolate

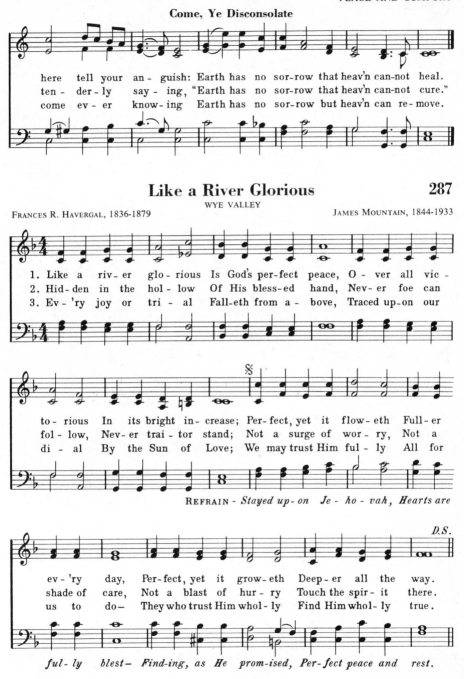

here tell your an-guish: Earth has no sor-row that heav'n can-not heal.
ten-der-ly say-ing, "Earth has no sor-row that heav'n can-not cure."
come ev-er know-ing Earth has no sor-row but heav'n can re-move.

Like a River Glorious 287

WYE VALLEY

FRANCES R. HAVERGAL, 1836-1879   JAMES MOUNTAIN, 1844-1933

1. Like a riv-er glo-rious Is God's per-fect peace, O-ver all vic-
2. Hid-den in the hol-low Of His bless-ed hand, Nev-er foe can
3. Ev-'ry joy or tri-al Fall-eth from a-bove, Traced up-on our

to-rious In its bright in-crease; Per-fect, yet it flow-eth Full-er
fol-low, Nev-er trai-tor stand; Not a surge of wor-ry, Not a
di-al By the Sun of Love; We may trust Him ful-ly All for

REFRAIN - *Stayed up-on Je-ho-vah, Hearts are*

D.S.

ev-'ry day, Per-fect, yet it grow-eth Deep-er all the way.
shade of care, Not a blast of hur-ry Touch the spir-it there.
us to do— They who trust Him whol-ly Find Him whol-ly true.

ful-ly blest— Find-ing, as He prom-ised, Per-fect peace and rest.

288

Wonderful Peace

W. D. Cornell, 19th century — alt.

W. G. Cooper, 19th century

1. Far a - way in the depths of my spir - it to - night Rolls a
2. What a treas - ure I have in this won - der - ful peace Bur - ied
3. I am rest - ing to - night in this won - der - ful peace, Rest - ing
4. And me - thinks when I rise to that cit - y of peace Where the
5. Ah! soul, are you here with - out com - fort and rest, March - ing

mel - o - dy sweet - er than psalm; In ce - les - tial-like strains it un -
deep in the heart of my soul, So se - cure that no pow - er can
sweet - ly in Je - sus' con - trol, For I'm kept from all dan - ger by
Au - thor of peace I shall see, That one strain of the song which the
down the rough path-way of time? Make Je - sus your friend ere the

CHORUS

ceas - ing - ly falls O'er my soul like an in - fi - nite calm.
mine it a - way While the years of e - ter - ni - ty roll.
night and by day, And His glo - ry is flood-ing my soul. Peace! peace!
ran-somed will sing In that heav - en - ly king-dom shall be:
shad-ows grow dark— O ac - cept this sweet peace so sub - lime!

won - der - ful peace, Com-ing down from the Fa - ther a - bove, Sweep o - ver my

spir - it for - ev - er, I pray, In fath-om-less bil-lows of love.

Does Jesus Care?

Frank E. Graeff, 1860-1919

J. Lincoln Hall, 1866-1930

1. Does Je-sus care when my heart is pained Too deep-ly for
2. Does Je-sus care when my way is dark With a name - less
3. Does Je-sus care when I've tried and failed To re - sist some temp-
4. Does Je-sus care when I've said good-bye To the dear-est on

mirth and song; As the bur-dens press, and the cares dis-tress,
dread and fear? As the day-light fades in-to deep night shades,
ta-tion strong; When for my deep grief I find no re-lief,
earth to me, And my sad heart aches till it near-ly breaks—

CHORUS

And the way grows wea-ry and long?
Does He care e-nough to be near?
Tho my tears flow all the night long?
Is it aught to Him? does He see?

O yes, He cares— I

know He cares! His heart is touched with my grief; When the

days are wea-ry, the long nights drear-y, I know my Sav-ior cares.(He cares.)

290

Be Still, My Soul

FINLANDIA

Katharina von Schlegel, 1697-?
Trans. by Jane L. Borthwick, 1813-1897

Jean Sibelius, 1865-1957

1. Be still, my soul— the Lord is on thy side! Bear pa-tient-ly the
2. Be still, my soul— thy God doth un-der-take To guide the fu-ture
3. Be still, my soul— the hour is has-t'ning on When we shall be for-

cross of grief or pain; Leave to thy God to or-der and pro-vide—
as He has the past; Thy hope, thy con-fi-dence let noth-ing shake—
ev-er with the Lord, When dis-ap-point-ment, grief, and fear are gone,

In ev-'ry change He faith-ful will re-main. Be still, my soul— thy
All now mys-te-rious shall be bright at last. Be still, my soul— the
Sor-row for-got, love's pur-est joys re-stored. Be still, my soul—when

best, thy heav'n-ly Friend Thru thorn-y ways leads to a joy-ful end.
waves and winds still know His voice who ruled them while He dwelt be-low.
change and tears are past, All safe and bless-ed we shall meet at last.

This tune in a lower key: 525

Guide Me, O Thou Great Jehovah

291

CWM RHONDDA

WILLIAM WILLIAMS, 1717-1791
Trans. by Peter Williams, 1722-1796, and others

JOHN HUGHES, 1873-1932
Arr. by Norman Johnson, 1928-

1. Guide me, O Thou great Je - ho-vah, Pil-grim thru this bar-ren land;
2. O - pen now the crys-tal foun-tain Whence the heal-ing stream doth flow;
3. When I tread the verge of Jor-dan, Bid my anx-ious fears sub-side;

I am weak, but Thou art might-y— Hold me with Thy pow'r-ful hand:
Let the fire and cloud-y pil-lar Lead me all my jour-ney thru:
Bear me thru the swell-ing cur-rent, Land me safe on Ca-naan's side:

Bread of Heav-en, Bread of Heav-en, Feed me till I want no
Strong De-liv-'rer, strong De-liv-'rer, Be Thou still my strength and
Songs of prais-es, songs of prais-es I will ev-er give to

more, (want no more,) Feed me till I want no more.
shield, (strength and shield,) Be Thou still my strength and shield.
Thee, (give to Thee,) I will ev-er give to Thee.

Music used by permission of the composer's daughter, Mrs. Dilys Webb.
Arr. ©1968 by Singspiration, Inc. All rights reserved.

292 Surely Goodness and Mercy

John W. Peterson, 1921-
and Alfred B. Smith, 1916-

John W. Peterson, 1921-
and Alfred B. Smith, 1916-

1. A pil-grim was I, and a-wan-d'ring, In the cold night of sin I did roam, When Je-sus the kind Shep-herd found me, And now I am on my way home.

2. He re-stor-eth my soul when I'm wea-ry, He giv-eth me strength day by day; He leads me be-side the still wa-ters, He guards me each step of the way.

3. When I walk thru the dark lone-some val-ley, My Sav-ior will walk with me there; And safe-ly His great hand will lead me To the man-sions He's gone to pre-pare.

CHORUS

Sure-ly good-ness and mer-cy shall fol-low me All the days, all the days of my life; Sure-ly good-ness and mer-cy shall fol-low me All the days, all the days of my life.

Surely Goodness and Mercy

May be omitted until final chorus:

And I shall dwell in the house of the Lord for-ev-er, And I shall feast at the ta-ble spread for me; Sure-ly good-ness and mer-cy shall fol-low me All the days, all the days of my life, All the days, all the days of my life.

The Lord's My Shepherd   293

CRIMOND

Psalm 23
From the *Scottish Psalter*, 1650

JESSIE SEYMOUR IRVINE, 1836-1887

1. The Lord's my Shep-herd— I'll not want; He makes me down to lie
2. My soul He doth re - store a - gain, And me to walk doth make
3. Yea, tho I walk thru death's dark vale, Yet will I fear no ill,
4. My ta - ble Thou hast fur - nish-ed In pres - ence of my foes;
5. Good-ness and mer - cy all my life Shall sure-ly fol - low me,

In pas - tures green— He lead - eth me The qui - et wa - ters by.
With-in the paths of right-eous-ness, E'en for His own name's sake.
For Thou art with me, and Thy rod And staff me com - fort still.
My head Thou dost with oil a - noint, And my cup o - ver - flows.
And in God's house for - ev - er-more My dwell-ing place shall be.

Alternate tunes: MARTYRDOM – 110, EVAN – 327

294 Savior, Like a Shepherd Lead Us

BRADBURY

From *Hymns for the Young,* 1836
Attr. to Dorothy A. Thrupp, 1779-1847

WILLIAM B. BRADBURY, 1816-1868

1. Sav - ior, like a shep-herd lead us, Much we need Thy ten-der care;
2. We are Thine—do Thou be - friend us, Be the Guard-ian of our way;
3. Thou hast prom-ised to re - ceive us, Poor and sin - ful tho we be;
4. Ear - ly let us seek Thy fa - vor, Ear - ly let us do Thy will;

In Thy pleas-ant pas-tures feed us, For our use Thy folds pre - pare:
Keep Thy flock, from sin de - fend us, Seek us when we go a - stray:
Thou hast mer - cy to re - lieve us, Grace to cleanse and pow'r to free:
Bless-ed Lord and on - ly Sav - ior, With Thy love our bos-oms fill:

Bless - ed Je - sus, Bless - ed Je - sus, Thou hast bought us, Thine we are;
Bless - ed Je - sus, Bless - ed Je - sus, Hear, O hear us when we pray;
Bless - ed Je - sus, Bless - ed Je - sus, Ear - ly let us turn to Thee;
Bless - ed Je - sus, Bless - ed Je - sus, Thou hast loved us, love us still;

Bless - ed Je - sus, Bless - ed Je - sus, Thou hast bought us, Thine we are.
Bless - ed Je - sus, Bless - ed Je - sus, Hear, O hear us when we pray.
Bless - ed Je - sus, Bless - ed Je - sus, Ear - ly let us turn to Thee.
Bless - ed Je - sus, Bless - ed Je - sus, Thou hast loved us, love us still.

He Leadeth Me

JOSEPH H. GILMORE, 1834-1918　　　　　WILLIAM B. BRADBURY, 1816-1868

1. He lead-eth me! O bless-ed thought! O words with heav'n-ly
2. Some-times 'mid scenes of deep-est gloom, Some-times where E - den's
3. Lord, I would clasp Thy hand in mine, Nor ev - er mur - mur
4. And when my task on earth is done, When by Thy grace the

com-fort fraught! What-e'er I do, wher-e'er I be, Still
bow-ers bloom, By wa - ters still, o'er trou-bled sea, Still
nor re - pine; Con - tent, what-ev - er lot I see, Since
vic - t'ry's won, E'en death's cold wave I will not flee, Since

CHORUS

'tis God's hand that lead - eth me.
'tis His hand that lead - eth me! He lead-eth me, He
'tis my God that lead - eth me!
God thru Jor - dan lead - eth me.

lead-eth me, By His own hand He lead-eth me; His faith-ful

fol - l'wer I would be, For by His hand He lead-eth me.

296 All the Way My Savior Leads Me

FANNY J. CROSBY, 1820-1915

ROBERT LOWRY, 1826-1899

1. All the way my Sav-ior leads me— What have I to ask be - side?
2. All the way my Sav-ior leads me— Cheers each wind-ing path I tread,
3. All the way my Sav-ior leads me— O the full - ness of His love!

Can I doubt His ten-der mer - cy, Who thru life has been my Guide?
Gives me grace for ev-'ry tri - al, Feeds me with the liv - ing bread.
Per - fect rest to me is prom-ised In my Fa - ther's house a - bove.

Heav'n - ly peace, di - vin-est com-fort, Here by faith in Him to dwell!
Tho my wea - ry steps may fal-ter And my soul a -thirst may be,
When my spir - it, clothed im-mor-tal, Wings its flight to realms of day,

For I know, what-e'er be - fall me, Je-sus do - eth all things well; well.
Gush-ing from the Rock be - fore me, Lo! a spring of joy I see; see.
This my song thru end-less a - ges: Je-sus led me all the way; way.

God Will Take Care of You

CIVILLA D. MARTIN, 1869-1948   W. STILLMAN MARTIN, 1862-1935

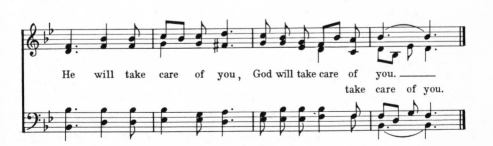

1. Be not dis-mayed what-e'er be-tide, God will take care of you;
2. Thru days of toil when heart doth fail, God will take care of you;
3. All you may need He will pro-vide, God will take care of you;
4. No mat-ter what may be the test, God will take care of you;

Be-neath His wings of love a-bide, God will take care of you.
When dan-gers fierce your path as-sail, God will take care of you.
Noth-ing you ask will be de-nied, God will take care of you.
Lean, wea-ry one, up-on His breast, God will take care of you.

CHORUS

God will take care of you, Thru ev-'ry day, O'er all the way;

He will take care of you, God will take care of you.
take care of you.

298

God Leads Us Along

G. A. Young, 19th century   G. A. Young, 19th century

1. In shad-y, green pas-tures, so rich and so sweet, God leads His dear
2. Some-times on the mount where the sun shines so bright, God leads His dear
3. Tho sor-rows be-fall us and Sa-tan op-pose, God leads His dear
4. A-way from the mire and a-way from the clay, God leads His dear

chil-dren a-long; Where the wa-ter's cool flow bathes the wea-ry one's feet,
chil-dren a-long; Some-times in the val-ley, in dark-est of night,
chil-dren a-long; Thru grace we can con-quer, de-feat all our foes,
chil-dren a-long; A-way up in glo-ry, e-ter-ni-ty's day,

CHORUS

God leads His dear chil-dren a-long. Some thru the wa-ters, some thru the flood,

Some thru the fire, but all thru the blood; Some thru great sor-row, but

God gives a song, In the night sea-son and all the day long.

Day by Day

Lina Sandell Berg, 1832-1903
Trans. by Andrew L. Skoog, 1856-1934

Oscar Ahnfelt, 1813-1882

1. Day by day and with each pass-ing mo-ment, Strength I find to
2. Ev - 'ry day the Lord Him-self is near me With a spe - cial
3. Help me then in ev - 'ry trib - u - la - tion So to trust Thy

meet my tri - als here; Trust-ing in my Fa-ther's wise be - stow-ment,
mer - cy for each hour; All my cares He fain would bear, and cheer me,
prom - is - es, O Lord, That I lose not faith's sweet con-so - la - tion

I've no cause for wor - ry or for fear. He whose heart is kind be -
He whose name is Coun-sel-lor and Pow'r. The pro - tec - tion of His
Of - fered me with-in Thy ho - ly word. Help me, Lord, when toil and

yond all meas-ure Gives un - to each day what He deems best— Lov - ing -
child and treas-ure Is a charge that on Him-self He laid; "As thy
trou - ble meet-ing, E'er to take, as from a fa-ther's hand, One by

ly, its part of pain and pleas-ure, Min-gling toil with peace and rest.
days, thy strength shall be in meas-ure," This the pledge to me He made.
one, the days, the mo-ments fleet-ing, Till I reach the prom-ised land.

300 More Secure Is No One Ever

TRYGGARE KAN INGEN VARA

LINA SANDELL BERG, 1832-1903
Composite translation

Swedish melody

1. More se-cure is no one ev-er Than the loved ones of the Sav-ior—
2. God His own doth tend and nour-ish, In His ho-ly courts they flour-ish;
3. Nei-ther life nor death can ev-er From the Lord His chil-dren sev-er,
4. Lit-tle flock, to joy then yield thee! Ja-cob's God will ev-er shield thee;
5. What He takes or what He gives us Shows the Fa-ther's love so pre-cious;

Not yon star on high a-bid-ing Nor the bird in home-nest hid-ing.
Like a fa-ther kind He spares them, In His lov-ing arms He bears them.
For His love and deep com-pas-sion Com-forts them in trib-u-la-tion.
Rest se-cure with this De-fend-er— At His will all foes sur-ren-der.
We may trust His pur-pose whol-ly— 'Tis His chil-dren's wel-fare sole-ly.

301 The King of Love My Shepherd Is

DOMINUS REGIT ME

From Psalm 23
HENRY W. BAKER, 1821-1877

JOHN B. DYKES, 1823-1876

1. The King of love my Shep-herd is, Whose good-ness fail-eth nev-er;
2. Where streams of liv-ing wa-ter flow My ran-somed soul He lead-eth,
3. Per-verse and fool-ish oft I strayed, But yet in love He sought me,
4. In death's dark vale I fear no ill With Thee, dear Lord, be-side me;
5. And so thru all the length of days Thy good-ness fail-eth nev-er:

I noth-ing lack if I am His And He is mine for-ev-er.
And, where the ver-dant pas-tures grow, With food ce-les-tial feed-eth.
And on His shoul-der gen-tly laid, And home re-joic-ing brought me.
Thy rod and staff my com-fort still, Thy cross be-fore to guide me.
Good Shep-herd, may I sing Thy praise With-in Thy house for-ev-er.

Lead Me, Savior

FRANK M. DAVIS, 1839-1896   FRANK M. DAVIS, 1839-1896

1. Sav - ior, lead me, lest I stray, (lest I stray,) Gen - tly
2. Thou the ref - uge of my soul, (of my soul,) When life's
3. Sav - ior, lead me, till at last, (till at last,) When the

1. Sav - ior, lead me, lest I stray, Gen -

lead me all the way; (all the way;) I am safe when by Thy
storm-y bil-lows roll; (bil-lows roll;) I am safe when Thou art
storm of life is past, (life is past,) I shall reach the end-less

tly lead me all the way; I am

side, (by Thy side,) I would in Thy love a - bide. (love a - bide.)
nigh, (Thou art nigh,) On Thy mer-cy I re - ly. (I re - ly.)
day, (end-less day,) Where all tears are wiped a - way. (wiped a - way.)

safe when by Thy side, I would in Thy love a - bide.

CHORUS

Lead me, lead me, Sav-ior, lead me, lest I stray; Gen - tly
lest I stray;

down the stream of time, Lead me, Sav-ior, all the way.
stream of time, all the way.

303

Jesus, Savior, Pilot Me

PILOT

EDWARD HOPPER, 1816-1888

JOHN E. GOULD, 1822-1875

Fine

1. Je - sus, Sav - ior, pi - lot me O - ver life's tem-pes-tuous sea:
2. As a moth - er stills her child, Thou canst hush the o - cean wild;
3. When at last I near the shore, And the fear - ful break-ers roar

D.C. — Chart and com - pass come from Thee— Je - sus, Sav - ior, pi - lot me!
D.C. — Won - drous Sov'reign of the sea, Je - sus, Sav - ior, pi - lot me!
D.C. — May I hear Thee say to me, "Fear not— I will pi - lot thee!"

D.C.

Un - known waves be - fore me roll, Hid - ing rocks and treach'rous shoal;
Bois-t'rous waves o - bey Thy will When Thou say'st to them, "Be still!"
'Twixt me and the peace-ful rest — Then, while lean-ing on Thy breast,

304

Savior, More Than Life to Me

FANNY J. CROSBY, 1820-1915

WILLIAM H. DOANE, 1832-1915

1. Sav - ior, more than life to me, I am cling-ing, cling-ing close to Thee;
2. Thru this chang-ing world be - low, Lead me gen - tly, gen - tly as I go;
3. Let me love Thee more and more Till this fleet-ing, fleet-ing life is o'er;

Fine

Let Thy pre - cious blood, ap - plied, Keep me ev - er, ev - er near Thy side.
Trust-ing Thee, I can - not stray— I can nev - er, nev - er lose my way.
Till my soul is lost in love In a bright-er, bright-er world a - bove.

D.S. — May Thy ten - der love to me Bind me clos - er, clos - er, Lord, to Thee.

Savior, More Than Life to Me

CHORUS

D.S.

Ev-'ry day, ev-'ry hour, Let me feel Thy cleans-ing pow'r;
Ev-'ry day and hour, ev-'ry day and hour,

Just One Step at a Time

305

JOHN W. PETERSON, 1921-

JOHN W. PETERSON, 1921-

1. The fu-ture veiled be-fore us lies, The path is hid-den from our eyes,
2. The road He takes we need not know, But fol-low in the steps that glow,
3. We need not fear what lies a-head, Nor anx-ious be nor filled with dread;

And Je-sus leads, while faith He tries, Just one step at a time.
And trust in Him as on we go— Just one step at a time.
The saints be-fore were safe-ly led, Just one step at a time.

CHORUS

Just one step at a time, Just one step at a time;
one step at a time,

That's the way He leads to glo-ry, Just one step at a time.
glo-ry, one step at a time.

A Passion for Souls

HERBERT G. TOVEY, 1888-   FOSS L. FELLERS, 1887-1924

1. Give me a pas-sion for souls, dear Lord, A   pas-sion to save the lost;
2. Tho there are dan-gers un - told and stern Con-front-ing me in   the way,
3. How shall this pas-sion for souls be mine? Lord, make Thou the an - swer clear;

O   that Thy love were by   all   a - dored, And wel-comed at an - y   cost!
Will-ing-ly still would I   go, nor turn, But trust Thee for grace each day.
Help me to throw out the old Life-Line To those who are strug-gling near.

CHORUS

Je - sus, I long, I   long to be win-ning   Men who are

lost,   and con-stant-ly sin - ning;   O   may this hour   be

one of be - gin-ning The   sto - ry of par-don to   tell.

I with Thee Would Begin

Lina Sandell Berg, 1832-1903
Trans. by A. Samuel Wallgren, 1885-1940

W. Theodor Söderberg, 1845-1922
Arr. by Norman Johnson, 1928-

1. I with Thee would be-gin, O my Sav-ior so dear,
2. I with Thee would be-gin, and go forth in Thy name
3. Let Thy word all-di-vine be my lamp in whose light
4. I with Thee would be-gin— yea, and hear one more prayer—

On the way that I still must pur-sue; I with Thee would be-
Which a-lone doth sal-va-tion be-stow; Fold me close to Thy
I may con-stant-ly keep to Thy way; And each day wouldst Thou
I would close with Thee too my brief day; And when day-light has

gin ev-'ry day grant-ed here, As my ear-nest re-solve
breast where found joy all who came— There is ref-uge for me
cleanse me a-new, make me white In the blood shed for me
failed let me sleep in Thy care, Un-til wak-ing Thy child

I re-new— To be and re-main Thine for-ev-er.
too, I know, Though all in this world is con-fu-sion.
on that day When death Thou didst suf-fer, Lord Je-sus.
Thou dost say, "Come, live with me ev-er in heav-en!"

Higher Ground

Johnson Oatman, Jr., 1856-1922

Charles H. Gabriel, 1856-1932

1. I'm press-ing on the up-ward way, New heights I'm gain-ing ev-'ry day—
2. My heart has no de-sire to stay Where doubts a-rise and fears dis-may;
3. I want to live a-bove the world, Tho Sa-tan's darts at me are hurled;
4. I want to scale the ut-most height And catch a gleam of glo-ry bright;

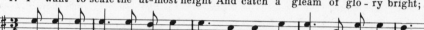

Still pray-ing as I'm on-ward bound, "Lord, plant my feet on high-er ground."
Tho some may dwell where these a-bound, My pray'r, my aim, is high-er ground.
For faith has caught the joy-ful sound, The song of saints on high-er ground.
But still I'll pray till heav'n I've found, "Lord, lead me on to high-er ground."

Chorus

Lord, lift me up and let me stand By faith on heav-en's ta-ble-land;

A high-er plane than I have found— Lord, plant my feet on high-er ground.

Beneath the Cross of Jesus

ST. CHRISTOPHER

ELIZABETH C. CLEPHANE, 1830-1869　　　　　　　　　　　FREDERICK C. MAKER, 1844-1927

1. Be - neath the cross of Je - sus I fain would take my stand,
2. Up - on that cross of Je - sus Mine eye at times can see
3. I take, O cross, thy shad - ow For my a - bid - ing - place —

The shad - ow of a might-y Rock With - in a wea - ry land;
The ver - y dy - ing form of One Who suf - fered there for me;
I ask no oth - er sun-shine than The sun-shine of His face;

A home with-in the wil - der - ness, A rest up - on the way
And from my smit-ten heart with tears Two won-ders I con - fess —
Con - tent to let the world go by, To know no gain nor loss,

From the burn-ing of the noon-day heat And the bur-den of the day.
The won-ders of His glo-rious love And my own worth-less-ness.
My sin - ful self my on - ly shame, My glo - ry all the cross.

310 Whiter Than Snow

JAMES NICHOLSON, c. 1828-1876 · WILLIAM G. FISCHER, 1835-1912

1. Lord Je - sus, I long to be per - fect - ly whole; I
2. Lord Je - sus, look down from Thy throne in the skies And
3. Lord Je - sus, for this I most hum - bly en - treat; I
4. Lord Je - sus, Thou se - est I pa - tient - ly wait; Come

want Thee for - ev - er to live in my soul. Break down ev - 'ry
help me to make a com - plete sac - ri - fice. I give up my -
wait, bless-ed Lord, at Thy cru - ci - fied feet. By faith, for my
now and with - in me a new heart cre - ate. To those who have

i - dol, cast out ev - 'ry foe— Now wash me and I shall be
self and what - ev - er I know— Now wash me and I shall be
cleans-ing I see Thy blood flow— Now wash me and I shall be
sought Thee Thou nev - er saidst "No"— Now wash me and I shall be

REFRAIN

whit - er than snow. Whit-er than snow, yes, whit - er than

snow— Now wash me and I shall be whit - er than snow.

We Would See Jesus

O PERFECT LOVE

ANNA B. WARNER, 1820-1915

JOSEPH BARNBY, 1838-1896

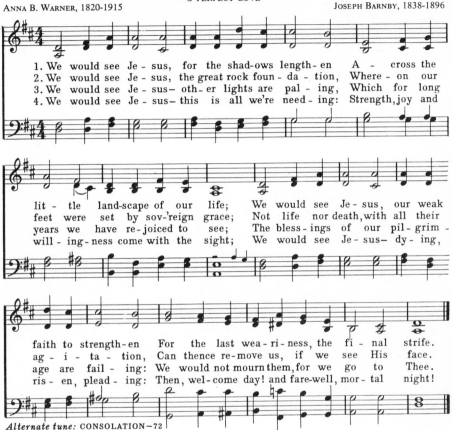

1. We would see Je - sus, for the shad-ows length- en A - cross the
2. We would see Je - sus, the great rock foun - da - tion, Where - on our
3. We would see Je - sus— oth - er lights are pal - ing, Which for long
4. We would see Je - sus— this is all we're need - ing: Strength, joy and

lit - tle land-scape of our life; We would see Je - sus, our weak
feet were set by sov-'reign grace; Not life nor death, with all their
years we have re - joiced to see; The bless - ings of our pil - grim -
will - ing - ness come with the sight; We would see Je - sus— dy - ing,

faith to strength-en For the last wea - ri - ness, the fi - nal strife.
ag - i - ta - tion, Can thence re - move us, if we see His face.
age are fail - ing: We would not mourn them, for we go to Thee.
ris - en, plead - ing: Then, wel - come day! and fare-well, mor - tal night!

Alternate tune: CONSOLATION—72

O Perfect Love

DOROTHY B. GURNEY, 1858-1932

To be sung to the above tune

1. O perfect Love, all human thought transcending,
   Lowly we kneel in prayer before Thy throne,
   That theirs may be the love which knows no ending,
   Whom Thou forevermore dost join in one.

2. O perfect Life, be Thou their full assurance
   Of tender charity and steadfast faith,
   Of patient hope and quiet, brave endurance,
   With childlike trust that fears no pain nor death.

3. Grant them the joy which brightens earthly sorrow,
   Grant them the peace which calms all earthly strife,
   And to life's day the glorious unknown morrow
   That dawns upon eternal love and life.

313   Stepping in the Light

ELIZA E. HEWITT, 1851-1920   WILLIAM J. KIRKPATRICK, 1838-1921

1. Try - ing to walk in the steps of the Sav-ior, Try - ing to fol - low our
2. Press-ing more close-ly to Him who is lead-ing—When we are tempt - ed to
3. Walk-ing in foot-steps of gen - tle for-bear-ance, Foot-steps of faith-ful - ness,
4. Try - ing to walk in the steps of the Sav-ior, Up - ward, still up-ward we'll

Sav - ior and King, Shap-ing our lives by His bless - ed ex - am - ple,
turn from the way, Trust-ing the arm that is strong to de - fend us,
mer - cy and love, Look-ing to Him for the grace free-ly prom - ised,
fol - low our Guide; When we shall see Him, the King in His beau - ty,

CHORUS

Hap - py, how hap-py, the songs that we bring.
Hap - py, how hap-py, our prais-es each day.
Hap - py, how hap-py, our jour-ney a - bove.   How beau-ti-ful to walk in the
Hap - py, how hap-py, our place at His side.

steps of the Sav - ior, Step-ping in the light, Step-ping in the light; How

beau-ti-ful to walk in the steps of the Sav-ior, Led in paths of light.

I Am Thine, O Lord

314

FANNY J. CROSBY, 1820-1915

WILLIAM H. DOANE, 1832-1915

1. I am Thine, O Lord— I have heard Thy voice, And it told Thy
2. Con - se - crate me now to Thy serv - ice, Lord, By the pow'r of
3. O the pure de - light of a sin - gle hour That be - fore Thy
4. There are depths of love that I can - not know Till I cross the

love to me; But I long to rise in the arms of faith
grace di - vine; Let my soul look up with a stead - fast hope
throne I spend, When I kneel in pray'r and with Thee, my God,
nar - row sea; There are heights of joy that I may not reach

CHORUS

And be clos - er drawn to Thee.
And my will be lost in Thine. Draw me near - er, near-er,
I com-mune as friend with friend. near - er, near-er,
Till I rest in peace with Thee.

bless-ed Lord, To the cross where Thou hast died; Draw me near - er,

near - er, near-er, bless-ed Lord, To Thy pre - cious, bleed - ing side.

315 Deeper and Deeper

Oswald J. Smith, 1890-

Oswald J. Smith, 1890-

1. In-to the heart of Je - sus Deep-er and deep-er I go,
2. In-to the will of Je - sus Deep-er and deep-er I go,
3. In-to the cross of Je - sus Deep-er and deep-er I go,
4. In-to the joy of Je - sus Deep-er and deep-er I go,
5. In-to the love of Je - sus Deep-er and deep-er I go,

Seek-ing to know the rea - son Why He should love me so—
Pray-ing for grace to fol - low, Seek-ing His way to know;
Fol - low-ing thru the gar - den, Fac - ing the dread-ed foe;
Ris - ing, with soul en - rap - tured, Far from the world be - low;
Prais-ing the One who brought me Out of my sin and woe;

Why He should stoop to lift me Up from the mir - y clay,
Bow - ing in full sur - ren - der Low at His bless - ed feet,
Drink-ing the cup of sor - row Sob-bing with bro - ken heart,
Joy in the place of sor - row, Peace in the midst of pain,
And thru e - ter - nal a - ges Grate-ful - ly I shall sing,

Sav - ing my soul, mak-ing me whole, Tho I had wan-dered a - way.
Bid-ding Him take, break me and make, Till I am mold-ed and meet.
"O Sav - ior, help! dear Sav-ior, help! Grace for my weak-ness im - part."
Je - sus will give, Je - sus will give— He will up-hold and sus - tain.
"O how He loved! O how He loved! Je - sus, my Lord and my King!"

O to Be Like Thee!

Thomas O. Chisholm, 1866-1960

William J. Kirkpatrick, 1838-1921

1. O to be like Thee! bless-ed Re-deem-er, This is my con-stant
2. O to be like Thee! full of com-pas-sion, Lov-ing, for-giv-ing,
3. O to be like Thee! low-ly in spir-it, Ho-ly and harm-less,
4. O to be like Thee! Lord, I am com-ing Now to re-ceive th'a-
5. O to be like Thee! while I am plead-ing, Pour out Thy Spir-it,

long-ing and prayer; Glad-ly I'll for-feit all of earth's treas-ures,
ten-der and kind; Help-ing the help-less, cheer-ing the faint-ing,
pa-tient and brave; Meek-ly en-dur-ing cru-el re-proach-es,
noint-ing di-vine; All that I am and have I am bring-ing—
fill with Thy love; Make me a tem-ple meet for Thy dwell-ing,

CHORUS

Je-sus Thy per-fect like-ness to wear.
Seek-ing the wan-d'ring sin-ner to find.
Will-ing to suf-fer oth-ers to save. O to be like Thee!
Lord, from this mo-ment all shall be Thine.
Fit me for life and heav-en a-bove.

O to be like Thee, Bless-ed Re-deem-er, pure as Thou art! Come in Thy

sweet-ness, come in Thy full-ness; Stamp Thine own im-age deep on my heart.

317 A Charge to Keep I Have

BOYLSTON

CHARLES WESLEY, 1707-1788 — alt.

LOWELL MASON, 1792-1872

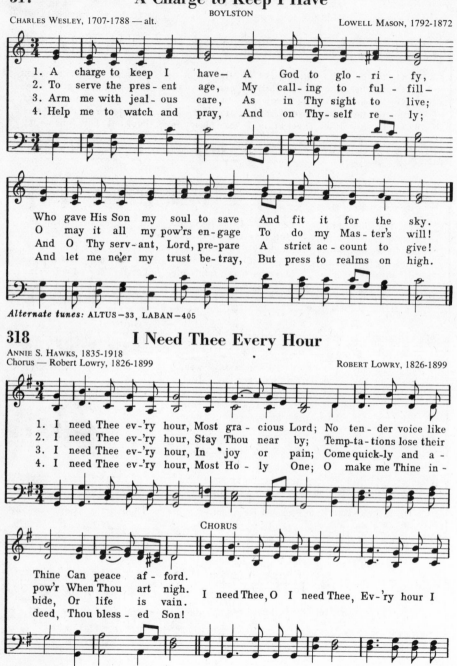

1. A charge to keep I have — A God to glo - ri - fy,
2. To serve the pres - ent age, My call - ing to ful - fill —
3. Arm me with jeal - ous care, As in Thy sight to live;
4. Help me to watch and pray, And on Thy - self re - ly;

Who gave His Son my soul to save And fit it for the sky.
O may it all my pow'rs en - gage To do my Mas - ter's will!
And O Thy serv - ant, Lord, pre-pare A strict ac - count to give!
And let me ne'er my trust be - tray, But press to realms on high.

Alternate tunes: ALTUS — 33, LABAN — 405

318 I Need Thee Every Hour

ANNIE S. HAWKS, 1835-1918
Chorus — Robert Lowry, 1826-1899

ROBERT LOWRY, 1826-1899

1. I need Thee ev - 'ry hour, Most gra - cious Lord; No ten - der voice like
2. I need Thee ev - 'ry hour, Stay Thou near by; Temp - ta - tions lose their
3. I need Thee ev - 'ry hour, In joy or pain; Come quick-ly and a -
4. I need Thee ev - 'ry hour, Most Ho - ly One; O make me Thine in -

CHORUS

Thine Can peace af - ford.
pow'r When Thou art nigh.
bide, Or life is vain.
deed, Thou bless - ed Son!

I need Thee, O I need Thee, Ev - 'ry hour I

I Need Thee Every Hour

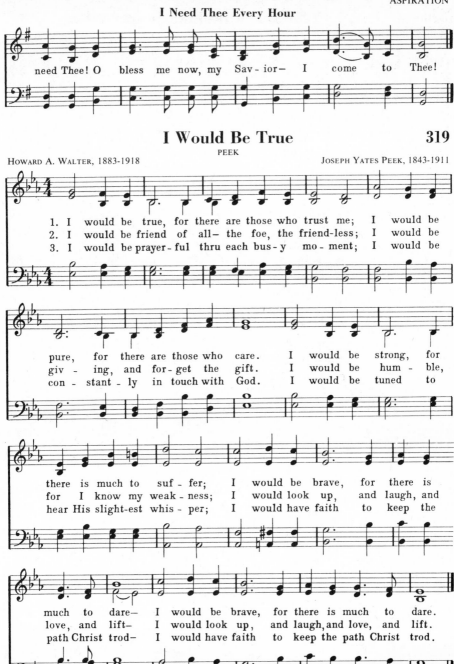

need Thee! O bless me now, my Sav-ior— I come to Thee!

I Would Be True

319

PEEK

HOWARD A. WALTER, 1883-1918

JOSEPH YATES PEEK, 1843-1911

1. I would be true, for there are those who trust me; I would be
2. I would be friend of all— the foe, the friend-less; I would be
3. I would be prayer-ful thru each bus-y mo-ment; I would be

pure, for there are those who care. I would be strong, for
giv - ing, and for - get the gift. I would be hum - ble,
con - stant - ly in touch with God. I would be tuned to

there is much to suf - fer; I would be brave, for there is
for I know my weak - ness; I would look up, and laugh, and
hear His slight-est whis - per; I would have faith to keep the

much to dare— I would be brave, for there is much to dare.
love, and lift— I would look up, and laugh, and love, and lift.
path Christ trod— I would have faith to keep the path Christ trod.

320

O I Want to Be Like Jesus

JOHN W. PETERSON, 1921-

JOHN W. PETERSON, 1921-

1. O I want to be like Je - sus As I walk a-
2. O I want to talk like Je - sus— Gra - cious are the
3. O I want to serve like Je - sus— Will-ing-ly He

long this pil-grim way; O I want to live like Je - sus,
words from Him we hear: Words of life and hope for sin - ners,
came from heav'n a - bove; On the earth He lived for oth - ers,

Show-ing forth His beau-ty ev-'ry day. This my prayer and deep-est
Ten - der, heal-ing words of love and cheer. O the pow - er and the
Spent His life in kind-ly deeds of love. I would fol - low where He

long - ing— To be pure with-out, with - in; O I want to
val - ue Of a fit - ly spok-en word! O I want to
leads me And His bid-ding al-ways do; O I want to

be like Je - sus, Cleansed from dross and free from self and sin.
talk like Je - sus An - y time or place my voice is heard.
serve like Je - sus Till my trav-'ling days on earth are through.

Nothing Between

CHARLES A. TINDLEY, 1851-1933
Arr. by Don Peterman, 1925-

CHARLES A. TINDLEY, 1851-1933

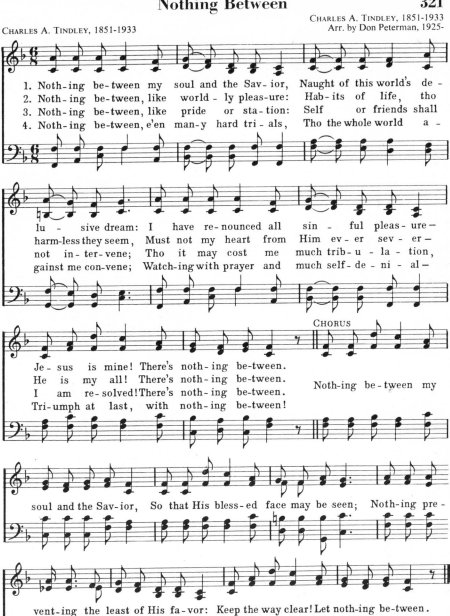

1. Noth-ing be-tween my soul and the Sav-ior, Naught of this world's de-
lu - sive dream: I have re-nounced all sin - ful pleas-ure — Je - sus is mine! There's noth-ing be-tween.

2. Noth-ing be-tween, like world - ly pleas-ure: Hab-its of life, tho
harm-less they seem, Must not my heart from Him ev - er sev - er — He is my all! There's noth-ing be-tween.

3. Noth-ing be-tween, like pride or sta-tion: Self or friends shall
not in-ter-vene; Tho it may cost me much trib-u-la-tion, I am re-solved! There's noth-ing be-tween.

4. Noth-ing be-tween, e'en man-y hard tri-als, Tho the whole world a-
gainst me con-vene; Watch-ing with prayer and much self-de-ni-al — Tri-umph at last, with noth-ing be-tween!

CHORUS

Noth-ing be-tween my soul and the Sav-ior, So that His bless-ed face may be seen; Noth-ing pre-vent-ing the least of His fa-vor: Keep the way clear! Let noth-ing be-tween.

322
Near to Thy Heart
SUSQUEHANNA

JOHN W. PETERSON, 1921-   JOHN W. PETERSON, 1921-

1. Near to Thy heart, O Christ di - vine, Lean-ing like John on Thy breast —
2. Near to Thy heart O may I be, Hear-ing Thy sweet words of love,
3. Near to Thy heart where all is peace, Lost in the light of Thy face,

Till with Thy glo - ry I will shine, Near to Thy heart I'd rest.
Learn-ing Thy pre - cious will for me, Seek-ing those things a - bove.
There will my faith and trust in - crease, There will I grow in grace.

323
More Love to Thee
MORE LOVE TO THEE

ELIZABETH PRENTISS, 1818-1878   WILLIAM H. DOANE, 1832-1915

1. More love to Thee, O Christ, More love to Thee! Hear Thou the
2. Once earth - ly joy I craved, Sought peace and rest; Now Thee a -
3. Let sor - row do its work, Send grief and pain; Sweet are Thy
4. Then shall my lat - est breath Whis - per Thy praise; This be the

prayer I make On bend - ed knee; This is my ear - nest plea:
lone I seek — Give what is best; This all my prayer shall be:
mes - sen - gers, Sweet their re - frain, When they can sing with me,
part - ing cry My heart shall raise; This still its prayer shall be:

ASPIRATION

More Love to Thee

More love, O Christ, to Thee, More love to Thee, More love to Thee!

A Student's Prayer

324

ELLESDIE

JOHN W. PETERSON, 1921-

From Leavitt's *Christian Lyre,* 1831
Possibly from W. A. Mozart, 1756-1791
Arr. by John W. Peterson, 1921-

1. God, the all-wise, and Cre-a-tor Of the hu-man in-tel-lect,
2. O how vast the shores of learn-ing—There are still un-chart-ed seas,
3. May the things we learn, so mea-ger, Nev-er lift our hearts in pride

Guide our search for truth and knowl-edge, All our thoughts and ways di-rect.
And they call to bold ad-ven-ture Those who turn from sloth and ease.
Till in fool-ish self-re-li-ance We would wan-der from Thy side.

Help us build the tow'rs of learn-ing That would make us wise, as-tute,
But we need Thy hand to guide us In the stud-ies we pur-sue,
Let them on-ly bind us clos-er, Lord, to Thee, in whom we find

On the rock of Ho-ly Scrip-ture: Truth re-vealed and ab-so-lute.
And the pres-ence of Thy Spir-it To il-lu-mine all we do.
Ver-y foun-tain-head of wis-dom, Light and life of all man-kind.

This tune in a higher key: 390   *Alternate tune:* HYFRYDOL — 49 (84)

325 More Like the Master

CHARLES H. GABRIEL, 1856-1932   CHARLES H. GABRIEL, 1856-1932

1. More like the Mas-ter I would ev - er be, More of His meek-ness,
2. More like the Mas-ter is my dai - ly prayer, More strength to car - ry
3. More like the Mas-ter I would live and grow, More of His love to

more hu-mil - i - ty; More zeal to la - bor, more cour-age to be true,
cross-es I must bear; More ear-nest ef - fort to bring His king-dom in,
oth- ers I would show; More self-de - ni - al, like His in Gal - i - lee,

rit.   CHORUS

More con-se-cra-tion for work He bids me do.   Take Thou my
More of His Spir - it, the wan-der- er to win.   Take my heart, O
More like the Mas - ter I long to ev - er be.

heart, I would be Thine a - lone; Take Thou my heart and
take my heart, I would be Thine a-lone; Take my heart, O take my heart and

make it all Thine own. Purge me from sin, O Lord, I now im-
make it all Thine own. Purge Thou me from ev'ry sin, O Lord, I

More Like the Master

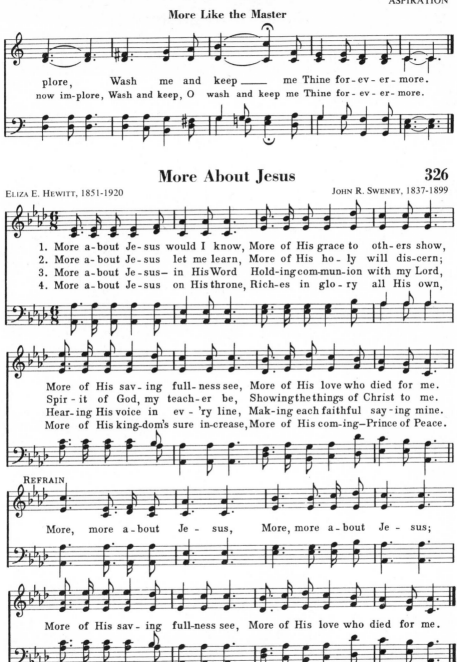

plore, Wash me and keep ___ me Thine for - ev - er - more.
now im-plore, Wash and keep, O wash and keep me Thine for - ev - er - more.

More About Jesus
326

ELIZA E. HEWITT, 1851-1920

JOHN R. SWENEY, 1837-1899

1. More a-bout Je-sus would I know, More of His grace to oth-ers show,
2. More a-bout Je-sus let me learn, More of His ho-ly will dis-cern;
3. More a-bout Je-sus— in His Word Hold-ing com-mun-ion with my Lord,
4. More a-bout Je-sus on His throne, Rich-es in glo-ry all His own,

More of His sav-ing full-ness see, More of His love who died for me.
Spir-it of God, my teach-er be, Showing the things of Christ to me.
Hear-ing His voice in ev-'ry line, Mak-ing each faithful say-ing mine.
More of His king-dom's sure in-crease, More of His com-ing—Prince of Peace.

REFRAIN

More, more a-bout Je-sus, More, more a-bout Je-sus;

More of His sav-ing full-ness see, More of His love who died for me.

327 O for a Faith That Will Not Shrink

EVAN

WILLIAM H. BATHURST, 1796-1877

WILLIAM H. HAVERGAL, 1793-1870

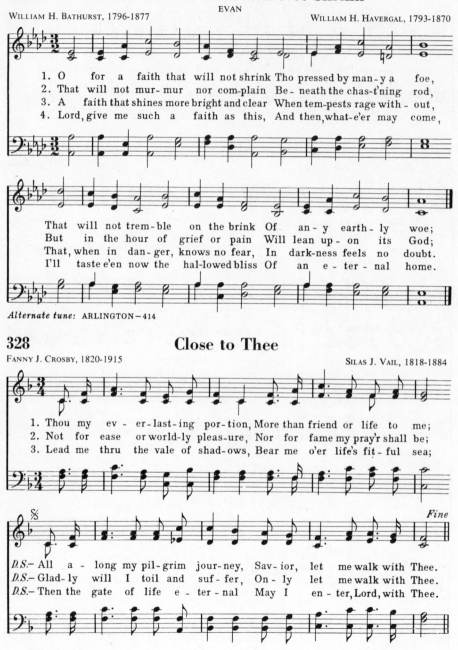

1. O for a faith that will not shrink Tho pressed by man-y a foe,
2. That will not mur-mur nor com-plain Be-neath the chas-t'ning rod,
3. A faith that shines more bright and clear When tem-pests rage with-out,
4. Lord, give me such a faith as this, And then, what-e'er may come,

That will not trem-ble on the brink Of an-y earth-ly woe;
But in the hour of grief or pain Will lean up-on its God;
That, when in dan-ger, knows no fear, In dark-ness feels no doubt.
I'll taste e'en now the hal-lowed bliss Of an e-ter-nal home.

Alternate tune: ARLINGTON—414

328 Close to Thee

FANNY J. CROSBY, 1820-1915

SILAS J. VAIL, 1818-1884

1. Thou my ev-er-last-ing por-tion, More than friend or life to me;
2. Not for ease or world-ly pleas-ure, Nor for fame my pray'r shall be;
3. Lead me thru the vale of shad-ows, Bear me o'er life's fit-ful sea;

Fine

D.S.— All a-long my pil-grim jour-ney, Sav-ior, let me walk with Thee.
D.S.— Glad-ly will I toil and suf-fer, On-ly let me walk with Thee.
D.S.— Then the gate of life e-ter-nal May I en-ter, Lord, with Thee.

Close to Thee

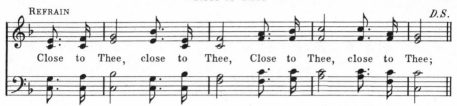

REFRAIN   *D.S.*

Close to Thee, close to Thee, Close to Thee, close to Thee;

Sitting at the Feet of Jesus   329
CONSTANCY

Source unknown   Source unknown

1. Sit - ting at the feet of Je - sus, O what words I hear Him say!
2. Sit - ting at the feet of Je - sus, Where can mor - tal be more blest?
3. Bless me, O my Sav - ior, bless me, As I sit low at Thy feet!

Hap - py place—so near, so pre - cious! May it find me there each day!
There I lay my sins and sor - rows, And, when wea - ry, find sweet rest.
O look down in love up - on me, Let me see Thy face so sweet!

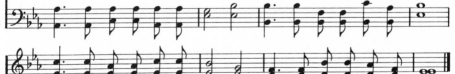

Sit - ting at the feet of Je - sus, I would look up - on the past,
Sit - ting at the feet of Je - sus, There I love to weep and pray,
Give me, Lord, the mind of Je - sus, Make me ho - ly as He is;

For His love has been so gra - cious— It has won my heart at last.
While I from His full - ness gath - er Grace and com - fort ev - 'ry day.
May I prove I've been with Je - sus, Who is all my right-eous - ness.

Alternate tunes: AUTUMN—145, HYFRYDOL—49(84)

330 Fill All My Vision

Avis B. Christiansen, 1895-   Homer Hammontree, 1884-1965

1. Fill all my vi - sion, Sav-ior, I pray, Let me see on - ly
2. Fill all my vi - sion— ev-'ry de - sire Keep for Thy glo - ry;
3. Fill all my vi - sion—let naught of sin Shad-ow the bright-ness

Je - sus to - day; When thru the val - ley Thou lead-est me,
my soul in - spire With Thy per - fec - tion, Thy ho - ly love
shin-ing with - in; Let me see on - ly Thy bless-ed face,

CHORUS

Give me Thy glo - ry and beau-ty to see.
Flood-ing my path-way with light from a - bove. Fill all my vi - sion,
Feast-ing my soul on Thine in - fi - nite grace.

Sav-ior di - vine, Till with Thy glo - ry my spir-it shall shine; Fill all my

vi - sion, that all may see Thy ho-ly im-age re-flect-ed in me.

Make Me a Channel of Blessing

HARPER G. SMYTH, 1873-1945   HARPER G. SMYTH, 1873-1945

1. Is your life a chan-nel of bless-ing? Is the love of God
2. Is your life a chan-nel of bless-ing? Are you bur-dened for
3. Is your life a chan-nel of bless-ing? Is it dai - ly
4. We can - not be chan-nels of bless-ing If our lives are not

flow-ing thru you? Are you tell-ing the lost of the Sav - ior?
those that are lost? Have you urged up-on those who are stray-ing
tell - ing for Him? Have you spo-ken the word of sal - va - tion
free from known sin; We will bar-ri-ers be and a hin - drance

CHORUS

Are you read-y His serv-ice to do?
The Sav-ior who died on the cross?
To those who are dy-ing in sin?
To those we are try-ing to win.

Make me a chan-nel of

bless-ing to-day, Make me a chan-nel of bless-ing, I pray; My life pos-

sess-ing, my serv-ice bless-ing, Make me a chan-nel of bless-ing to-day.

332 My Jesus, I Love Thee

GORDON

WILLIAM R. FEATHERSTON, 1846-1873

ADONIRAM J. GORDON, 1836-1895

1. My Je - sus, I love Thee, I know Thou art mine— For Thee all the
2. I love Thee be - cause Thou hast first lov - ed me And pur - chased my
3. I'll love Thee in life, I will love Thee in death, And praise Thee as
4. In man - sions of glo - ry and end - less de - light, I'll ev - er a -

fol - lies of sin I re - sign; My gra - cious Re - deem - er, my
par - don on Cal - va - ry's tree; I love Thee for wear - ing the
long as Thou lend - est me breath; And say when the death - dew lies
dore Thee in heav - en so bright; I'll sing with the glit - ter - ing

Sav - ior art Thou: If ev - er I loved Thee, my Je - sus, 'tis now.
thorns on Thy brow: If ev - er I loved Thee, my Je - sus, 'tis now.
cold on my brow, "If ev - er I loved Thee, my Je - sus, 'tis now."
crown on my brow, "If ev - er I loved Thee, my Je - sus, 'tis now."

333 May the Mind of Christ, My Savior

ST. LEONARDS

KATE B. WILKINSON, 1859-1928

A. CYRIL BARHAM-GOULD, 1891-1953

1. May the mind of Christ, my Sav - ior, Live in me from day to day,
2. May the Word of God dwell rich - ly In my heart from hour to hour,
3. May the peace of God, my Fa - ther, Rule my life in ev - 'ry - thing,
4. May the love of Je - sus fill me, As the wa - ters fill the sea;
5. May I run the race be - fore me, Strong and brave to face the foe,
6. May His beau - ty rest up - on me As I seek the lost to win,

May the Mind of Christ, My Savior

By His love and pow'r con-trol-ling All I do and say.
So that all may see I tri - umph On - ly thru His pow'r.
That I may be calm to com-fort Sick and sor - row - ing.
Him ex - alt - ing, self a - bas-ing— This is vic - to - ry.
Look-ing on - ly un - to Je - sus As I on - ward go.
And may they for - get the chan-nel, See-ing on - ly Him.

Be Thou My Vision 334

SLANE

Irish hymn, c. 8th century
Trans. by Mary E. Byrne, 1880-1931
Versified by Eleanor H. Hull, 1860-1935

Irish melody
Arr. by Norman Johnson, 1928-

1. Be Thou my Vi - sion, O Lord of my heart— Nought be all
2. Be Thou my Wis - dom, and Thou my true Word— I ev - er
3. Rich - es I heed not, nor man's emp-ty praise— Thou mine in -
4. High King of heav-en, my vic - to - ry won, May I reach

else to me, save that Thou art; Thou my best thought, by
with Thee and Thou with me, Lord; Thou my great Fa - ther,
her - it - ance, now and al - ways; Thou and Thou on - ly,
heav-en's joys, O bright heav'n's Sun! Heart of my own heart, what -

day or by night— Wak-ing or sleep-ing, Thy pres-ence my light.
I Thy true son— Thou in me dwell-ing, and I with Thee one.
first in my heart— High King of heav - en, my Treas-ure Thou art.
ev - er be - fall, Still be my Vi - sion, O Rul - er of all.

335 God of Our Youth

BURNING TREE

WILLIAM BYRON FORBUSH, 1868-1928 — alt.

JOHN W. PETERSON, 1921-

1. God of our youth, to whom we yield The trib-ute of our ea - ger praise,
2. Stur - dy of limb, with bounding health, And quick to play the he - ro's part,
3. When from the field of friend-ly strife, Con-test-ing strength or skill or speed,

Up - on the well - con-test-ed field And 'mid the glo - ry of these days:
Grant to us each that great-er wealth— An un - de - filed and loy-al heart:
We face the stern-er fights of life— As then our strength in time of need:

God of our youth, be with us yet Lest we for - get, lest we for-get.
God of our youth, be Thou our might To do the right, to do the right.
God of our youth, in-spire us still To do Thy will, to do Thy will.

336 O for a Closer Walk with God

BEATITUDO

WILLIAM COWPER, 1731-1800

JOHN B. DYKES, 1823-1876

1. O for a clos - er walk with God, A calm and heav'n - ly frame,
2. Re - turn, O ho - ly Dove, re - turn, Sweet mes-sen - ger of rest;
3. The dear-est i - dol I have known, What-e'er that i - dol be,
4. So shall my walk be close with God, Calm and se - rene my frame;

This tune in a higher key: 523

O for a Closer Walk with God

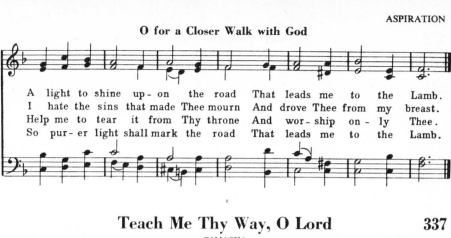

A light to shine up-on the road That leads me to the Lamb.
I hate the sins that made Thee mourn And drove Thee from my breast.
Help me to tear it from Thy throne And wor-ship on-ly Thee.
So pur-er light shall mark the road That leads me to the Lamb.

Teach Me Thy Way, O Lord   337

CAMACHA

B. Mansell Ramsey, 1849-1923   B. Mansell Ramsey, 1849-1923

1. Teach me Thy Way, O Lord, Teach me Thy Way! Thy guid-ing
2. When I am sad at heart, Teach me Thy Way! When earth-ly
3. When doubts and fears a-rise, Teach me Thy Way! When storms o'er-
4. Long as my life shall last, Teach me Thy Way! Wher-e'er my

grace af-ford— Teach me Thy Way! Help me to walk a-right,
joys de-part, Teach me Thy Way! In hours of lone-li-ness,
spread the skies, Teach me Thy Way! Shine thru the cloud and rain,
lot be cast, Teach me Thy Way! Un-til the race is run,

More by faith, less by sight; Lead me with heav'n-ly light— Teach me Thy Way!
In times of dire dis-tress, In fail-ure or suc-cess, Teach me Thy Way!
Thru sor-row, toil and pain; Make Thou my path-way plain—Teach me Thy Way!
Un-til the jour-ney's done, Un-til the crown is won, Teach me Thy Way!

338 O Grant Thy Touch
LINDSBORG

JOHN W. PETERSON, 1921-   JOHN W. PETERSON, 1921-

1. O grant Thy touch of fire, Lord, And set my heart a - flame,
2. O grant Thy touch of peace, Lord, And heal my trou - bled mind;
3. O grant Thy touch of joy, Lord, Un - til its spring shall flow
4. O grant Thy touch of strength, Lord, My giv - en place to fill —

Un - til I've one de - sire, Lord— To glo - ri - fy Thy name.
May faith and trust in - crease, Lord, With fear and doubt be - hind.
Un - checked—tho things an - noy, Lord, And sor - row's sting I know.
To go to an - y length, Lord, To do Thy bless - ed will.

339 O Love That Wilt Not Let Me Go
ST. MARGARET

GEORGE MATHESON, 1842-1906   ALBERT L. PEACE, 1844-1912

1. O Love that wilt not let me go,   I rest my wea - ry
2. O Light that fol - l'west all my way,   I yield my flick - 'ring
3. O Joy that seek - est me thru pain,   I can - not close my
4. O Cross that lift - est up my head,   I dare not ask to

soul in Thee;   I give Thee back the life I owe,   That
torch to Thee;   My heart re - stores its bor - rowed ray,   That
heart to Thee;   I trace the rain - bow thru the rain,   And
fly from Thee;   I lay in dust life's glo - ry dead,   And

O Love That Wilt Not Let Me Go

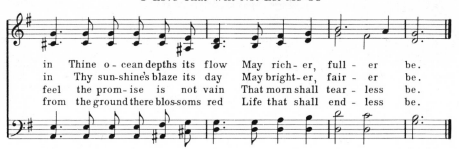

in | Thine o - cean depths its flow | May rich- er, full - er be.
in | Thy sun-shine's blaze its day | May bright- er, fair - er be.
feel | the prom- ise is not vain | That morn shall tear - less be.
from | the ground there blos-soms red | Life that shall end - less be.

Nearer, Still Nearer 340

MORRIS

Lelia N. Morris, 1862-1929   Lelia N. Morris, 1862-1929

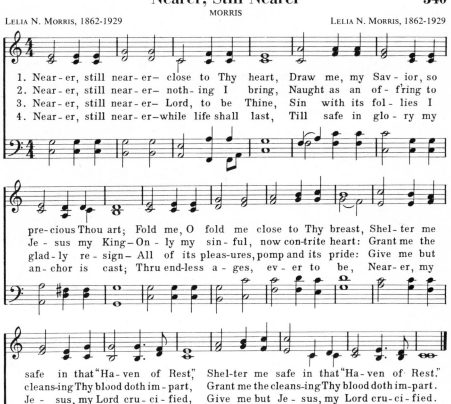

1. Near - er, still near - er— close to Thy heart, Draw me, my Sav - ior, so
2. Near - er, still near - er— noth- ing I bring, Naught as an of - f'ring to
3. Near - er, still near - er— Lord, to be Thine, Sin with its fol - lies I
4. Near - er, still near - er—while life shall last, Till safe in glo - ry my

pre-cious Thou art; Fold me, O fold me close to Thy breast, Shel- ter me
Je - sus my King— On - ly my sin- ful, now con-trite heart: Grant me the
glad - ly re- sign— All of its pleas-ures, pomp and its pride: Give me but
an - chor is cast; Thru end-less a - ges, ev - er to be, Near- er, my

safe in that "Ha- ven of Rest," Shel-ter me safe in that "Ha- ven of Rest."
cleans-ing Thy blood doth im - part, Grant me the cleans-ing Thy blood doth im-part.
Je - sus, my Lord cru - ci - fied, Give me but Je - sus, my Lord cru-ci - fied.
Sav - ior, still near - er to Thee, Near- er, my Sav - ior, still near- er to Thee.

ASPIRATION

341 Something for Thee

SOMETHING FOR JESUS

SYLVANUS D. PHELPS, 1816-1895

ROBERT LOWRY, 1826-1899
Arr. by Jon Drevits, 1928-

1. Sav - ior, Thy dy - ing love Thou gav - est me, Nor should I
2. At the blest mer - cy seat, Plead - ing for me, My fee - ble
3. Give me a faith-ful heart, Like - ness to Thee, That each de -
4. All that I am and have— Thy gifts so free— In joy, in

aught with-hold, Dear Lord, from Thee: In love my soul would bow,
faith looks up, Je - sus, to Thee: Help me the cross to bear,
part - ing day Hence-forth may see Some work of love be - gun,
grief, thru life, Dear Lord, for Thee! And when Thy face I see,

My heart ful-fill its vow, Some of-f'ring bring Thee now, Some-thing for Thee.
Thy won-drous love de-clare, Some song to raise, or prayer, Some-thing for Thee.
Some deed of kind-ness done, Some wan-d'rer sought and won, Some-thing for Thee.
My ran-somed soul shall be, Thru all e - ter - ni - ty, Some-thing for Thee.

342 Must Jesus Bear the Cross Alone?

MAITLAND

THOMAS SHEPHERD, 1665-1739

GEORGE N. ALLEN, 1812-1877

1. Must Je - sus bear the cross a - lone And all the world go free?
2. The con - se - crat - ed cross I'll bear Till death shall set me free,
3. Up - on the crys - tal pave-ment, down At Je - sus' pierc-ed feet,
4. O pre-cious cross! O glo - rious crown! O res - ur - rec - tion day!

Must Jesus Bear the Cross Alone?

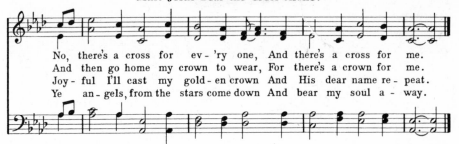

No, there's a cross for ev- 'ry one, And there's a cross for me.
And then go home my crown to wear, For there's a crown for me.
Joy- ful I'll cast my gold- en crown And His dear name re - peat.
Ye an - gels, from the stars come down And bear my soul a - way.

I Want a Principle Within 343

GERALD

CHARLES WESLEY, 1707-1788   LOUIS SPOHR, 1784-1859

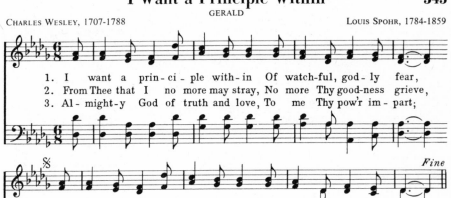

1. I want a prin- ci - ple with- in Of watch-ful, god- ly fear,
2. From Thee that I no more may stray, No more Thy good-ness grieve,
3. Al- might-y God of truth and love, To me Thy pow'r im - part;

Fine

A sen- si- bil- i - ty of sin, A pain to feel it near.
Grant me the fil - ial awe, I pray, The ten- der con-science give.
The bur- den from my soul re- move, The hard-ness from my heart.

D.S.— To catch the wan-d'ring of my will And quench the kind- ling fire.
D.S.— A - wake my soul when sin is nigh And keep it still a - wake.
D.S.— And drive me to that grace a-gain Which makes the wound- ed whole.

D.S.

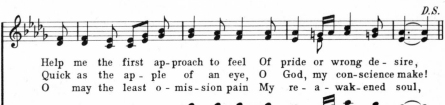

Help me the first ap-proach to feel Of pride or wrong de - sire,
Quick as the ap - ple of an eye, O God, my con-science make!
O may the least o - mis-sion pain My re - a - wak-ened soul,

Alternate tune: GREEN HILL—114

344 I Must Tell Jesus

ELISHA A. HOFFMAN, 1839-1929   ELISHA A. HOFFMAN, 1839-1929

1. I must tell Je - sus all of my tri - als, I can-not bear these
2. I must tell Je - sus all of my trou-bles, He is a kind, com-
3. Tempt-ed and tried, I need a great Sav - ior, One who can help my
4. O how the world to e - vil al - lures me! O how my heart is

bur - dens a - lone; In my dis - tress He kind-ly will help me,
pas - sion-ate Friend; If I but ask Him, He will de - liv - er,
bur - dens to bear; I must tell Je - sus, I must tell Je - sus,
tempt_ed to sin! I must tell Je - sus, and He will help me

CHORUS

He ev - er loves and cares for His own.
Make of my trou - bles quick-ly an end.
He all my cares and sor-rows will share.   I must tell Je - sus!
O - ver the world the vic - t'ry to win.

I must tell Je-sus! I can-not bear my bur-dens a - lone; I must tell

Je - sus! I must tell Je-sus! Je-sus can help me, Je-sus a - lone.

'Tis the Blessed Hour of Prayer

Fanny J. Crosby, 1820-1915

William H. Doane, 1832-1915

1. 'Tis the bless-ed hour of prayer, when our hearts low-ly bend, And we
2. 'Tis the bless-ed hour of prayer, when the Sav-ior draws near With a
3. 'Tis the bless-ed hour of prayer, when the tempt-ed and tried To the
4. At the bless-ed hour of prayer, trust-ing Him we be-lieve That the

gath-er to Je-sus, our Sav-ior and Friend; If we come to Him in
ten-der com-pas-sion, His chil-dren to hear; When He tells us we may
Sav-ior who loves them their sor-row con-fide; With a sym-pa-thiz-ing
bless-ings we're need-ing we'll sure-ly re-ceive; In the full-ness of this

faith, His pro-tec-tion to share, What a balm for the wea-ry!
cast at His feet ev-'ry care, What a balm for the wea-ry!
heart He re-moves ev-'ry care— What a balm for the wea-ry!
trust we shall lose ev-'ry care— What a balm for the wea-ry!

CHORUS

O how sweet to be there! Bless-ed hour of prayer, Bless-ed hour of

prayer—What a balm for the wea-ry! O how sweet to be there!

346 Teach Me to Pray

ALBERT S. REITZ, 1879-   ALBERT S. REITZ, 1879-

1. Teach me to pray, Lord, teach me to pray; This is my heart-cry day un-to day; I long to know Thy will and Thy way; Teach me to pray, Lord, teach me to pray.

2. Pow-er in prayer, Lord, pow-er in prayer, Here 'mid earth's sin and sor-row and care; Men lost and dy-ing, souls in de-spair— O give me pow-er, pow-er in prayer!

3. My weak-ened will, Lord, Thou canst re-new; My sin-ful na-ture Thou canst sub-due; Fill me just now with pow-er a-new, Pow-er to pray and pow-er to do!

4. Teach me to pray, Lord, teach me to pray; Thou art my Pat-tern day un-to day; Thou art my Sure-ty now and for aye; Teach me to pray, Lord, teach me to pray.

CHORUS

Liv-ing in Thee, Lord, and Thou in me; Con-stant a-bid-ing, this is my plea; Grant me Thy pow-er, bound-less and free: Pow-er with men and pow-er with Thee.

Tell It to Jesus

JEREMIAH E. RANKIN, 1828-1904

EDMUND S. LORENZ, 1854-1942

1. Are you wea-ry, are you heav-y-heart-ed? Tell it to Je-sus,
2. Do the tears flow down your cheeks un-bid-den? Tell it to Je-sus,
3. Do you fear the gath-'ring clouds of sor-row? Tell it to Je-sus,
4. Are you trou-bled at the thought of dy-ing? Tell it to Je-sus,

Tell it to Je-sus; Are you griev-ing o-ver joys de-part-ed?
Tell it to Je-sus; Have you sins that to men's eyes are hid-den?
Tell it to Je-sus; Are you anx-ious what shall be to-mor-row?
Tell it to Je-sus; For Christ's com-ing king-dom are you sigh-ing?

CHORUS

Tell it to Je-sus a-lone. Tell it to Je-sus, tell it to

Je-sus, He is a friend that's well-known; You've no oth-er

such a friend or broth-er, Tell it to Je-sus a-lone.

348 The Beautiful Garden of Prayer

ELEANOR ALLEN SCHROLL, 20th century   JAMES H. FILLMORE, 1849-1936

1. There's a gar-den where Je-sus is wait-ing, There's a place that is
2. There's a gar-den where Je-sus is wait-ing, And I go, with my
3. There's a gar-den where Je-sus is wait-ing, And He bids you to

won-drous-ly fair, For it glows with the light of His pres-ence— 'Tis the
bur-den and care, Just to learn from His lips words of com-fort— In the
come meet Him there, Just to bow and re-ceive a new bless-ing— In the

REFRAIN

beau-ti-ful gar-den of prayer.
beau-ti-ful gar-den of prayer. O the beau-ti-ful gar-den, the
beau-ti-ful gar-den of prayer.

gar-den of prayer, O the beau-ti-ful gar-den of prayer! There my Sav-ior a-

waits, and He o-pens the gates To the beau-ti-ful gar-den of prayer.

There Shall Be Showers of Blessing 349

DANIEL W. WHITTLE, 1840-1901　　　　　　　　JAMES McGRANAHAN, 1840-1907

1. "There shall be show-ers of bless-ing"— This is the prom-ise of love;
2. "There shall be show-ers of bless-ing"— Pre - cious re-viv-ing a - gain;
3. "There shall be show-ers of bless-ing"— Send them up-on us, O Lord;
4. "There shall be show-ers of bless-ing"— O that to-day they might fall,

There shall be sea-sons re - fresh-ing, Sent from the Sav-ior a - bove.
O - ver the hills and the val - leys Sound of a - bun-dance of rain.
Grant to us now a re - fresh-ing, Come and now hon-or Thy Word.
Now as to God we're con - fess-ing, Now as on Je - sus we call!

CHORUS

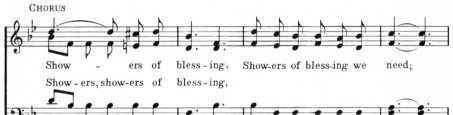

Show - ers of bless-ing, Show-ers of bless-ing we need;
Show - ers, show-ers of bless-ing,

Mer-cy-drops round us are fall - ing, But for the show-ers we plead.

350

Teach Me to Trust

DINJAN

John W. Peterson, 1921-

John W. Peterson, 1921-

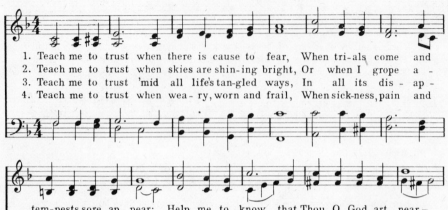

1. Teach me to trust when there is cause to fear, When tri-als come and
2. Teach me to trust when skies are shin-ing bright, Or when I grope a -
3. Teach me to trust 'mid all life's tan-gled ways, In all its dis - ap -
4. Teach me to trust when wea - ry, worn and frail, When sick-ness, pain and

tem-pests sore ap - pear; Help me to know that Thou, O God, art near —
lone in sor-row's night; Thy love pro-vides what-ev-er's best and right —
point-ments and de-lays; Give me a song — a sac - ri - fice of praise!
oth - er ills as-sail; Thy grace sus-tains, Thy prom-ise will not fail—

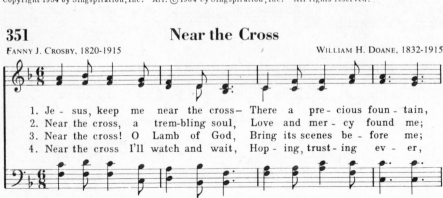

Teach me to trust, Teach me to trust.
Teach, O teach me to trust,

351

Near the Cross

Fanny J. Crosby, 1820-1915

William H. Doane, 1832-1915

1. Je - sus, keep me near the cross— There a pre - cious foun - tain,
2. Near the cross, a trem-bling soul, Love and mer - cy found me;
3. Near the cross! O Lamb of God, Bring its scenes be - fore me;
4. Near the cross I'll watch and wait, Hop - ing, trust - ing ev - er,

Near the Cross

Fine

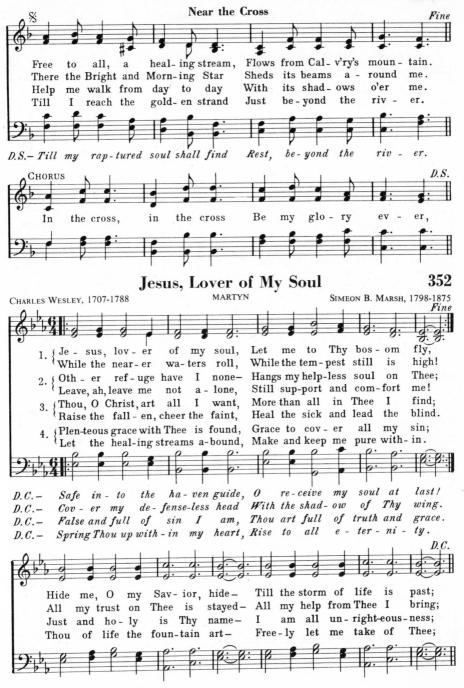

Free   to   all,   a   heal-ing stream,   Flows from Cal-v'ry's moun-tain.
There the Bright and Morn-ing Star   Sheds   its beams   a-round   me.
Help   me walk from   day   to   day   With   its shad-ows   o'er   me.
Till   I   reach the   gold-en strand   Just   be-yond   the   riv-er.

D.S.— Till my rap-tured soul shall find   Rest, be-yond the   riv-er.

CHORUS   *D.S.*

In   the cross,   in   the cross   Be   my glo-ry   ev-er,

Jesus, Lover of My Soul   352

CHARLES WESLEY, 1707-1788   MARTYN   SIMEON B. MARSH, 1798-1875

Fine

1. { Je-sus, lov-er   of my soul,   Let me to Thy bos-om   fly,
   { While the near-er   wa-ters roll,   While the tem-pest still   is   high!

2. { Oth-er   ref-uge have I   none—   Hangs my help-less soul on   Thee;
   { Leave, ah, leave me   not   a-lone,   Still sup-port and com-fort   me!

3. { Thou, O Christ, art   all   I want,   More than all   in Thee I   find;
   { Raise the fall-en, cheer the faint,   Heal the sick and lead the   blind.

4. { Plen-teous grace with Thee is found,   Grace to cov-er   all   my   sin;
   { Let   the heal-ing streams a-bound,   Make and keep me   pure with-in.

D.C.— Safe in-to the ha-ven guide, O re-ceive my soul at last!
D.C.— Cov-er my de-fense-less head With the shad-ow of Thy wing.
D.C.— False and full of sin I am, Thou art full of truth and grace.
D.C.— Spring Thou up with-in my heart, Rise to all e-ter-ni-ty.

D.C.

Hide me, O my Sav-ior, hide—   Till the storm of life is   past;
All   my trust on Thee is stayed—   All my help from Thee I   bring;
Just and ho-ly   is Thy name—   I   am all un-right-eous-ness;
Thou of life the foun-tain art—   Free-ly let me take of   Thee;

353

Leave It There

CHARLES A. TINDLEY, 1851-1933

CHARLES A. TINDLEY, 1851-1933
Arr. by Harold DeCou, 1932-

1. If the world from you with-hold of its sil - ver and its gold, And you
2. If your bod - y suf - fers pain and your health you can't re - gain, And your
3. When your en - e - mies as - sail and your heart be - gins to fail, Don't for -
4. When your youth-ful days are gone and old age is steal-ing on, And your

have to get a - long with mea - ger fare, Just re - mem-ber, in His Word,
soul is al-most sink-ing in de - spair, Je - sus knows the pain you feel,
get that God in heav - en an - swers prayer; He will make a way for you
bod - y bends be-neath the weight of care, He will nev - er leave you then,

how He feeds the lit - tle bird— Take your bur-den to the Lord and leave it there.
He can save and He can heal— Take your bur-den to the Lord and leave it there.
and will lead you safe-ly thru— Take your bur-den to the Lord and leave it there.
He'll go with you to the end— Take your bur-den to the Lord and leave it there.

CHORUS

Leave it there, leave it there, Take your bur-den to the
Leave it there, leave it there,

Lord and leave it there; If you trust and nev - er doubt, He will
leave it there;

Leave It There

sure-ly bring you out— Take your bur-den to the Lord and leave it there.

What a Friend We Have in Jesus 354

CONVERSE

JOSEPH SCRIVEN, 1819-1886

CHARLES C. CONVERSE, 1832-1918

1. What a Friend we have in Je - sus, All our sins and griefs to bear!
2. Have we tri - als and temp-ta - tions? Is there trou-ble an - y - where?
3. Are we weak and heav-y - la - den, Cum-bered with a load of care?

What a priv - i - lege to car - ry Ev - 'ry-thing to God in prayer!
We should nev-er be dis - cour-aged— Take it to the Lord in prayer.
Pre - cious Sav-ior, still our ref - uge— Take it to the Lord in prayer.

O what peace we oft - en for - feit, O what need-less pain we bear,
Can we find a friend so faith- ful Who will all our sor-rows share?
Do thy friends de-spise, for- sake thee? Take it to the Lord in prayer;

All be - cause we do not car - ry Ev - 'ry-thing to God in prayer!
Je - sus knows our ev-'ry weak-ness— Take it to the Lord in prayer.
In His arms He'll take and shield thee— Thou wilt find a sol - ace there.

355
From Every Stormy Wind That Blows

RETREAT

HUGH STOWELL, 1799-1865

THOMAS HASTINGS, 1784-1872
Arr. by John W. Peterson, 1921-

1. From ev-'ry storm-y wind that blows, From ev-'ry swell-ing tide of woes,
2. There is a place where Je - sus sheds The oil of glad-ness on our heads,
3. There is a scene where spir - its blend, Where friend holds fel-low-ship with friend;
4. Ah! whith-er could we flee for aid When tempt-ed, des - o - late, dis-mayed,
5. Ah! there on ea - gle wings we soar, And sin and sense mo-lest no more;

There is a calm, a sure re-treat— 'Tis found be-neath the mer-cy seat.
A place than all be-sides more sweet— It is the blood-bought mer-cy seat.
Tho sun-dered far, by faith they meet A - round one com-mon mer-cy seat.
Or how the hosts of hell de-feat, Had suf-f'ring saints no mer-cy seat?
And heav'n comes down our souls to greet, While glo - ry crowns the mer - cy seat.

356
Near to the Heart of God

CLELAND B. MCAFEE, 1866-1944

CLELAND B. MCAFEE, 1866-1944

1. There is a place of qui - et rest, Near to the heart of God,
2. There is a place of com - fort sweet, Near to the heart of God,
3. There is a place of full re - lease, Near to the heart of God,

A place where sin can - not mo - lest, Near to the heart of God.
A place where we our Sav - ior meet, Near to the heart of God.
A place where all is joy and peace, Near to the heart of God.

Near to the Heart of God

CHORUS

O Je - sus, blest Re - deem - er, Sent from the heart of God,

Hold us who wait be - fore Thee Near to the heart of God.

Nearer, My God, to Thee 357

BETHANY

SARAH F. ADAMS, 1805-1848   LOWELL MASON, 1792-1872

1. Near - er, my God, to Thee, Near - er to Thee! E'en tho it
2. Tho like the wan - der - er, The sun gone down, Dark-ness be
3. There let the way ap - pear, Steps un - to heav'n; All that Thou
4. Then with my wak-ing thoughts, Bright with Thy praise, Out of my
5. Or if on joy-ful wing, Cleav- ing the sky, Sun, moon, and

be a cross That rais-eth me; Still all my song shall be,
o - ver me, My rest a stone, Yet in my dreams I'd be
send - est me, In mer - cy giv'n— An - gels to beck - on me
ston - y griefs, Beth - el I raise; So by my woes to be
stars for-got, Up - ward I fly, Still all my song shall be,

Near-er, my God, to Thee, Near-er, my God, to Thee, Near- er to Thee!

358 Dear Lord and Father of Mankind
REST

JOHN G. WHITTIER, 1807-1892

FREDERICK C. MAKER, 1844-1927

1. Dear Lord and Fa - ther of man - kind, For - give our fe - v'rish
2. In sim - ple trust like theirs who heard, Be - side the Syr - ian
3. O Sab - bath rest by Gal - i - lee! O calm of hills a -
4. Drop thy still dews of qui - et - ness Till all our striv - ings
5. Breathe thru the heats of our de - sire Thy cool - ness and thy

ways! Re - clothe us in our right - ful mind; In pur - er
sea, The gra - cious call - ing of the Lord, Let us, like
bove, Where Je - sus knelt to share with thee The si - lence
cease; Take from our souls the strain and stress, And let our
balm; Let sense be dumb, let flesh re - tire; Speak thru the

lives Thy serv - ice find, In deep - er rev - 'rence, praise.
them, with - out a word Rise up and fol - low Thee.
of e - ter - ni - ty, In - ter - pret - ed by love—
or - dered lives con - fess The beau - ty of Thy peace.
earth-quake, wind, and fire, O still small voice of calm!

359 My Faith Looks Up to Thee
OLIVET

RAY PALMER, 1808-1887

LOWELL MASON, 1792-1872

1. My faith looks up to Thee, Thou Lamb of Cal - va - ry,
2. May Thy rich grace im - part Strength to my faint - ing heart,
3. While life's dark maze I tread And griefs a - round me spread,
4. When ends life's tran - sient dream, When death's cold sul - len stream

My Faith Looks Up to Thee

Sav - ior di - vine; Now hear me when I pray, Take all my
My zeal in - spire; As Thou hast died for me, O may my
Be Thou my guide; Bid dark-ness turn to day, Wipe sor - row's
Shall o'er me roll, Blest Sav - ior, then, in love, Fear and dis -

sin a-way, O let me from this day Be whol - ly Thine!
love to Thee Pure, warm and change-less be— A liv - ing fire!
tears a-way, Nor let me ev - er stray From Thee a - side.
trust re-move— O bear me safe a-bove, A ran-somed soul.

Speak, Lord, in the Stillness   360

QUIET HOUR

E. MAY GRIMES, 1868-1927

Source unknown
Arr. by Alfred B. Smith, 1916-

1. Speak, Lord, in the still - ness, While I wait on Thee;
2. Speak, O bless - ed Mas - ter, In this qui - et hour;
3. For the words Thou speak - est, They are life in - deed;
4. All to Thee is yield - ed— I am not my own!
5. Fill me with the knowl - edge Of Thy glo - rious will;
6. Like a wa - tered gar - den Full of fra - grance rare,

Hush'd my heart to lis - ten, In ex - pect - an - cy.
Let me see Thy face, Lord, Feel Thy touch of pow'r.
Liv - ing Bread from heav - en, Now my spir - it feed!
Bliss - ful, glad sur - ren - der— I am Thine a - lone!
All Thine own good plea - sure In Thy child ful - fill.
Lin - g'ring in Thy pres - ence, Let my life ap - pear.

361 Sweet Hour of Prayer

SWEET HOUR

WILLIAM W. WALFORD, 1772-1850　　　　　　　　　　　WILLIAM B. BRADBURY, 1816-1868

1. Sweet hour of prayer, sweet hour of prayer, That calls me from a world of care
2. Sweet hour of prayer, sweet hour of prayer, Thy wings shall my pe - ti - tion bear
3. Sweet hour of prayer, sweet hour of prayer, May I thy con - so - la - tion share,

Fine

And bids me at my Fa-ther's throne Make all my wants and wish- es known!
To Him whose truth and faith-ful-ness En - gage the wait - ing soul to bless;
Till from Mount Pis-gah's loft - y height I view my home and take my flight:

D.S.—And oft es-caped the tempt-er's snare By thy re - turn, sweet hour of prayer.
D.S.—I'll cast on Him my ev -'ry care, And wait for thee, sweet hour of prayer.
D.S.—And shout, while pass-ing thru the air, "Fare-well, fare-well, sweet hour of prayer!"

D.S.

In sea-sons of dis-tress and grief My soul has oft - en found re- lief,
And since He bids me seek His face, Be - lieve His Word and trust His grace,
This robe of flesh I'll drop, and rise To seize the ev - er - last- ing prize,

362 More Holiness Give Me

MY PRAYER

PHILIP P. BLISS, 1838-1876　　　　　　　　　　　PHILIP P. BLISS, 1838-1876

1. More ho - li - ness give me, More striv-ing with-in, More pa - tience in
2. More grat - i - tude give me, More trust in the Lord, More pride in His
3. More pur - i - ty give me, More strength to o'er-come, More free-dom from

More Holiness Give Me

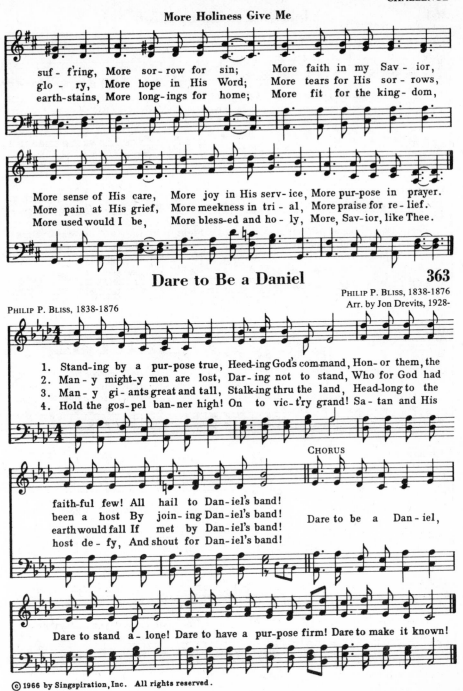

suf - f'ring, More sor - row for sin;
glo - ry, More hope in His Word;
earth-stains, More long-ings for home;

More faith in my Sav - ior,
More tears for His sor - rows,
More fit for the king - dom,

More sense of His care, More joy in His serv - ice, More pur-pose in prayer.
More pain at His grief, More meekness in tri - al, More praise for re - lief.
More used would I be, More bless-ed and ho - ly, More, Sav-ior, like Thee.

Dare to Be a Daniel 363

PHILIP P. BLISS, 1838-1876
Arr. by Jon Drevits, 1928-

PHILIP P. BLISS, 1838-1876

1. Stand-ing by a pur-pose true, Heed-ing God's com-mand, Hon-or them, the
2. Man - y might-y men are lost, Dar - ing not to stand, Who for God had
3. Man - y gi - ants great and tall, Stalk-ing thru the land, Head-long to the
4. Hold the gos-pel ban-ner high! On to vic-t'ry grand! Sa - tan and His

CHORUS

faith-ful few! All hail to Dan-iel's band!
been a host By join-ing Dan-iel's band!
earth would fall If met by Dan-iel's band!
host de - fy, And shout for Dan-iel's band!

Dare to be a Dan - iel,

Dare to stand a - lone! Dare to have a pur-pose firm! Dare to make it known!

Yield Not to Temptation

HORATIO R. PALMER, 1834-1907
Arr. by Norman Johnson, 1928-

HORATIO R. PALMER, 1834-1907

1. Yield not to temp-ta-tion For yield-ing is sin, Each vic-t'ry will help you Some oth-er to win; Fight man-ful-ly on-ward, Dark pas-sions sub-due, Look ev-er to Je-sus— He'll car-ry you through.
2. Shun e-vil com-pan-ions, Bad lan-guage dis-dain, God's name hold in rev-'rence, Nor take it in vain; Be thought-ful and ear-nest, Kind-heart-ed and true, Look ev-er to Je-sus— He'll car-ry you through.
3. To him that o'er-com-eth God giv-eth a crown, Thru faith we will con-quer Tho oft-en cast down; He who is our Sav-ior Our strength will re-new, Look ev-er to Je-sus— He'll car-ry you through.

CHORUS

Ask the Sav-ior to help you, Com-fort, strength-en and keep you; He is will-ing to aid you— He will car-ry you through.

"Are Ye Able," Said the Master

BEACON HILL

Earl Marlatt, 1892-

Harry S. Mason, 1881-1964

1. "Are ye   a-ble," said the Mas-ter, "To   be   cru-ci-fied with Me?"
2. "Are ye   a-ble" to   re-mem-ber, When a   thief lifts up   his   eyes,
3. "Are ye   a-ble," when the shad-ows Close a-round you with the   sod,
4. "Are ye   a-ble?" still the Mas-ter Whis-pers down e-ter-ni-ty,

"Yea," the stur-dy dream-ers an-swered, "To the death we fol-low Thee:"
That his par-doned soul is wor-thy Of a   place in par-a-dise?
To be-lieve that spir-it tri-umphs, To com-mend your soul to God?
And he-ro-ic spir-its an-swer, Now, as then in Gal-i-lee:

CHORUS

"Lord, we are a-ble"— our spir-its are Thine; Re-mold them—

make us   like Thee, di-vine: Thy guid-ing ra-diance a-

bove us shall be   A bea-con to God, to   love and loy-al-ty.

Give Me Thy Heart

ELIZA E. HEWITT, 1851-1920

WILLIAM J. KIRKPATRICK, 1838-1921

1. "Give me thy heart," says the Fa-ther a-bove— No gift so pre-cious to
2. "Give me thy heart," says the Sav-ior of men, Call-ing in mer-cy a-
3. "Give me thy heart," says the Spir-it di-vine, "All that thou hast to my

Him as our love; Soft-ly He whis-pers wher-ev-er thou art,
gain and a-gain; "Turn now from sin and from e-vil de-part—
keep-ing re-sign; Grace more a-bound-ing is mine to im-part—

CHORUS

"Grate-ful-ly trust me and give me thy heart."
Have I not died for thee? give me thy heart." "Give me thy heart,
Make full sur-ren-der and give me thy heart."

Give me thy heart"— Hear the soft whisper, wher-ev-er thou art; From this dark

world He would draw thee a-part, Speak-ing so ten-der-ly, "Give me thy heart."

His Way with Thee

CYRUS S. NUSBAUM, 1861-1937

CYRUS S. NUSBAUM, 1861-1937

1. Would you live for Je-sus and be al-ways pure and good? Would you walk with
2. Would you have Him make you free, and fol-low at His call? Would you know the
3. Would you in His king-dom find a place of con-stant rest? Would you prove Him

Him with-in the nar-row road? Would you have Him bear your bur-den, car-ry
peace that comes by giv-ing all? Would you have Him save you, so that you can
true in prov-i-den-tial test? Would you in His serv-ice la-bor al-ways

CHORUS

all your load? Let Him have His way with thee.
nev-er fall? Let Him have His way with thee. His pow'r can make you what you
at your best? Let Him have His way with thee.

ought to be, His blood can cleanse your heart and make you free, His love can

fill your soul, and you will see 'Twas best for Him to have His way with thee.

368 Have I Done My Best for Jesus?

ENSIGN EDWIN YOUNG, 1895-

HARRY E. STORRS, 20th century

1. I won-der, have I done my best for Je - sus, Who died up - on the
2. The hours that I have wast-ed are so man - y, The hours I've spent for
3. I won-der, have I cared e-nough for oth-ers, Or have I let them
4. No long-er will I stay with-in the val - ley— I'll climb to moun-tain

cru - el tree? To think of His great sac - ri - fice at Cal - v'ry! I
Christ so few; Be - cause of all my lack of love for Je - sus, I
die a - lone? I might have helped a wan-d'rer to the Sav - ior, The
heights a - bove; The world is dy - ing now for want of some-one To

CHORUS

know my Lord ex-pects the best from me.
won - der if His heart is break-ing too. How man-y are the lost that
seed of pre-cious Life I might have sown.
tell them of the Sav-ior's match-less love.

I have lift - ed? How man-y are the chained I've helped to free? I

won-der, have I done my best for Je - sus, When He has done so much for me?

Give of Your Best to the Master

369

HOWARD B. GROSE, 1851-1939   CHARLOTTE A. BARNARD, 1830-1869

1. Give of your best to the Mas - ter, Give of the strength of your youth;
2. Give of your best to the Mas - ter, Give Him first place in your heart;
3. Give of your best to the Mas - ter, Nought else is wor - thy His love;

REFRAIN—*Give of your best to the Mas - ter, Give of the strength of your youth;*

Fine

Throw your soul's fresh, glowing ar - dor In - to the bat - tle for truth.
Give Him first place in your serv - ice, Con - se - crate ev - 'ry part.
He gave Him-self for your ran - som, Gave up His glo - ry a - bove:

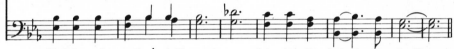

Clad in sal - va-tion's full ar - mor, Join in the bat - tle for truth.

Je - sus has set the ex - am - ple— Daunt-less was He, young and brave;
Give and to you shall be giv - en— God His be - lov - ed Son gave;
Laid down His life with-out mur - mur, You from sin's ru - in to save;

D.C.

Give Him your loy - al de - vo - tion, Give Him the best that you have.
Grate-ful - ly seek-ing to serve Him, Give Him the best that you have.
Give Him your heart's ad-o - ra - tion, Give Him the best that you have.

370 Count Your Blessings

JOHNSON OATMAN, JR., 1856-1922   EDWIN O. EXCELL, 1851-1921

1. When up-on life's bil-lows you are tem-pest-tossed, When you are dis-
2. Are you ev-er bur-dened with a load of care? Does the cross seem
3. When you look at oth-ers with their lands and gold, Think that Christ has
4. So a-mid the con-flict, wheth-er great or small, Do not be dis-

cour-aged, think-ing all is lost, Count your man-y bless-ings—name them
heav-y you are called to bear? Count your man-y bless-ings— ev-'ry
prom-ised you His wealth un-told; Count your man-y bless-ings— mon-ey
cour-aged—God is o-ver all; Count your man-y bless-ings— an-gels

one by one, And it will sur-prise you what the Lord hath done.
doubt will fly, And you will be sing-ing as the days go by.
can-not buy Your re-ward in heav-en nor your home on high.
will at-tend, Help and com-fort give you to your jour-ney's end.

CHORUS

Count your bless-ings—name them one by one; Count your
Count your man-y bless-ings— name them one by one; Count your man-y

bless-ings— see what God hath done; Count your bless-ings—
bless-ings— see what God hath done; Count your man-y bless-ings—

372 Who Is on the Lord's Side?

ARMAGEDDON

FRANCES R. HAVERGAL, 1836-1879

C. LUISE REICHARDT, c. 1780-1826
Arr. by John Goss, 1800-1880

1. Who is on the Lord's side? Who will serve the King? Who will
2. Not for weight of glo - ry, Not for crown and palm, En - ter
3. Je - sus, Thou hast bought us, Not with gold or gem, But with
4. Fierce may be the con - flict, Strong may be the foe, But the

be His help - ers, Oth - er lives to bring? Who will leave the
we the ar - my, Raise the war-rior - psalm; But for Love that
Thine own life - blood, For Thy di - a - dem; With Thy bless - ing
King's own ar - my None can o - ver - throw; Round His stan - dard

world's side? Who will face the foe? Who is on the
claim - eth Lives for whom He died: He whom Je - sus
fill - ing Each who comes to Thee, Thou hast made us
rang - ing, Vic - t'ry is se - cure, For His truth un -

Lords side? Who for Him will go? By Thy call of mer - cy,
nam - eth Must be on His side. By Thy love con-strain - ing,
will - ing, Thou hast made us free. By Thy grand re - demp - tion,
chang-ing Makes the tri - umph sure. Joy - ful - ly en - list - ing,

By Thy grace di - vine, We are on the Lord's side— Sav-ior, we are Thine!

You May Have the Joy-Bells

373

WILLIAM J. KIRKPATRICK, 1838-1921

J. EDWARD RUARK, 19th century

Arr. by Harold DeCou, 1932-

1. You may have the joy-bells ring-ing in your heart, And a peace that
2. Love of Je-sus in its full-ness you may know, And this love to
3. You will meet with tri-als as you jour-ney home— Grace suf-fi-cient
4. Let your life speak well of Je-sus ev-'ry day, Own His right to

from you nev-er will de-part; Walk the straight and nar-row way, Live for
those a-round you sweet-ly show; Words of kind-ness al-ways say, Deeds of
He will give to o-ver-come; Tho un-seen by mor-tal eye, He is
ev-'ry serv-ice you can pay; Sin-ners you can help to win If your

Je-sus ev-'ry day— He will keep the joy-bells ring-ing in your heart.
mer-cy do each day— Then He'll keep the joy-bells ring-ing in your heart.
with you ev-er nigh— And He'll keep the joy-bells ring-ing in your heart.
life is pure and clean, And you keep the joy-bells ring-ing in your heart.

D.S.— He will keep the joy-bells ring-ing in your heart.

CHORUS

Joy-bells ring-ing in your heart, Joy-bells ring-ing in your heart!

Take the Sav-ior, here be-low, With you ev-'ry-where you go—

374

Jesus Calls Us

GALILEE

CECIL F. ALEXANDER, 1818-1895

WILLIAM H. JUDE, 1851-1922

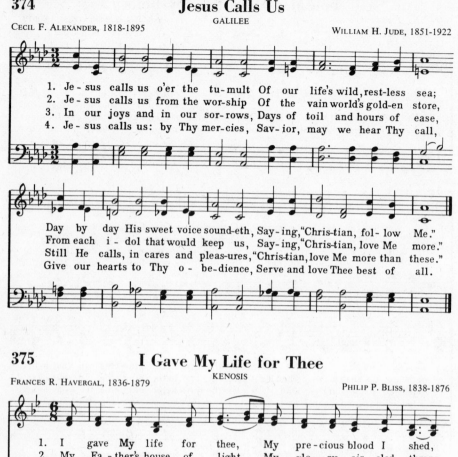

1. Je-sus calls us o'er the tu-mult Of our life's wild, rest-less sea;
2. Je-sus calls us from the wor-ship Of the vain world's gold-en store,
3. In our joys and in our sor-rows, Days of toil and hours of ease,
4. Je-sus calls us: by Thy mer-cies, Sav-ior, may we hear Thy call,

Day by day His sweet voice sound-eth, Say-ing, "Chris-tian, fol-low Me."
From each i-dol that would keep us, Say-ing, "Chris-tian, love Me more."
Still He calls, in cares and pleas-ures, "Chris-tian, love Me more than these."
Give our hearts to Thy o-be-dience, Serve and love Thee best of all.

375

I Gave My Life for Thee

KENOSIS

FRANCES R. HAVERGAL, 1836-1879

PHILIP P. BLISS, 1838-1876

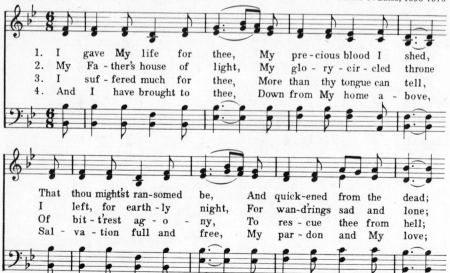

1. I gave My life for thee, My pre-cious blood I shed,
2. My Fa-ther's house of light, My glo-ry-cir-cled throne
3. I suf-fered much for thee, More than thy tongue can tell,
4. And I have brought to thee, Down from My home a-bove,

That thou might'st ran-somed be, And quick-ened from the dead;
I left, for earth-ly night, For wan-d'rings sad and lone;
Of bit-t'rest ag-o-ny, To res-cue thee from hell;
Sal-va-tion full and free, My par-don and My love;

I Gave My Life for Thee

I gave, I gave My life for thee—What hast thou giv'n for Me?
I left, I left it all for thee—Hast thou left aught for Me?
I've borne, I've borne it all for thee—What hast thou borne for Me?
I bring, I bring rich gifts to thee—What hast thou brought to Me?

Take Time to Be Holy   376

HOLINESS

WILLIAM D. LONGSTAFF, 1822-1894   GEORGE C. STEBBINS, 1846-1945

1. Take time to be ho-ly, Speak oft with thy Lord; A-bide in Him
2. Take time to be ho-ly, The world rush-es on; Spend much time in
3. Take time to be ho-ly, Let Him be thy guide, And run not be-
4. Take time to be ho-ly, Be calm in thy soul— Each thought and each

al-ways And feed on His Word. Make friends of God's chil-dren,
se-cret With Je-sus a-lone. By look-ing to Je-sus,
fore Him, What-ev-er be-tide. In joy or in sor-row
mo-tive Be-neath His con-trol. Thus led by His Spir-it

Help those who are weak, For-get-ting in noth-ing His bless-ing to seek.
Like Him thou shalt be; Thy friends in thy con-duct His like-ness shall see.
Still fol-low thy Lord, And, look-ing to Je-sus, Still trust in His Word.
To foun-tains of love, Thou soon shalt be fit-ted For serv-ice a-bove.

Stand Up for Jesus

GEIBEL

GEORGE DUFFIELD, 1818-1888

ADAM GEIBEL, 1885-1933
Arr. by Harold DeCou, 1932-

Unison

1. Stand up, stand up for Je - sus, Ye sol-diers of the cross!
2. Stand up, stand up for Je - sus, The trum-pet call o - bey;
3. Stand up, stand up for Je - sus, The strife will not be long;

Lift high His roy - al ban - ner— It must not suf - fer loss.
Forth to the might - y con - flict In this His glo - rious day:
This day the noise of bat - tle— The next, the vic - tor's song.

From vic - t'ry un - to vic - t'ry His ar - my shall He lead,
Ye that are men now serve Him A - gainst un - num-bered foes;
To Him that o - ver - com - eth A crown of life shall be:

rit.

Till ev - 'ry foe is van - quished And Christ is Lord in - deed.
Let cour - age rise with dan - ger And strength to strength op - pose.
He with the King of glo - ry Shall reign e - ter - nal - ly.

CHORUS
Parts

Stand up for Je - sus, Ye sol-diers of the cross! Lift
stand up

Stand Up for Jesus

high His roy-al ban-ner— It must not, it must not suf-fer loss!

Stand Up for Jesus 378

WEBB

George Duffield, 1818-1888   George J. Webb, 1803-1887

1. Stand up, stand up for Je-sus, Ye sol-diers of the cross!
2. Stand up, stand up for Je-sus, The trum-pet call o - bey;
3. Stand up, stand up for Je-sus, Stand in His strength a - lone;
4. Stand up, stand up for Je-sus, The strife will not be long;

Lift high His roy-al ban-ner— It must not suf-fer loss.
Forth to the might-y con-flict In this His glo-rious day.
The arm of flesh will fail you— Ye dare not trust your own.
This day the noise of bat-tle— The next, the vic-tor's song.

From vic-t'ry un-to vic-t'ry His ar-my shall He lead,
Ye that are men now serve Him A - gainst un-num-bered foes;
Put on the gos-pel ar-mor, Each piece put on with prayer;
To Him that o - ver-com-eth A crown of life shall be:

Till ev-'ry foe is van-quished And Christ is Lord in - deed.
Let cour-age rise with dan-ger And strength to strength op - pose.
Where du-ty calls or dan-ger, Be nev-er want-ing there.
He with the King of glo-ry Shall reign e - ter-nal-ly.

379 Fight the Good Fight

PENTECOST

John S. B. Monsell, 1811-1875   William Boyd, 1847-1928

1. Fight the good fight with all thy might! Christ is thy strength and Christ thy right;
2. Run the straight race thru God's good grace, Lift up thine eyes and seek His face;
3. Cast care a - side, lean on thy Guide, His bound-less mer - cy will pro - vide;
4. Faint not nor fear, for He is near, He chang-eth not and thou art dear;

Lay hold on life and it shall be Thy joy and crown e - ter - nal - ly.
Life with its way be - fore us lies, Christ is the path and Christ the prize.
Trust, and thy trust-ing soul shall prove Christ is its life and Christ its love.
On - ly be - lieve, and thou shalt see That Christ is all in all to thee.

380 Rise Up, O Men of God!

FESTAL SONG

William P. Merrill, 1867-1954   William H. Walter, 1825-1893

1. Rise up, O men of God! Have done with less - er things;
2. Rise up, O men of God! His King - dom tar - ries long;
3. Rise up, O men of God! The Church for you doth wait,
4. Lift high the cross of Christ! Tread where His feet have trod;

Give heart and soul and mind and strength To serve the King of kings.
Bring in the day of broth-er - hood And end the night of wrong.
Her strength un - e - qual to her task; Rise up, and make her great!
As broth - ers of the Son of Man, Rise up, O men of God!

Alternate tune: ST. THOMAS — 23, 188
Words used by permission of "The Presbyterian Outlook," Richmond, Va.

Is Your All on the Altar?

ELISHA A. HOFFMAN, 1839-1929

ELISHA A. HOFFMAN, 1839-1929

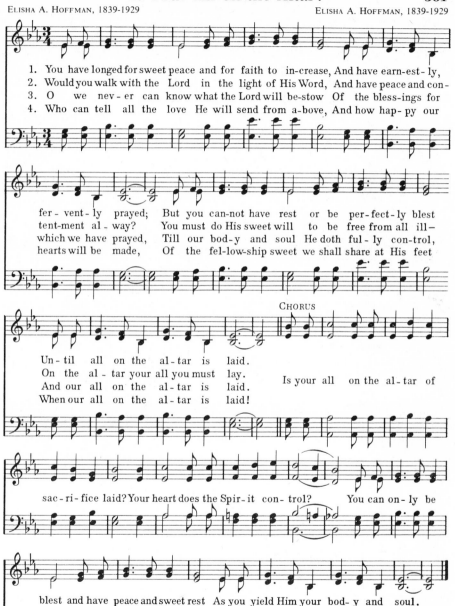

1. You have longed for sweet peace and for faith to in-crease, And have earn-est-ly
2. Would you walk with the Lord in the light of His Word, And have peace and con-
3. O we nev-er can know what the Lord will be-stow Of the bless-ings for
4. Who can tell all the love He will send from a-bove, And how hap-py our

fer - vent-ly prayed; But you can-not have rest or be per-fect-ly blest
tent-ment al - way? You must do His sweet will to be free from all ill—
which we have prayed, Till our bod-y and soul He doth ful-ly con-trol,
hearts will be made, Of the fel-low-ship sweet we shall share at His feet

CHORUS

Un - til all on the al-tar is laid.
On the al - tar your all you must lay.
And our all on the al-tar is laid.
When our all on the al-tar is laid!

Is your all on the al-tar of

sac - ri - fice laid? Your heart does the Spir-it con-trol? You can on-ly be

blest and have peace and sweet rest As you yield Him your bod-y and soul.

382   Trust, Try, and Prove Me

Lida S. Leech, 1873-1962   Lida S. Leech, 1873-1962

1. Bring ye all the tithes in-to the store-house, All your mon-ey tal-ents, time and love; Con-se-crate them all up-on the al-tar, While your Sav-ior from a-bove speaks sweet-ly,

2. When my wa-v'ring faith in tri-al fal-ters, When His guid-ing hand I can-not see, Then in won-drous love and ten-der mer-cy, Through His Word He says to me, My child, just

3. I have yield-ed Him my life for-ev-er, All I am, or have, or hope to be; Naught on earth my hold on Him can sev-er, While I hear Him say to me, My child, just

Chorus

Trust Me, try Me, Prove Me, saith the Lord of hosts, And see if a bless-ing, un-meas-ured bless-ing, I will not pour out on thee.

Trust Me, yes, then try Me, prove Me,

COMMITMENT

Follow, I Will Follow Thee

383

Howard L. Brown, 1889-1965
and Margaret W. Brown, 1892-

Howard L. Brown, 1889-1965
and Margaret W. Brown, 1892-

1. Je-sus calls me— I must fol-low, Fol-low Him to - day;
2. Je-sus calls me— I must fol-low, Fol-low ev - 'ry hour,
3. Je-sus calls me— I must fol-low, Fol-low Him al - way;

When His ten-der voice is plead-ing How can I de - lay?
Know the bless-ing of His pres-ence, Full-ness of His pow'r.
When my Sav-ior goes be-fore me I can nev-er stray.

CHORUS

Fol - low, I will fol-low Thee, my Lord, Fol - low ev - 'ry
pass-ing day; I'll fol-low ev-'ry day; My to - mor-rows are all

known to Thee, Thou wilt lead me all the way. all the way.

COMMITMENT

384

Upbeat

Where He Leads Me

E. W. Blandy, 19th century

John S. Norris, 1844-1907

1. I can hear my Sav - ior call - ing, I can hear my Sav - ior call - ing,
2. I'll go with Him thru the gar - den, I'll go with Him thru the gar - den,
3. I'll go with Him thru the judg - ment, I'll go with Him thru the judg - ment,
4. He will give me grace and glo - ry, He will give me grace and glo - ry,

Chorus—*Where He leads me I will fol - low, Where He leads me I will fol - low,*

D.C.

I can hear my Sav - ior call - ing, "Take thy cross and fol - low, fol - low Me."
I'll go with Him thru the gar - den, I'll go with Him, with Him all the way.
I'll go with Him thru the judg - ment, I'll go with Him, with Him all the way.
He will give me grace and glo - ry, And go with me, with me all the way.

Where He leads me I will fol - low— I'll go with Him, with Him all the way.

385 *Take the World, but Give Me Jesus*

Fanny J. Crosby, 1820-1915

John R. Sweney, 1837-1899

1. Take the world, but give me Je - sus— All its joys are but a name;
2. Take the world, but give me Je - sus— Sweetest com - fort of my soul;
3. Take the world, but give me Je - sus— Let me view His con - stant smile;
4. Take the world, but give me Je - sus— In His cross my trust shall be;

But His love a - bid - eth ev - er, Thru e - ter - nal years the same.
With my Sav - ior watch - ing o'er me, I can sing tho bil - lows roll.
Then thru - out my pil - grim jour - ney Light will cheer me all the while.
Till, with clear - er, bright - er vi - sion, Face to face my Lord I see.

Take the World, but Give Me Jesus

CHORUS

O the height and depth of mer - cy! O the length and breadth of love!

O the full - ness of re - demp - tion— Pledge of end - less life a - bove!

All for Jesus

386

CONSTANCY

MARY D. JAMES, 19th century

Source unknown

1. All for Je - sus, all for Je - sus! All my be - ing's ran-somed pow'rs:
2. Let my hands per-form His bid - ding, Let my feet run in His ways;
3. Since my eyes were fixed on Je - sus, I've lost sight of all be - side,
4. O what won-der! how a - maz - ing! Je - sus, glo-rious King of kings,

All my tho'ts and words and do - ings, All my days and all my hours:
Let my eyes see Je - sus on - ly, All my lips speak forth His praise:
So en-chained my spir-it's vi - sion, Look-ing at the Cru - ci - fied:
Deigns to call me His be - lov - ed, Lets me rest be-neath His wings:

1. 2.

All for Je - sus! all for Je - sus! All my days and all my hours; hours.
All for Je - sus! all for Je - sus! Let my lips speak forth His praise; praise.
All for Je - sus! all for Je - sus! Look-ing at the Cru - ci - fied; fied.
All for Je - sus! all for Je - sus! Rest-ing now be-neath His wings; wings.

True-Hearted, Whole-Hearted

FRANCES R. HAVERGAL, 1836-1879

GEORGE C. STEBBINS, 1846-1945

1. True-heart-ed, whole-heart-ed, faith-ful and loy-al, King of our
2. True-heart-ed, whole-heart-ed, full-est al-le-giance Yield-ing hence-
3. True-heart-ed, whole-heart-ed, Sav-ior all-glo-rious! Take Thy great

lives, by Thy grace we will be; Un-der the stan-dard ex-
forth to our glo-ri-ous King; Val-iant en-deav-or and
pow-er and reign there a-lone, O-ver our wills and af-

alt-ed and roy-al, Strong in Thy strength we will bat-tle for Thee.
lov-ing o-be-dience, Free-ly and joy-ous-ly now would we bring.
fec-tions vic-to-rious, Free-ly sur-ren-dered and whol-ly Thine own.

CHORUS

Peal out the watch-word! si-lence it nev-er! Song of our
Peal out the watch-word! si-lence it nev-er! Song of our

spir-its, re-joic-ing and free; Peal out the watch-word!
spir-its, re-joic-ing and free; Peal out the watch-word!

True-Hearted, Whole-Hearted

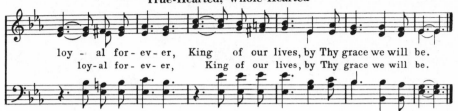

loy - al for - ev - er, King of our lives, by Thy grace we will be.
loy-al for- ev - er, King of our lives, by Thy grace we will be.

Have Thine Own Way, Lord! 388

ADELAIDE A. POLLARD, 1862-1934   GEORGE C. STEBBINS, 1846-1945

1. Have Thine own way, Lord! Have Thine own way! Thou art the
2. Have Thine own way, Lord! Have Thine own way! Search me and
3. Have Thine own way, Lord! Have Thine own way! Wound-ed and
4. Have Thine own way, Lord! Have Thine own way! Hold o'er my

Pot - ter, I am the clay: Mould me and make me
try me, Mas-ter, to - day! Whit - er than snow, Lord,
wea - ry, Help me, I pray! Pow - er, all pow - er,
be - ing Ab - so - lute sway! Fill with Thy Spir - it

Aft - er Thy will, While I am wait-ing, Yield-ed and still.
Wash me just now, As in Thy pres-ence Hum-bly I bow.
Sure-ly is Thine! Touch me and heal me, Sav - ior di - vine!
Till all shall see Christ on - ly, al - ways, Liv - ing in me!

I Am Resolved

PALMER HARTSOUGH, 1844-1932

JAMES H. FILLMORE, 1849-1936

1. I am re-solved no lon-ger to lin-ger, Charmed by the world's de-light;
2. I am re-solved to go to the Sav-ior, Leav - ing my sin and strife;
3. I am re-solved to fol-low the Sav-ior, Faith-ful and true each day;
4. I am re-solved to en-ter the king-dom, Leav - ing the paths of sin;
5. I am re-solved, and who will go with me? Come, friends, without de - lay;

Things that are high-er, things that are no-bler— These have al-lured my sight.
He is the true one, He is the just one— He hath the words of life.
Heed what He say-eth, do what He will-eth— He is the liv-ing way.
Friends may op-pose me, foes may be-set me, Still will I en-ter in.
Taught by the Bi-ble, led by the Spir-it, We'll walk the heav'n-ly way.

CHORUS

I will has-ten to Him, Has-ten so glad and free;
I will has-ten, has-ten, glad and free;

Je - sus, great-est, high-est, I will come to Thee.
Je - sus, Je - sus,

Jesus, I My Cross Have Taken

390

ELLESDIE

From Leavitt's *Christian Lyre,* 1831
Possibly from W. A. Mozart, 1756-1791
Arr. by John W. Peterson, 1921-

HENRY F. LYTE, 1793-1847

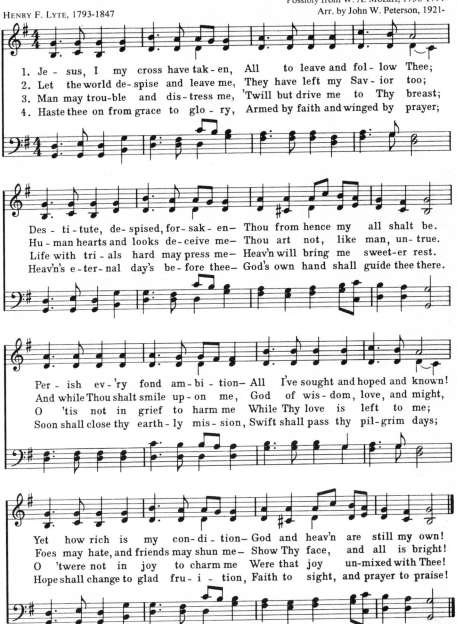

1. Je - sus, I my cross have tak-en, All to leave and fol-low Thee;
2. Let the world de-spise and leave me, They have left my Sav-ior too;
3. Man may trou-ble and dis-tress me, 'Twill but drive me to Thy breast;
4. Haste thee on from grace to glo-ry, Armed by faith and winged by prayer;

Des - ti-tute, de-spised, for-sak-en— Thou from hence my all shalt be.
Hu - man hearts and looks de-ceive me— Thou art not, like man, un-true.
Life with tri-als hard may press me— Heav'n will bring me sweet-er rest.
Heav'n's e-ter-nal day's be-fore thee— God's own hand shall guide thee there.

Per - ish ev-'ry fond am-bi-tion— All I've sought and hoped and known!
And while Thou shalt smile up-on me, God of wis-dom, love, and might,
O 'tis not in grief to harm me While Thy love is left to me;
Soon shall close thy earth-ly mis-sion, Swift shall pass thy pil-grim days;

Yet how rich is my con-di-tion— God and heav'n are still my own!
Foes may hate, and friends may shun me— Show Thy face, and all is bright!
O 'twere not in joy to charm me Were that joy un-mixed with Thee!
Hope shall change to glad fru-i-tion, Faith to sight, and prayer to praise!

This tune in a lower key: 324

391   A Flag to Follow

JOHN W. PETERSON, 1921-   JOHN W. PETERSON, 1921-

1. I sought a flag to fol - low, A cause for which to stand,
2. I sought a ring - ing an - swer For all my doubts in - side,
3. I sought for sat - is - fac - tion For yearn-ings deep with - in,

I sought a val - iant lead - er Who could my love com - mand;
A torch of truth up - lift - ed, My search-ing steps to guide;
I sought for full de - liv - 'rance From chains of guilt and sin;

I sought a stir - ring chal - lenge, Some no - ble work to try,
I sought a word of wis - dom, A true au - thor - i - ty,
I sought for peace and par - don, For free-dom from my fears,

To give my life ful - fill - ment, My dreams to sat - is - fy.
I sought to know life's pur - pose, To solve its mys - ter - y.
I sought a hope to cling to Be - yond these pass-ing years.

REFRAIN

I found them all in Je - sus, The Life, the Truth, the Way; Be - neath His

A Flag to Follow

CODA - *optional*

flag I'll take my stand And fol-low Him to-day. I'll fol-low Him to-day!

O Jesus, I Have Promised

ANGEL'S STORY

392

ARTHUR H. MANN, 1850-1929
Arr. by Harold DeCou, 1932-

JOHN E. BODE, 1816-1874

1. O Je-sus, I have prom-ised to serve Thee to the end;
2. O let me feel Thee near me— the world is ev-er near;
3. O Je-sus, Thou hast prom-ised to all who fol-low Thee,

Be Thou for-ev-er near me, my Mas-ter and my Friend.
I see the sights that daz-zle, the tempt-ing sounds I hear.
That where Thou art in glo-ry, there shall Thy serv-ant be.

I shall not fear the bat-tle if Thou art by my side,
My foes are ev-er near me, a-round me and with-in;
And, Je-sus, I have prom-ised to serve Thee to the end:

Nor wan-der from the path-way if Thou wilt be my guide.
But, Je-sus, draw Thou near-er and shield my soul from sin.
O give me grace to fol-low, my Mas-ter and my Friend.

393 Take My Life and Let It Be

HENDON

FRANCES R. HAVERGAL, 1836-1879

H. A. CÉSAR MALAN, 1787-1864

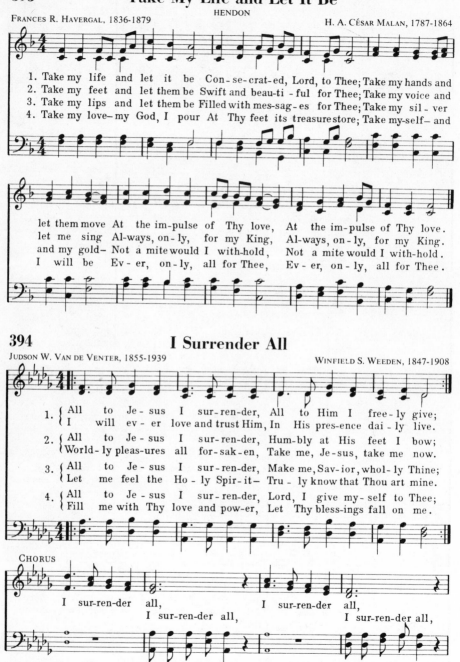

1. Take my life and let it be Con-se-crat-ed, Lord, to Thee; Take my hands and
2. Take my feet and let them be Swift and beau-ti-ful for Thee; Take my voice and
3. Take my lips and let them be Filled with mes-sag-es for Thee; Take my sil-ver
4. Take my love—my God, I pour At Thy feet its treasure store; Take my-self—and

let them move At the im-pulse of Thy love, At the im-pulse of Thy love.
let me sing Al-ways, on-ly, for my King, Al-ways, on-ly, for my King.
and my gold— Not a mite would I with-hold, Not a mite would I with-hold.
I will be Ev-er, on-ly, all for Thee, Ev-er, on-ly, all for Thee.

394 I Surrender All

JUDSON W. VAN DE VENTER, 1855-1939

WINFIELD S. WEEDEN, 1847-1908

1. { All to Je-sus I sur-ren-der, All to Him I free-ly give;
   { I will ev-er love and trust Him, In His pres-ence dai-ly live.

2. { All to Je-sus I sur-ren-der, Hum-bly at His feet I bow;
   { World-ly pleas-ures all for-sak-en, Take me, Je-sus, take me now.

3. { All to Je-sus I sur-ren-der, Make me, Sav-ior, whol-ly Thine;
   { Let me feel the Ho-ly Spir-it— Tru-ly know that Thou art mine.

4. { All to Je-sus I sur-ren-der, Lord, I give my-self to Thee;
   { Fill me with Thy love and pow-er, Let Thy bless-ings fall on me.

CHORUS

I sur-ren-der all, I sur-ren-der all,
I sur-ren-der all, I sur-ren-der all,

I Surrender All

All to Thee, my bless-ed Sav-ior, I sur-ren-der all.

Only One Life
395

Avis B. Christiansen, 1895-

Merrill Dunlop, 1905-

1. On-ly one life to of-fer— Je-sus, my Lord and King;
2. On-ly this hour is mine, Lord— May it be used for Thee;
3. On-ly one life to of-fer— Take it, dear Lord, I pray;

On-ly one tongue to praise Thee And of Thy mer-cy sing (for-ev-er);
May ev-'ry pass-ing mo-ment Count for e-ter-ni-ty (my Sav-ior);
Nothing from Thee with-hold-ing, Thy will I now o-bey (my Je-sus);

On-ly one heart's de-vo-tion— Sav-ior, O may it be Con-se-
Souls all a-bout are dy-ing, Dy-ing in sin and shame; Help me
Thou who hast free-ly giv-en Thine all in all for me, Claim this

crat-ed a-lone to Thy match-less glo-ry, Yield-ed ful-ly to Thee.
bring them the mes-sage of Cal-v'ry's re-demp-tion In Thy glo-ri-ous name.
life for Thine own to be used, my Sav-ior, Ev-'ry mo-ment for Thee.

396 I'll Live for Him

RALPH E. HUDSON, 1843-1901

C. R. DUNBAR, 19th century

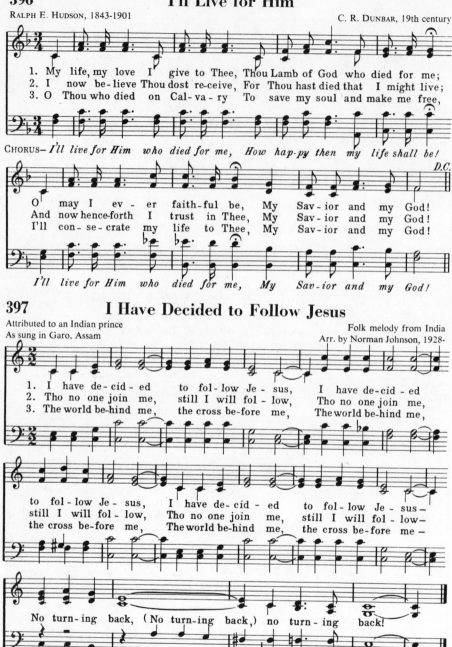

1. My life, my love I give to Thee, Thou Lamb of God who died for me;
2. I now be-lieve Thou dost re-ceive, For Thou hast died that I might live;
3. O Thou who died on Cal-va-ry To save my soul and make me free,

CHORUS—I'll live for Him who died for me, How hap-py then my life shall be!

O may I ev - er faith-ful be, My Sav-ior and my God!
And now hence-forth I trust in Thee, My Sav-ior and my God!
I'll con-se-crate my life to Thee, My Sav-ior and my God!

I'll live for Him who died for me, My Sav-ior and my God!

D.C.

397 I Have Decided to Follow Jesus

Attributed to an Indian prince
As sung in Garo, Assam

Folk melody from India
Arr. by Norman Johnson, 1928-

1. I have de-cid-ed to fol-low Je-sus, I have de-cid-ed
2. Tho no one join me, still I will fol-low, Tho no one join me,
3. The world be-hind me, the cross be-fore me, The world be-hind me,

to fol-low Je-sus, I have de-cid-ed to fol-low Je-sus—
still I will fol-low, Tho no one join me, still I will fol-low—
the cross be-fore me, The world be-hind me, the cross be-fore me—

No turn-ing back, (No turn-ing back,) no turn-ing back!

Follow On

William O. Cushing, 1823-1902

Robert Lowry, 1826-1899

1. Down in the val-ley with my Sav-ior I would go, Where the flowers are
2. Down in the val-ley with my Sav-ior I would go, Where the storms are
3. Down in the val-ley or up - on the moun-tain steep, Close be - side my

bloom-ing and the sweet wa-ters flow; Ev - 'ry-where He leads me I would
sweep-ing and the dark wa-ters flow; With His hand to lead me I will
Sav - ior would my soul ev - er keep; He will lead me safe-ly in the

fol-low, fol-low on, Walk-ing in His foot-steps till the crown be won.
nev-er, nev-er fear, Dan - ger can-not fright me if my Lord is near.
path that He has trod, Up to where they gath-er on the hills of God.

Chorus

Fol - low! fol - low! I would fol-low Je - sus! An - y-where, ev-'ry-where,

1. I would fol-low on!

2. Ev - 'ry-where He leads me I would fol - low on!

399 My Heart's Prayer

SAN GABRIEL

H. P. BLANCHARD, 20th century

RALPH E. STEWART, 1898-1956

1. My new life I owe to Thee, Je-sus, Lamb of Cal-va-ry;
2. Hum-bly at Thy cross I'd stay— Je-sus, keep me there, I pray;
3. Grant me wis-dom, grace and pow'r— Lord, I need Thee ev-'ry hour;
4. Sav-ior, Thou hast heard my plea— Thou art near, so near to me;

Sin was can-celed on the tree— Je-sus, bless-ed Je - sus!
Teach me more of Thee each day, Je-sus, bless-ed Je - sus!
Let my will be lost in Thine, Je-sus, bless-ed Je - sus!
Now I feel Thy strength'ning pow'r, Je-sus, bless-ed Je - sus!

400 Jesus, and Shall It Ever Be?

JOSEPH GRIGG, c. 1720-1768
Alt. by Benjamin Francis, 1734-1799

FEDERAL STREET

HENRY K. OLIVER, 1800-1885

1. Je-sus, and shall it ev-er be— A mor-tal man a-shamed of Thee?
2. A-shamed of Je-sus! soon-er far Let eve-ning blush to own a star;
3. A-shamed of Je-sus! that dear Friend On whom my hopes of heav'n de-pend!
4. A-shamed of Je-sus! yes, I may, When I've no guilt to wash a-way;
5. Till then, nor is my boast-ing vain, Till then I boast a Sav-ior slain;

A-shamed of Thee, whom an-gels praise, Whose glo-ries shine thru end-less days?
He sheds the beams of light di-vine O'er this be-night-ed soul of mine.
No—when I blush, be this my shame, That I no more re-vere His name.
No tear to wipe, no good to crave, No fears to quell, no soul to save.
And O may this my glo-ry be, That Christ is not a-shamed of me!

Alternate tunes: BREWSTER—180, GERMANY—217 (521)

Where He Leads I'll Follow

WILLIAM A. OGDEN, 1841-1897

WILLIAM A. OGDEN, 1841-1897

1. Sweet are the prom-is-es, Kind is the word, Dear-er far than
2. Sweet is the ten-der love Je-sus hath shown, Sweet-er far than
3. List to His lov-ing words, "Come un-to me!" Wea-ry, heav-y-

an-y mes-sage man ev-er heard; Pure was the mind of Christ,
an-y love that mor-tals have known; Kind to the err-ing one,
la-den, there is sweet rest for thee; Trust in His prom-is-es,

Sin-less, I see, He the great ex-am-ple is, and pat-tern for me.
Faith-ful is He, He the great ex-am-ple is, and pat-tern for me.
Faith-ful and sure, Lean up-on the Sav-ior and thy soul is se-cure.

CHORUS

Where_____ He leads I'll fol - - low,
Where He leads I'll fol-low, Where He leads I'll fol-low,

1
Fol - - low all the way;
Fol-low all the way, yes, fol-low all the way;

2
Fol-low Je-sus ev'-ry day.

402 Faith Is the Victory

JOHN H. YATES, 1837-1900

IRA D. SANKEY, 1840-1908

1. En-camped a-long the hills of light, Ye Chris-tian sol-diers, rise,
2. His ban-ner o-ver us is love, Our sword the Word of God;
3. On ev-'ry hand the foe we find Drawn up in dread ar-ray;
4. To him that o-ver-comes the foe White rai-ment shall be giv'n;

And press the bat-tle ere the night Shall veil the glow-ing skies.
We tread the road the saints a-bove With shouts of tri-umph trod.
Let tents of ease be left be-hind, And on-ward to the fray!
Be-fore the an-gels he shall know His name con-fessed in heav'n.

A-gainst the foe in vales be-low Let all our strength be hurled;
By faith they like a whirl-wind's breath Swept on o'er ev-'ry field;
Sal-va-tion's hel-met on each head, With truth all girt a-bout:
Then on-ward from the hills of light, Our hearts with love a-flame;

Faith is the vic-to-ry, we know That o-ver-comes the world.
The faith by which they con-quered death Is still our shin-ing shield.
The earth shall trem-ble 'neath our tread And ech-o with our shout.
We'll van-quish all the hosts of night In Je-sus' con-q'ring name.

CHORUS

Faith is the vic-to-ry! Faith is the vic-to-ry!
Faith is the vic-to-ry! Faith is the vic-to-ry!

Faith Is the Victory

O glo - ri - ous vic - to - ry That o - ver-comes the world.

Soldiers of Christ, Arise 403

DIADEMATA

CHARLES WESLEY, 1707-1788   GEORGE J. ELVEY, 1816-1893

1. Sol - diers of Christ, a - rise   And   put your ar - mor   on,
2. Stand then in His great might,   With   all His strength en - dued,
3. Leave no un-guard - ed   place,   No   weak-ness of the   soul;

Strong in the strength which God sup-plies Thru His e - ter - nal Son;
And take, to arm you for the fight, The pan - o - ply of God;
Take ev - 'ry vir - tue, ev - 'ry grace, And for - ti - fy the whole.

Strong in the Lord of hosts And in His might - y pow'r: Who
That hav - ing all things done, And all your con - flicts past, Ye
From strength to strength go on, Wres - tle and fight and pray; Tread

in the strength of Je - sus trusts Is more than con - quer - or.
may o'er - come thru Christ a - lone And stand en - tire at last.
all the pow'rs of dark - ness down And win the well - fought day.

This tune in a lower key: 62

404

The Fight Is On

LELIA N. MORRIS, 1862-1929   LELIA N. MORRIS, 1862-1929

1. The fight is on— the trum-pet sound is ring-ing out, The cry "To
2. The fight is on— a - rouse, ye sol-diers brave and true! Je - ho - vah
3. The Lord is lead - ing on to cer-tain vic - to - ry, The bow of

arms!" is heard a - far and near; The Lord of hosts is march-ing
leads, and vic - t'ry will as - sure; Go buck - le on the ar - mor
prom - ise spans the east-ern sky; His glo-rious name in ev - 'ry

on to vic - to - ry, The tri - umph of the Christ will soon ap-pear.
God has giv - en you, And in His strength un - to the end en-dure.
land shall hon-ored be, The morn will break— the dawn of peace is nigh.

CHORUS

The fight is on, O Chris-tian sol - dier, And face to face in stern ar - ray,

With ar-mor gleam-ing and col-ors streaming, The right and wrong engage to-day!

The Fight Is On

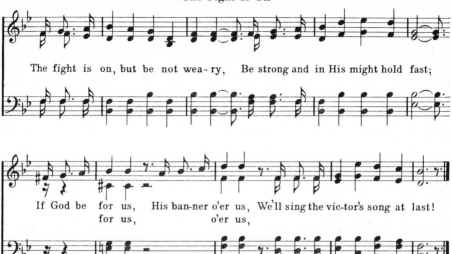

The fight is on, but be not wea-ry, Be strong and in His might hold fast;

If God be for us, His ban-ner o'er us, We'll sing the vic-tor's song at last!
for us, o'er us,

My Soul, Be on Thy Guard 405
LABAN

GEORGE HEATH, 1750-1822　　　　　　　　　　　　LOWELL MASON, 1792-1872

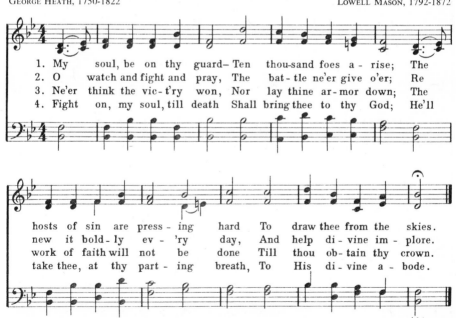

1. My　soul, be on thy guard— Ten thou-sand foes a - rise; The
2. O　watch and fight and pray, The bat - tle ne'er give o'er; Re
3. Ne'er think the vic-t'ry won, Nor lay thine ar-mor down; The
4. Fight　on, my soul, till death Shall bring thee to thy God; He'll

hosts of sin are press - ing hard To draw thee from the skies.
new it bold - ly ev - 'ry day, And help di - vine im - plore.
work of faith will not be done Till thou ob - tain thy crown.
take thee, at thy part - ing breath, To His di - vine a - bode.

Alternate tunes: BOYLSTON—317, ST. THOMAS—23 (188)

406 I'm a Soldier

JOHN W. PETERSON, 1921-

JOHN W. PETERSON, 1921-

1. A sol-dier in the ar-my of the King of kings am I,
2. The bat-tle fierce is rag-ing o-ver land and o-ver sea,
3. Some day the bat-tle will be o-ver, vic-to-ry will come—

He called me to His col-ors and for Him I'll live or die;
Wher-ev-er men have borne the news of Christ and Cal-va-ry;
I won-der if I'll share the full re-ward a-wait-ing some;

I'll go wher-e'er He bids me and I'll do His least com-mand,
The fight for souls must not be lost— I can-not fal-ter, no!
Will I have bat-tle scars to show in heav-en when we meet?

Be-neath the ban-ner of the cross I glad-ly take my stand.
But in the strength of Christ my Lord I'll on-ly for-ward go.
How man-y crowns and tro-phies will I cast at Je-sus' feet?

CHORUS

I'm a sol-dier in the ar-my, And the call to bat-tle loud-ly rings;

I'm a Soldier

I'm a sol-dier in the ar-my, In the ar-my of the King of kings.

Lead On, O King Eternal

407

LANCASHIRE

HENRY SMART, 1813-1879

Arr. by Jon Drevits, 1928-

ERNEST W. SHURTLEFF, 1862-1917

1. Lead on, O King E - ter - nal, The day of march has come!
2. Lead on, O King E - ter - nal, Till sin's fierce war shall cease
3. Lead on, O King E - ter - nal, We fol - low— not with fears!

Hence-forth in fields of con - quest Thy tents shall be our home;
And ho - li - ness shall whis - per The sweet A - men of peace;
For glad-ness breaks like morn - ing Wher-e'er Thy face ap - pears;

Thru days of prep - a - ra - tion Thy grace has made us strong,
For not with swords loud clash - ing Nor roll of stir - ring drums—
Thy cross is lift - ed o'er us— We jour-ney in its light:

And now, O King E - ter - nal, We lift our bat - tle song.
With deeds of love and mer - cy The heav'n-ly king-dom comes.
The crown a - waits the con - quest—Lead on, O God of might.

408 Loyalty to Christ

E. Taylor Cassel, 1849-1930

Flora H. Cassel, 1852-1911

1. From o - ver hill and plain There comes the sig-nal strain— 'Tis loy-al-ty,
2. O hear, ye brave, the sound That moves the earth a-round— 'Tis loy-al-ty,
3. Come, join our loy-al throng—We'll rout the gi-ant wrong— 'Tis loy-al-ty,
4. The strength of youth we lay At Je-sus' feet to-day— 'Tis loy-al-ty,

loy-al-ty, loy-al-ty to Christ; Its mu-sic rolls a-long, The
loy-al-ty, loy-al-ty to Christ; A - rise to dare and do, Ring
loy-al-ty, loy-al-ty to Christ; Where Sa-tan's ban-ners float We'll
loy-al-ty, loy-al-ty to Christ; His gos-pel we'll pro-claim Thru-

hills take up the song, Of loy-al-ty, loy-al-ty, yes, loy-al-ty to Christ.
out the watch-word true, Of loy-al-ty, loy-al-ty, yes, loy-al-ty to Christ.
send the bu-gle note, Of loy-al-ty, loy-al-ty, yes, loy-al-ty to Christ.
out the world's do-main, Of loy-al-ty, loy-al-ty, yes, loy-al-ty to Christ.

CHORUS

"On to vic-to-ry! On to vic-to-ry!" Cries our great Com-mand-er,

"On!"_____ We'll move at His com-mand— We'll soon pos-sess the
great Com-mand-er, "On!"

Loyalty to Christ

land, Thru loy-al-ty, loy-al-ty, yes, loy-al-ty to Christ!

Hold the Fort
409

PHILIP P. BLISS, 1838-1876

PHILIP P. BLISS, 1838-1876

1. Ho, my com-rades, see the sig-nal Wav-ing in the sky!
2. See the might-y host ad-vanc-ing, Sa-tan lead-ing on;
3. See the glo-rious ban-ner wav-ing! Hear the trum-pet blow!
4. Fierce and long the bat-tle rag-es, But our help is near;

Re-in-force-ments now ap-pear-ing, Vic-to-ry is nigh.
Might-y men a-round us fall-ing, Cour-age al-most gone!
In our Lead-er's name we tri-umph O-ver ev-'ry foe.
On-ward comes our great Com-mand-er— Cheer, my com-rades, cheer!

CHORUS

"Hold the fort, for I am com-ing," Je-sus sig-nals still;

Wave the an-swer back to heav-en, "By Thy grace we will."

410 The Banner of the Cross

DANIEL W. WHITTLE, 1840-1901

JAMES McGRANAHAN, 1840-1907

1. There's a roy-al ban-ner giv-en for dis-play To the sol-diers
2. Though the foe may rage and gath-er as the flood, Let the stan-dard
3. O - ver land and sea, wher-ev-er men may dwell, Make the glo-rious
4. When the glo-ry dawns—'tis draw-ing ver-y near— It is hast-'ning

of the King;   As an en-sign fair we lift it up to-day,
be dis-played;   And be-neath its folds, as sol-diers of the Lord,
ti - dings known;   Of the crim-son ban-ner now the sto-ry tell,
day by day—   Then be-fore our King the foe shall dis-ap-pear,

CHORUS

While as ran-somed ones we sing.   Marching on,   march-ing
For the truth be not dis-mayed.   on, on,
While the Lord shall claim His own.
And the cross the world shall sway.

on,   For Christ count ev-'ry-thing but loss!   And to
on, on,   ev-'ry-thing,   ev-'ry-thing but loss!

crown Him King,   toil and sing   'Neath the ban-ner of the cross!
we'll   Be - neath

Victory Through Grace

FANNY J. CROSBY, 1820-1915

JOHN R. SWENEY, 1837-1899

1. Con-quer-ing now and still to con-quer, Rid-eth a King in His might!
2. Con-quer-ing now and still to con-quer, Who is this won-der-ful King?
3. Con-quer-ing now and still to con-quer, Je-sus, Thou Rul-er of all!

Lead - ing the host of all the faith-ful In - to the midst of the fight;
Whence are the ar-mies which He lead-eth, While of His glo - ry they sing?
Thrones and their scep-ters all shall per-ish, Crowns and their splen-dor shall fall,

See them with cour-age ad - vanc-ing, Clad in their bril-liant ar - ray,
He is our Lord and Re - deem-er, Sav-ior and Mon-arch di - vine;
Yet shall the ar-mies Thou lead-est, Faith-ful and true to the last,

Shout-ing the name of their Lead-er, Hear them ex-ult-ing-ly say:
They are the stars that for - ev - er Bright in His King-dom will shine.
Find in Thy man-sions e - ter - nal Rest, when their war-fare is past.

Fine

D.S.— Yet to the true and the faith-ful Vic-t'ry is prom-ised through grace.

D.S.

CHORUS

Not to the strong is the bat - tle, Not to the swift is the race,

412 The Son of God Goes Forth to War

ALL SAINTS NEW

REGINALD HEBER, 1783-1826   HENRY S. CUTLER, 1824-1902

1. The Son of God goes forth to war, A king-ly crown to gain;
2. The mar-tyr first, whose ea-gle eye Could pierce be-yond the grave,
3. A glo-rious band, the cho-sen few On whom the Spir-it came,
4. A no-ble ar-my, men and boys, The ma-tron and the maid,

His blood-red ban-ner streams a-far: Who fol-lows in His train?
Who saw his Mas-ter in the sky And called on Him to save—
Twelve val-iant saints, their hope they knew, And mocked the cross and flame—
A-round the Sav-ior's throne re-joice, In robes of light ar-rayed—

Who best can drink his cup of woe, Tri-um-phant o-ver pain,
Like Him, with par-don on his tongue In midst of mor-tal pain,
They met the ty-rant's bran-dished steel, The li-on's gor-y mane,
They climbed the steep as-cent of heav'n Thru per-il, toil, and pain:

Who pa-tient bears his cross be-low, He fol-lows in His train.
He prayed for them that did the wrong: Who fol-lows in his train?
They bowed their necks the death to feel: Who fol-lows in their train?
O God, to us may grace be giv'n To fol-low in their train!

Sound the Battle Cry!

William F. Sherwin, 1826-1888

William F. Sherwin, 1826-1888

1. Sound the bat-tle cry! see— the foe is nigh! Raise the stan-dard high
2. Strong to meet the foe, march-ing on we go, While our cause, we know,
3. O thou God of all, hear us when we call, Help us one and all

for the Lord: Gird your ar-mor on, stand firm, ev-'ry-one;
must pre-vail; Shield and ban-ner bright gleam-ing in the light,
by Thy grace; When the bat-tle's done and the vic-t'ry won,

CHORUS

Rest your cause up-on His ho-ly Word.
Bat-tling for the right we ne'er can fail. Rouse, then, sol-diers, ral-ly
May we wear the crown be-fore Thy face.

round the ban-ner! Read-y, stead-y— pass the word a-long; On-ward, for-ward,

shout a-loud ho-san-na! Christ is Cap-tain of the might-y throng!

414 Am I a Soldier of the Cross?

ARLINGTON

ISAAC WATTS, 1674-1748

THOMAS A. ARNE, 1710-1778

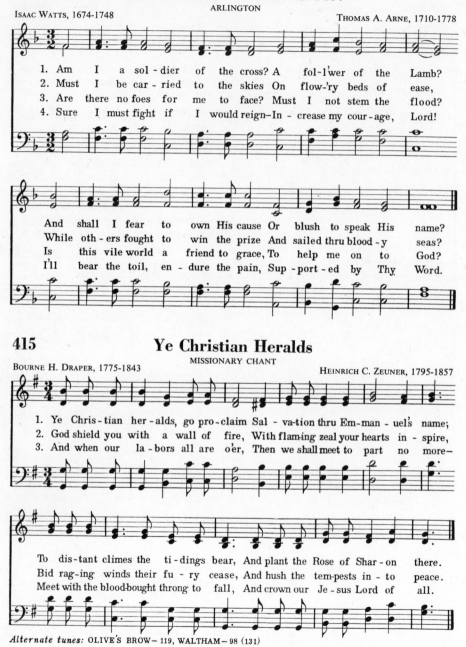

1. Am I a sol - dier of the cross? A fol-l'wer of the Lamb?
2. Must I be car - ried to the skies On flow-'ry beds of ease,
3. Are there no foes for me to face? Must I not stem the flood?
4. Sure I must fight if I would reign—In - crease my cour-age, Lord!

And shall I fear to own His cause Or blush to speak His name?
While oth - ers fought to win the prize And sailed thru blood-y seas?
Is this vile world a friend to grace, To help me on to God?
I'll bear the toil, en - dure the pain, Sup -port - ed by Thy Word.

415 Ye Christian Heralds

MISSIONARY CHANT

BOURNE H. DRAPER, 1775-1843

HEINRICH C. ZEUNER, 1795-1857

1. Ye Chris - tian her - alds, go pro-claim Sal - va-tion thru Em-man - uel's name;
2. God shield you with a wall of fire, With flam-ing zeal your hearts in - spire,
3. And when our la - bors all are o'er, Then we shall meet to part no more—

To dis-tant climes the ti - dings bear, And plant the Rose of Shar - on there.
Bid rag-ing winds their fu - ry cease, And hush the tem-pests in - to peace.
Meet with the blood-bought throng to fall, And crown our Je - sus Lord of all.

Alternate tunes: OLIVE'S BROW— 119, WALTHAM— 98 (131)

So Send I You

E. Margaret Clarkson, 1915-   John W. Peterson, 1921-

1. So send I you to la-bor un-re-ward-ed, To serve un-
2. So send I you to bind the bruised and bro-ken, O'er wan-d'ring
3. So send I you to lone-li-ness and long-ing, With heart a-
4. So send I you to leave your life's am-bi-tion, To die to
5. So send I you to hearts made hard by ha-tred, To eyes made

paid, un-loved, un-sought, un-known, To bear re-buke, to suf-fer
souls to work, to weep, to wake, To bear the bur-dens of a
hung-'ring for the loved and known, For-sak-ing home and kin-dred,
dear de-sire, self-will re-sign, To la-bor long and love where
blind be-cause they will not see, To spend— tho it be blood— to

scorn and scoff-ing— So send I you to toil for Me a-lone.
world a-wea-ry— So send I you to suf-fer for My sake.
friend and dear one— So send I you to know My love a-lone.
men re-vile you— So send I you to lose your life in Mine.
spend and spare not— So send I you to taste of Cal-va-

1-4 D.C.

ry. "As the Fa-ther hath sent Me, So send I you."

417 In Christ There Is No East or West

ST. PETER

JOHN OXENHAM, 1852-1941

ALEXANDER R. REINAGLE, 1799-1877

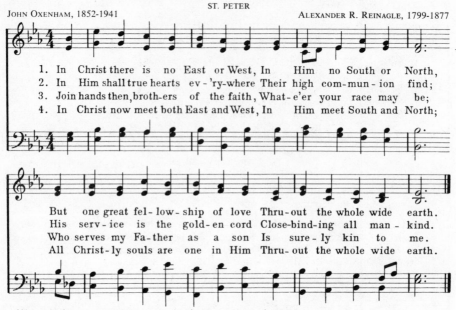

1. In Christ there is no East or West, In Him no South or North,
2. In Him shall true hearts ev-'ry-where Their high com-mun-ion find;
3. Join hands then, broth-ers of the faith, What-e'er your race may be;
4. In Christ now meet both East and West, In Him meet South and North;

But one great fel-low-ship of love Thru-out the whole wide earth.
His serv-ice is the gold-en cord Close-bind-ing all man-kind.
Who serves my Fa-ther as a son Is sure-ly kin to me.
All Christ-ly souls are one in Him Thru-out the whole wide earth.

Alternate tunes: ORTONVILLE—52 (267), ST. ANNE—10 (182)
Words from "Bees in Amber" by John Oxenham. Used by permission of Miss Theo. Oxenham.

418 Must I Go, and Empty-Handed?

CHARLES C. LUTHER, 1847-1924

GEORGE C. STEBBINS, 1846-1945

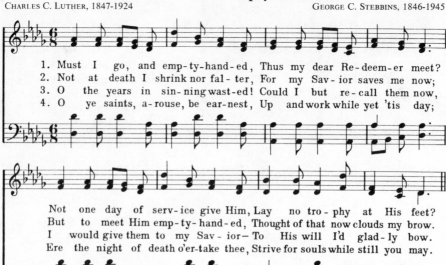

1. Must I go, and emp-ty-hand-ed, Thus my dear Re-deem-er meet?
2. Not at death I shrink nor fal-ter, For my Sav-ior saves me now;
3. O the years in sin-ning wast-ed! Could I but re-call them now,
4. O ye saints, a-rouse, be ear-nest, Up and work while yet 'tis day;

Not one day of serv-ice give Him, Lay no tro-phy at His feet?
But to meet Him emp-ty-hand-ed, Thought of that now clouds my brow.
I would give them to my Sav-ior— To His will I'd glad-ly bow.
Ere the night of death o'er-take thee, Strive for souls while still you may.

Must I Go, and Empty-Handed?

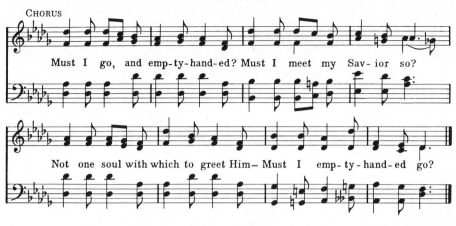

CHORUS

Must I go, and emp-ty-hand-ed? Must I meet my Sav-ior so?

Not one soul with which to greet Him— Must I emp-ty-hand-ed go?

The Call for Reapers 419

JOHN O. THOMPSON, 1782-1818   J. B. O. CLEMM, 19th century

1. Far   and near the fields are teem-ing With the waves of ri - pened grain;
2. Send them forth with morn's first beaming, Send them in the noon-tide's glare;
3. O thou, whom thy Lord is send-ing, Gath-er now the sheaves of gold;

Fine

Far   and near their gold is gleam-ing O'er the sun - ny slope and plain.
When the sun's last rays are gleam-ing, Bid them gath-er ev - 'ry-where.
Heav'n-ward then at eve - ning wend-ing, Thou shalt come with joy un-told.

D.S.- Send them now the sheaves to gath - er, Ere the har - vest-time pass by.

CHORUS   *D.S.*

Lord of har-vest, send forth reap-ers! Hear us, Lord, to Thee we cry;

Bringing In the Sheaves

KNOWLES SHAW, 1834-1878

GEORGE A. MINOR, 1845-1904

1. Sow-ing in the morn-ing, sow-ing seeds of kind-ness, Sow-ing in the
2. Sow-ing in the sun-shine, sow-ing in the shad-ows, Fear-ing nei-ther
3. Go - ing forth with weep-ing, sow-ing for the Mas-ter, Tho the loss sus -

noon- tide and the dew- y eve, Wait-ing for the har-vest and the
clouds nor win-ter's chill-ing breeze; By and by the har-vest and the
tained our spir - it oft - en grieves; When our weep-ing's o - ver He will

time of reap-ing— We shall come re-joic-ing, bring-ing in the sheaves.
la - bor end - ed— We shall come re-joic-ing, bring-ing in the sheaves.
bid us wel-come— We shall come re-joic-ing, bring-ing in the sheaves.

CHORUS

Bring-ing in the sheaves, bring-ing in the sheaves, We shall come re-

1
joic - ing, bring-ing in the sheaves.

2
joic - ing, bring-ing in the sheaves.

Go Tell the Untold Millions

JOHN W. PETERSON, 1921-   JOHN W. PETERSON, 1921-

1. Out in the dark-ness of sin they are wait - ing,
2. Go in the pow - er the Lord will pro - vide you,
3. Moved and con-strained by the love of the Sav - ior,

Lost and a - way from the fold; Who'll bear the mes - sage of
Led by the Spir - it each day; You can-not fail on the
Leave friends and com-forts be - hind; Yield all your tal - ents and

Christ and re-demp-tion? See! they have nev - er been told. (been told.)
mis - sion He sends you— Go then, no long-er de - lay. (de - lay.)
time to His serv-ice— Go now, the lost ones to find. (to find.)

CHORUS

Go tell the un-told mil - lions O - ver the whole world wide;
far and wide;

Go tell the un-told mil - lions, Tell of the Cru - ci - fied.

422 Anywhere with Jesus

1, 2 – Jessie B. Pounds, 1861-1921
3, 4 – Helen G. Alexander, 1877-?

Daniel B. Towner, 1850-1919

1. An-y-where with Je-sus I can safe-ly go, An-y-where He
2. An-y-where with Je-sus I am not a-lone, Oth-er friends may
3. An-y-where with Je-sus o-ver land and sea, Tell-ing souls in
4. An-y-where with Je-sus I can go to sleep, When the dark-'ning

leads me in this world be-low; An-y-where with-out Him dear-est
fail me— He is still my own; Tho His hand may lead me o-ver
dark-ness of sal-va-tion free; Read-y as He sum-mons me to
shad-ows round a-bout me creep; Know-ing I shall wak-en, nev-er

joys would fade, An-y-where with Je-sus I am not a-fraid.
drear-y ways, An-y-where with Je-sus is a house of praise.
go or stay, An-y-where with Je-sus when He points the way.
more to roam, An-y-where with Je-sus will be home, sweet home.

CHORUS

An-y-where! an-y-where! Fear I can-not know;

An-y-where with Je-sus I can safe-ly go.

We've a Story to Tell

H. Ernest Nichol, 1862-1928   H. Ernest Nichol, 1862-1928

1. We've a sto - ry to tell to the na - tions That shall turn their
2. We've a song to be sung to the na - tions That shall lift their
3. We've a mes - sage to give to the na - tions—That the Lord who
4. We've a Sav - ior to show to the na - tions Who the path of

hearts to the right, A sto - ry of truth and mer - cy, A
hearts to the Lord, A song that shall con - quer e - vil And
reign- eth a - bove Hath sent us His Son to save us And
sor - row hath trod, That all of the world's great peo - ples Might

sto - ry of peace and light, A sto - ry of peace and light.
shat - ter the spear and sword, And shat- ter the spear and sword.
show us that God is love, And show us that God is love.
come to the truth of God, Might come to the truth of God.

CHORUS

For the dark-ness shall turn to dawn-ing, And the dawn-ing to noon-day bright,

And Christ's great king-dom shall come to earth, The king-dom of love and light.

Send the Light!

CHARLES H. GABRIEL, 1856-1932   CHARLES H. GABRIEL, 1856-1932

1. There's a call comes ring-ing o'er the rest-less wave, "Send the light!
2. We have heard the Mac-e-do-nian call to-day, "Send the light!
3. Let us pray that grace may ev-'ry-where a-bound, Send the light!
4. Let us not grow wea-ry in the work of love, Send the light!

Send the light!

Send the light!"   There are souls to res-cue, there are souls to save,
Send the light!"   And a gold-en of-f'ring at the cross we lay,
Send the light!   And a Christ-like spir-it ev-'ry-where be found,
Send the light!   Let us gath-er jew-els for a crown a-bove,

Send the light!

CHORUS

Send the light!   Send the light!   Send the light, the
Send the light!   Send the light!   Send the light,

1

bless-ed gos-pel light; Let it shine from shore to
the bless-ed gos-pel light; Let it shine

2

shore!   shine   for-ev-er-more!
from shore to shore!   Let it shine   for-ev-er-more!

Seeking the Lost

WILLIAM A. OGDEN, 1841-1897

WILLIAM A. OGDEN, 1841-1897

1. Seek-ing the lost— yes, kind-ly en-treat-ing Wan-der-ers on the
2. Seek-ing the lost— and point-ing to Je-sus Souls that are weak and
3. Thus I would go on mis-sions of mer-cy, Fol-low-ing Christ from

moun-tain a - stray; "Come un-to Me," His mes-sage re-peat-ing,
hearts that are sore, Lead-ing them forth in ways of sal-va-tion,
day un-to day, Cheer-ing the faint and rais-ing the fall-en,

CHORUS

Words of the Mas-ter speak-ing to-day.
Show-ing the path to life ev-er-more.
Point-ing the lost to Je-sus, the Way.

Go - ing a -
In - to the

Go - ing a - far
In - to the fold

up-on the moun-tain,
of my Re-deem-er,

far _____ up - on the moun - tain, _____ Bring-ing the
fold _____ of my Re - deem - er, _____ Je - sus, the

1.
Bring-ing the wan-d'rer back a - gain, back a-gain,
Je - sus, the Lamb for sin - ners

2.
slain, for sin-ners slain.

wan - - d'rer back a - gain, _____
Lamb _____ for sin - ners

slain. _____

Throw Out the Life-Line

Edward S. Ufford, 1851-1929

Edward S. Ufford, 1851-1929
Arr. by Don Peterman, 1925-

1. Throw out the Life-Line a - cross the dark wave! There is a broth-er whom
2. Throw out the Life-Line with hand quick and strong—Why do you tar - ry, why
3. Throw out the Life-Line to dan-ger-fraught men, Sink-ing in an-guish where
4. Soon will the sea-son of res - cue be o'er, Soon will they drift to e -

some-one should save— Some-bod-y's broth-er! O who then will dare To
lin - ger so long? See, he is sink-ing! O has-ten to - day, And
you've nev-er been; Winds of temp-ta-tion and bil-lows of woe Will
ter - ni - ty's shore; Haste then, my broth-er— no time for de-lay, But

CHORUS

throw out the Life-Line, his per - il to share?
out with the Life-Boat! a - way, then, a - way!   Throw out the Life-Line!
soon hurl them out where the dark wa - ters flow.
throw out the Life-Line and save them to - day.

Throw out the Life-Line! Some-one is drift-ing a - way; Throw out the

Life-Line! Throw out the Life-Line! Some-one is sink-ing to - day.

Go Ye into All the World

James McGranahan, 1840-1907   James McGranahan, 1840-1907

1. Far, far a-way, in hea-then darkness dwell-ing, Mil-lions of souls for-
2. See o'er the world wide o-pen doors in-vit - ing— Sol-diers of Christ, a -
3. "Why will ye die?" the voice of God is call- ing, "Why will ye die?" re-
4. God speed the day, when those of ev-'ry na-tion "Glo-ry to God!" tri-

ev - er may be lost; Who, who will go, sal - va-tion's sto-ry tell - ing,
rise and en - ter in! Christians, a-wake! your forc - es all u - nit - ing,
ech - o in His name; Je _ sus hath died to save from death ap-pall - ing,
um-phant-ly shall sing; Ran-somed, re-deemed, re - joic - ing in sal - va-tion,

CHORUS

Look - ing to Je - sus, mind-ing not the cost?
Send forth the gos-pel, break the chains of sin.   "All pow'r is giv - en
Life and sal - va-tion there-fore go pro-claim.
Shout "Hal - le - lu - jah, for the Lord is King!"

un - to Me, All pow'r is giv - en un - to Me, Go ye in - to

all the world and preach the gos-pel, And lo, I am with you al - way."

To the Work!

FANNY J. CROSBY, 1820-1915

WILLIAM H. DOANE, 1832-1915

1. To the work! to the work! we are serv-ants of God, Let us fol-low the
2. To the work! to the work! let the hun-gry be fed, To the foun-tain of
3. To the work! to the work! there is la-bor for all, For the king-dom of
4. To the work! to the work! in the strength of the Lord, And a robe and a

path that our Mas-ter has trod; With the balm of His coun-sel our
life let the wea-ry be led; In the cross and its ban-ner our
dark-ness and er-ror shall fall; And the name of Je-ho-vah ex-
crown shall our la-bor re-ward When the home of the faith-ful our

strength to re-new, Let us do with our might what our hands find to do.
glo-ry shall be, While we her-ald the ti-dings, "Sal-va-tion is free!"
alt-ed shall be In the loud swell-ing cho-rus, "Sal-va-tion is free!"
dwell-ing shall be And we shout with the ran-somed, "Sal-va-tion is free!"

CHORUS

Toil-ing on, toil-ing on, Toil-ing
Toil-ing on, toil-ing on,

on, toil-ing on; Let us hope,
Toil-ing on, toil-ing on; and trust,

To the Work

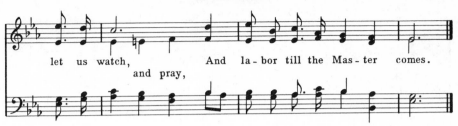

let us watch, and pray, And la-bor till the Mas-ter comes.

Ready 429

A. C. PALMER, 1845-1882

CHARLES D. TILLMAN, 1861-1943

1. Read-y to suf-fer grief or pain, Read-y to stand the test;
2. Read-y to go, read-y to bear, Read-y to watch and pray;
3. Read-y to speak, read-y to think, Read-y with heart and mind;
4. Read-y to speak, read-y to warn, Read-y o'er souls to yearn;

Read-y to stay at home and send Oth-ers if He sees best.
Read-y to stand a-side and give Till He shall clear the way.
Read-y to stand where He sees fit, Read-y His will to find.
Read-y in life or read-y in death, Read-y for His re-turn.

CHORUS

Read-y to go, read-y to stay, Read-y my place to fill;

Read-y for serv-ice low-ly or great, Read-y to do His will.

O Zion, Haste

TIDINGS

MARY ANN THOMSON, 1834-1923   JAMES WALCH, 1837-1901

1. O   Zi - on,   haste,   thy   mis - sion high ful - fill - ing,
2. Be - hold how   man - y   thou-sands still   are   ly - ing
3. Pro - claim to   ev - 'ry   peo - ple, tongue and   na - tion
4. Give   of thy   sons   to   bear the mes - sage glo - rious,

To   tell   to   all   the world that God   is   Light;   That   He   who
Bound in   the   dark - some pris - on - house of   sin,   With   none   to
That   God   in whom   they   live and move is   Love: Tell   how   He
Give   of thy wealth   to speed them on their   way;   Pour   out   thy

made   all   na - tions is   not   will - ing   One   soul should per - ish,
tell   them   of   the   Sav - ior's   dy - ing   Or   of   the   life   He
stooped   to   save   His   lost cre - a - tion   And   died   on   earth that
soul   for   them   in prayer vic - to - rious,   And   all   thou   spend - est

REFRAIN

lost   in shades of   night.
died   for   them   to   win.   Pub - lish glad   ti - dings,   Ti - dings of
man might   live a - bove.
Je - sus   will re - pay.

peace,   Ti - dings of   Je - sus— Re - demp - tion and   re - lease.

I Love to Tell the Story

A. Catherine Hankey, 1834-1911

William G. Fischer, 1835-1912

1. I love to tell the sto - ry Of un - seen things a - bove, Of Je - sus and His glo - ry, Of Je - sus and His love; I love to tell the sto - ry Be - cause I know 'tis true, It sat - is - fies my long - ings As noth - ing else can do.

2. I love to tell the sto - ry— More won - der - ful it seems Than all the gold-en fan - cies Of all our gold-en dreams; I love to tell the sto - ry— It did so much for me, And that is just the rea - son I tell it now to thee.

3. I love to tell the sto - ry— 'Tis pleas-ant to re - peat What seems, each time I tell it, More won-der-ful - ly sweet; I love to tell the sto - ry For some have nev - er heard The mes - sage of sal - va - tion From God's own ho - ly Word.

4. I love to tell the sto - ry, For those who know it best Seem hun - ger - ing and thirst-ing To hear it like the rest; And when in scenes of glo - ry I sing the new, new song, 'Twill be the old, old sto - ry That I have loved so long.

Refrain

I love to tell the sto - ry! 'Twill be my theme in glo - ry— To tell the old, old sto - ry Of Je - sus and His love.

Rescue the Perishing

FANNY J. CROSBY, 1820-1915

WILLIAM H. DOANE, 1832-1915

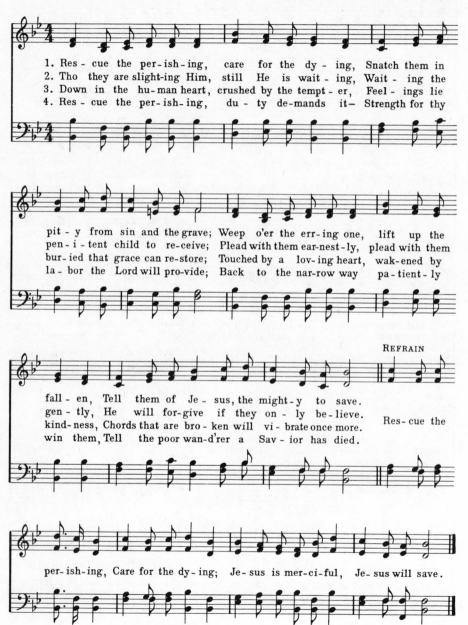

1. Res - cue the per-ish-ing, care for the dy - ing, Snatch them in
2. Tho they are slight-ing Him, still He is wait - ing, Wait - ing the
3. Down in the hu-man heart, crushed by the tempt - er, Feel - ings lie
4. Res - cue the per-ish-ing, du - ty de-mands it— Strength for thy

pit - y from sin and the grave; Weep o'er the err-ing one, lift up the
pen - i - tent child to re-ceive; Plead with them ear-nest-ly, plead with them
bur - ied that grace can re-store; Touched by a lov-ing heart, wak-ened by
la - bor the Lord will pro-vide; Back to the nar-row way pa - tient-ly

REFRAIN

fall - en, Tell them of Je - sus, the might-y to save.
gen - tly, He will for-give if they on - ly be-lieve.
kind - ness, Chords that are bro - ken will vi - brate once more.   Res - cue the
win them, Tell the poor wan-d'rer a Sav - ior has died.

per-ish-ing, Care for the dy - ing; Je - sus is mer-ci-ful, Je - sus will save.

From Greenland's Icy Mountains

MISSIONARY HYMN

REGINALD HEBER, 1783-1826   LOWELL MASON, 1792-1872

1. From Green-land's i - cy moun - tains, From In - dia's cor-al strand,
2. What though the spi - cy breez - es Blow soft o'er Cey-lon's isle,
3. Shall we, whose souls are light - ed With wis-dom from on high,
4. Waft, waft, ye winds, His sto - ry, And you, ye wa-ters, roll,

Where Af-ric's sun-ny foun-tains Roll down their gold-en sand,
Though ev-'ry pros-pect pleas-es And on - ly man is vile;
Shall we to men be-night-ed The lamp of life de - ny?
Till like a sea of glo - ry It spreads from pole to pole,

From man-y an an-cient riv - er, From man-y a palm - y plain,
In vain with lav - ish kind-ness The gifts of God are strown,
Sal - va-tion! O sal - va - tion! The joy - ful sound pro - claim,
Till o'er our ran-somed na - ture The Lamb for sin - ners slain,

They call us to de - liv - er Their land from er-ror's chain.
The hea-then in his blind-ness Bows down to wood and stone.
Till earth's re-mot-est na - tion Has learned Mes-si-ah's name.
Re - deem-er, King, Cre - a - tor, In bliss re-turns to reign.

434 Hail to the Brightness

WESLEY

THOMAS HASTINGS, 1784-1872

LOWELL MASON, 1792-1872

1. Hail to the bright-ness of Zi - on's glad morn-ing! Joy to the
2. Hail to the bright-ness of Zi - on's glad morn-ing, Long by the
3. Lo, in the des - ert rich flow-ers are spring-ing, Streams ev - er
4. See from all lands, from the isles of the o - cean, Praise to Je -

lands that in dark-ness have lain! Hushed be the ac - cents of
proph - ets of Is - rael fore - told! Hail to the mil - lions from
co - pious are glid-ing a - long; Loud from the moun-tain - tops
ho - vah as-cend-ing on high; Fall - en the en-gines of

sor-row and mourn-ing, Zi - on in tri-umph be - gins her mild reign.
bond-age re - turn-ing! Gen - tiles and Jews the blest vi-sion be - hold.
ech - oes are ring-ing, Wastes rise in ver-dure and min-gle in song.
war and com-mo-tion, Shouts of sal - va-tion are rend-ing the sky.

435 Lord, Speak to Me

CANONBURY

FRANCES R. HAVERGAL, 1836-1879

ROBERT SCHUMANN, 1810-1856

1. Lord, speak to me, that I may speak In liv-ing ech - oes of Thy tone;
2. O lead me, Lord, that I may lead The wan-d'ring and the wav-'ring feet;
3. O teach me, Lord, that I may teach The pre-cious things Thou dost im - part;
4. O fill me with Thy full-ness, Lord, Un - til my ver - y heart o'er-flow
5. O use me, Lord, use e - ven me, Just as Thou wilt, and when, and where,

Lord, Speak to Me

As Thou hast sought, so let me seek Thy err-ing chil-dren lost and lone.
O feed me, Lord, that I may feed The hun-g'ring ones with man-na sweet.
And wing my words that they may reach The hid-den depths of man-y a heart.
In kin-dling tho't and glow-ing word, Thy love to tell, Thy praise to show.
Un-til Thy bless-ed face I see— Thy rest, Thy joy, Thy glo-ry share.

Bring Them In

436

ALEXCENAH THOMAS, 19th century

WILLIAM A. OGDEN, 1841-1897

1. Hark! 'tis the Shep-herd's voice I hear, Out in the des-ert dark and drear,
2. Who'll go and help this Shep-herd kind, Help Him the wan-d'ring ones to find?
3. Out in the des-ert hear their cry, Out on the moun-tains wild and high;

Call-ing the sheep who've gone a-stray Far from the Shep-herd's fold a-way.
Who'll bring the lost ones to the fold Where they'll be shel-tered from the cold?
Hark! 'tis the Mas-ter speaks to thee, "Go find my sheep wher-e'er they be."

CHORUS

Bring them in, bring them in, Bring them in from the fields of sin;

Bring them in, bring them in, Bring the wan-d'ring ones to Je-sus.

437   O Master, Let Me Walk with Thee
MARYTON
WASHINGTON GLADDEN, 1836-1918   H. PERCY SMITH, 1825-1898

1. O Mas-ter, let me walk with Thee   In low-ly paths of serv-ice free;
2. Help me the slow of heart to move   By some clear, win-ning word of love;
3. Teach me Thy pa-tience! still with Thee   In clos-er, dear-er com-pa-ny,
4. In hope that sends a shin-ing ray   Far down the fu-ture's broad-ning way,

Tell me Thy se-cret— help me bear   The strain of toil, the fret of care.
Teach me the way-ward feet to stay   And guide them in the home-ward way.
In work that keeps faith sweet and strong, In trust that tri-umphs o-ver wrong.
In peace that on-ly Thou canst give, With Thee, O Mas-ter, let me live.

438   Footsteps of Jesus
MARY B. C. SLADE, 1826-1882   ASA B. EVERETT, 1828-1875

✓1. Sweet-ly, Lord, have we heard Thee call-ing, "Come, fol-low Me!" And we
2. Tho they lead o'er the cold, dark moun-tains, Seek-ing His sheep, Or a-
✓3. If they lead thru the tem-ple ho-ly, Preach-ing the Word, Or in
✓4. Then at last, when on high He sees us, Our jour-ney done, We will

CHORUS

see where Thy foot-prints fall-ing Lead us to Thee.
long by Si-lo-am's foun-tains, Help-ing the weak:
homes of the poor and low-ly, Serv-ing the Lord:
rest where the steps of Je-sus End at His throne.

Foot-prints of Je-sus, that

Footsteps of Jesus

make the path-way glow! We will fol-low the steps of Je-sus wher-e'er they go.

Work, for the Night Is Coming   439

ANNIE L. COGHILL, 1836-1907

LOWELL MASON, 1792-1872

1. Work, for the night is com - ing, Work thru the morn - ing hours;
2. Work, for the night is com - ing, Work thru the sun - ny noon;
3. Work, for the night is com - ing, Un - der the sun - set skies:

Work while the dew is spark - ling, Work 'mid spring-ing flow'rs.
Fill bright-est hours with la - bor— Rest comes sure and soon.
While their bright tints are glow - ing, Work, for day-light flies.

Work when the day grows bright - er, Work in the glow-ing sun;
Give ev-'ry fly - ing min - ute Some-thing to keep in store;
Work till the last beam fad - eth, Fad - eth to shine no more;

Work, for the night is com - ing, When man's work is done.
Work, for the night is com - ing, When man works no more.
Work, while the night is dark - 'ning, When man's work is o'er.

440   I'll Go Where You Want Me to Go

1 – MARY BROWN, 19th century
2, 3 – CHARLES E. PRIOR, 1856-1927

CARRIE E. ROUNSEFELL, 1861-1930

1. It may not be on the mountain's height Or o-ver the storm-y sea,
2. Per-haps to-day there are lov-ing words Which Je-sus would have me speak,
3. There's sure-ly some-where a low-ly place In earth's har-vest fields so wide,

It may not be at the bat-tle's front My Lord will have need of me;
There may be now, in the paths of sin, Some wan-d'rer whom I should seek;
Where I may la-bor thru life's short day For Je-sus the Cru-ci-fied;

But if by a still, small voice He calls To paths I do not know,
O Sav-ior, if Thou wilt be my Guide, Tho dark and rug-ged the way,
So, trust-ing my all un-to Thy care— I know Thou lov-est me—

Fine

I'll an-swer, dear Lord, with my hand in Thine, I'll go where You want me to go.
My voice shall ech-o the mes-sage sweet, I'll say what You want me to say.
I'll do Thy will with a heart sin-cere, I'll be what You want me to be.

D.S.- *I'll say what You want me to say, dear Lord, I'll be what You want me to be.*

CHORUS

D.S.

I'll go where You want me to go, dear Lord, O'er moun-tain or plain or sea;

Love Lifted Me

441

James Rowe, 1865-1933

Howard E. Smith, 1863-1918

1. I was sink-ing deep in sin, Far from the peace-ful shore, Ver-y deep-ly
2. All my heart to Him I give, Ev-er to Him I'll cling, In His bless-ed
3. Souls in dan-ger, look a-bove, Je-sus com-plete-ly saves; He will lift you

stained with-in, Sink-ing to rise no more; But the Mas-ter of the sea
pres-ence live, Ev-er His prais-es sing. Love so might-y and so true
by His love Out of the an-gry waves. He's the Mas-ter of the sea,

Heard my de-spair-ing cry, From the wa-ters lift-ed me—Now safe am I.
Mer-its my soul's best songs; Faith-ful, lov-ing serv-ice too To Him be-longs.
Bil-lows His will o-bey; He your Sav-ior wants to be—Be saved to-day.

CHORUS

Love lift-ed me, —— Love lift-ed me, —— When noth-ing
e-ven me, e-ven me,

1. else could help, Love lift-ed me;
2. Love lift-ed me.

442 Praise Him! Praise Him!

FANNY J. CROSBY, 1820-1915   CHESTER G. ALLEN, 1838-1878

1. Praise Him! praise Him! Je-sus, our bless-ed Re-deem-er! Sing, O
2. Praise Him! praise Him! Je-sus, our bless-ed Re-deem-er! For our
3. Praise Him! praise Him! Je-sus, our bless-ed Re-deem-er! Heav'n-ly

earth— His won-der-ful love pro-claim! Hail Him! hail Him! high-est arch-
sins He suf-fered and bled and died; He our Rock, our hope of e-
por-tals loud with ho-san-nas ring! Je-sus, Sav-ior, reign-eth for

an-gels in glo-ry, Strength and hon-or give to His ho-ly name!
ter-nal sal-va-tion, Hail Him! hail Him! Je-sus the Cru-ci-fied.
ev-er and ev-er, Crown Him! crown Him! Proph-et and Priest and King!

Like a shep-herd Je-sus will guard His chil-dren— In His arms He
Sound His prais-es— Je-sus who bore our sor-rows— Love un-bound-ed,
Christ is com-ing, o-ver the world vic-to-rious— Pow'r and glo-ry

REFRAIN

car-ries them all day long: Praise Him! praise Him! tell of His
won-der-ful, deep and strong: Praise Him! praise Him! tell of His
un-to the Lord be-long: Praise Him! praise Him! tell of His

Praise Him! Praise Him!

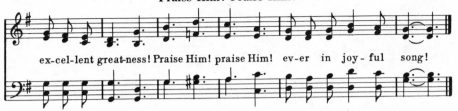

ex-cel-lent great-ness! Praise Him! praise Him! ev-er in joy-ful song!

There Is No Name So Sweet on Earth 443

GEORGE W. BETHUNE, 1805-1862

WILLIAM B. BRADBURY, 1816-1868

1. There is no name so sweet on earth, No name so sweet in heav-en—
2. 'Twas Ga-briel first that did pro-claim, To His most bless-ed moth-er,
3. And when He hung up-on the tree They wrote His name a-bove Him,
4. So now, up-on His Fa-ther's throne, Al-might-y to re-lease us
5. O Je-sus! by that matchless name Thy grace shall fail us nev-er;
6. To Je-sus ev-'ry knee shall bow And ev-'ry tongue con-fess Him,

Fine

The name, be-fore His won-drous birth, To Christ the Sav-ior giv-en.
That name which now and ev-er-more We praise a-bove all oth-er.
That all might see the rea-son we For ev-er-more must love Him.
From sin and pain, He ev-er reigns— The Prince and Sav-ior, Je-sus.
To-day as yes-ter-day the same, Thou art the same for-ev-er!
And we u-nite with saints in light, Our on-ly Lord, to bless Him.

D.S.—For there's no word ear ev-er heard So dear, so sweet as "Je-sus!"

REFRAIN

D.S.

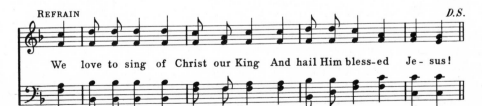

We love to sing of Christ our King And hail Him bless-ed Je-sus!

444 There's a Wideness in God's Mercy

WELLESLEY

FREDERICK W. FABER, 1814-1863

LIZZIE S. TOURJÉE, 1858-1913
Arr. by Jon Drevits, 1928-

1. There's a wide-ness in God's mer-cy Like the wide-ness of the sea;
2. There is wel-come for the sin-ner And more grac-es for the good;
3. For the love of God is broad-er Than the meas-ure of man's mind,
4. If our love were but more sim-ple, We should take Him at His word,

There's a kind-ness in His jus-tice Which is more than lib-er-ty.
There is mer-cy with the Sav-ior, There is heal-ing in His blood.
And the heart of the E-ter-nal Is most won-der-ful-ly kind.
And our lives would be all sun-shine In the sweet-ness of our Lord.

445 No, Not One!

JOHNSON OATMAN, JR., 1856-1922

GEORGE C. HUGG, 1848-1907

1. There's not a friend like the low-ly Je-sus— No, not one! no, not one!
2. No friend like Him is so high and ho-ly— No, not one! no, not one!
3. There's not an hour that He is not near us— No, not one! no, not one!
4. Did ev-er saint find this Friend for-sake Him? No, not one! no, not one!
5. Was e'er a gift like the Sav-ior giv-en? No, not one! no, not one!

Fine

None else could heal all our soul's dis-eas-es— No, not one! no, not one!
And yet no friend is so meek and low-ly— No, not one! no, not one!
No night so dark but His love can cheer us— No, not one! no, not one!
Or sin-ner find that He would not take him? No, not one! no, not one!
Will He re-fuse us a home in heav-en? No, not one! no, not one!

D.S.—*There's not a friend like the low-ly Je-sus— No, not one! no, not one!*

No, Not One!

CHORUS

D.S.

Je-sus knows all a-bout our strug-gles, He will guide till the day is done;

Satisfied

446

CLARA TEAR WILLIAMS, 1858-1937

RALPH E. HUDSON, 1843-1901

1. All my life long I had pant- ed For a draught, from some clear spring,
2. Feed-ing on the husks a-round me, Till my strength was al-most gone,
3. Poor I was, and sought for rich- es, Something that would sat - is - fy,
4. Well of wa- ter, ev - er spring-ing, Bread of life so rich and free,

That I hoped would quench the burn-ing Of the thirst I felt with- in.
Longed my soul for some-thing bet- ter, On- ly still to hun- ger on.
But the dust I gath- ered round me On- ly mocked my soul's sad cry.
Un - told wealth that nev - er fail- eth, My Re- deem-er is to me.

CHORUS

Hal- le - lu - jah! I have found Him Whom my soul so long has craved!

Je- sus sat - is-fies my long-ings—Thru His blood I now am saved.

447 The Lily of the Valley

CHARLES W. FRY, 1837-1882   WILLIAM S. HAYS, 1837-1907

1. I have found a friend in Je-sus— He's ev-'ry-thing to me, He's the
2. He all my griefs has tak-en and all my sor-rows borne, In temp-
3. He will nev-er, nev-er leave me nor yet for-sake me here, While I

fair-est of ten thou-sand to my soul; The Lil-y of the Val-ley— in
ta-tion He's my strong and might-y tow'r; I have all for Him for-sak-en and
live by faith and do His bless-ed will; A wall of fire a-bout me, I've

D.S.- Lil-y of the Val-ley, the

Fine

Him a-lone I see All I need to cleanse and make me ful-ly whole.
all my i-dols torn From my heart, and now He keeps me by His pow'r.
noth-ing now to fear— With His man-na He my hun-gry soul shall fill.

Bright and Morn-ing Star, He's the fair-est of ten thou-sand to my soul.

In sor-row He's my com-fort, in trou-ble He's my stay,
Tho all the world for-sake me and Sa-tan tempt me sore,
Then sweep-ing up to glo-ry I'll see His bless-ed face,

D.S.

He tells me ev-'ry care on Him to roll; He's the
Thru Je-sus I shall safe-ly reach the goal; He's the
Where riv-ers of de-light shall ev-er roll; He's the

Hal-le-lu-jah!

He Ransomed Me

JULIA H. JOHNSTON, 1849-1919   J. W. HENDERSON, 20th century

1. There's a sweet and bless-ed sto - ry Of the Christ who came from
2. From the depth of sin and sad-ness To the heights of joy and
3. By and by with joy in-creas-ing And with grat - i - tude un -

glo - ry Just to res-cue me from sin and mis - e - ry; He in
glad-ness Je - sus lift - ed me in mer - cy full and free; With His
ceas-ing, Lift - ed up to be with Christ e - ter-nal - ly, I will

lov - ing-kind-ness sought me And from sin and shame has brought me— Hal - le -
pre-cious blood He bought me, When I knew Him not He sought me, And in
join the hosts there sing-ing, In the an - them ev - er ring-ing, To the

D.S.— ev - er tell the sto - ry, Shout-ing,"Glo - ry, glo - ry, glo - ry!" Hal-le-

Fine CHORUS

lu - jah! Je - sus ran-somed me.
love di - vine He ran-somed me.   Hal-le-lu-jah! what a Sav-ior Who can
King of Love who ran-somed me.

lu-jah! Je - sus ran-somed me.

D.S.

take a poor lost sin-ner, Lift him from the mi - ry clay and set him free! I will

449 To God Be the Glory

FANNY J. CROSBY, 1820-1915

WILLIAM H. DOANE, 1832-1915

1. To God be the glo-ry—great things He hath done! So loved He the
2. O per-fect re-demp-tion, the pur-chase of blood! To ev-'ry be-
3. Great things He hath taught us, great things He hath done, And great our re-

world that He gave us His Son, Who yield-ed His life an a-
liev-er the prom-ise of God; The vil-est of-fen-der who
joic-ing thru Je-sus the Son; But pur-er and high-er and

tone-ment for sin And o-pened the Life-gate that all may go in.
tru-ly be-lieves, That mo-ment from Je-sus a par-don re-ceives.
great-er will be Our won-der, our trans-port, when Je-sus we see.

D. S.—Je-sus the Son, And give Him the glo-ry—great things He hath done.

CHORUS

Praise the Lord, Praise the Lord, Let the earth hear His voice! Praise the Lord,

Praise the Lord, Let the peo-ple re-joice! O come to the Fa-ther thru

Isn't the Love of Jesus Something Wonderful! 450

JOHN W. PETERSON, 1921-   JOHN W. PETERSON, 1921-

1. There will nev-er be a sweet-er sto-ry— Sto-ry of the Sav-ior's
2. Bound-less as the u-ni-verse a-round me, Reach-ing to the far-thest
3. Love be-yond our hu-man com-pre-hend-ing, Love of God in Christ—how

love di-vine,   Love that bro't Him from the realms of glo-ry
soul a-way—   Sav-ing, keep-ing love it was that found me,
can it be!   This will be my theme and nev-er end-ing,

Just to save a sin-ful soul like mine.
That is why my heart can tru-ly say:
Great re-deem-ing love of Cal-va-ry.

CHORUS

Is-n't the love of Je-sus

some-thing won-der-ful, won-der-ful, won-der-ful; O is-n't the love of
it is

Je-sus some-thing won-der-ful! Won-der-ful it is to me.
to me.

451 Wonderful, Wonderful Jesus!

ANNA B. RUSSELL, 1862-1954

ERNEST O. SELLERS, 1869-1952

1. There is nev-er a day so drear-y, There is nev-er a night so
2. There is nev-er a cross so heav-y, There is nev-er a weight of
3. There is nev-er a care or bur-den, There is nev-er a grief or
4. There is nev-er a guilt-y sin-ner, There is nev-er a wan-d'ring

long, But the soul that is trust-ing Je - sus Will some-where
woe, But that Je-sus will help to car - ry Be - cause He
loss, But that Je-sus in love will light - en When car - ried
one, But that God can in mer - cy par - don Thru Je - sus

CHORUS

find a song.
lov - eth so.
to the cross.
Christ, His Son. Won-der-ful, won-der-ful Je - sus! In the

heart He im-plant-eth a song; A song of de-liv-'rance,

im - plant-eth a song;

of cour-age, of strength— In the heart He im-plant-eth a song.

My Savior's Love

Charles H. Gabriel, 1856-1932

Charles H. Gabriel, 1856-1932

1. I stand a-mazed in the pres-ence Of Je - sus the Naz-a - rene,
2. For me it was in the gar - den He prayed, "Not My will, but Thine;"
3. In pit - y an - gels be-held Him, And came from the world of light
4. He took my sins and my sor - rows, He made them His ver - y own;
5. When with the ran-somed in glo - ry His face I at last shall see,

And won-der how He could love me, A sin - ner condemned, un - clean.
He had no tears for His own griefs But sweat-drops of blood for mine.
To com-fort Him in the sor-rows He bore for my soul that night.
He bore the bur-den to Cal-v'ry And suf-fered and died a - lone.
'Twill be my joy thru the a - ges To sing of His love for me.

CHORUS

How mar-vel-ous! how won-der-ful! And my song shall ev - er be:
O how mar-vel-ous! O how won-der-ful!

How mar-vel-ous! how won-der-ful Is my Sav-ior's love for me!
O how mar-vel-ous! O how won-der-ful

453 He Keeps Me Singing

LUTHER B. BRIDGERS, 1884-1948 LUTHER B. BRIDGERS, 1884-1948

Downbeat

1. There's with-in my heart a mel-o-dy— Je-sus whis-pers sweet and low,
2. All my life was wrecked by sin and strife, Dis-cord filled my heart with pain;
3. Feasting on the rich-es of His grace, Rest-ing 'neath His shelt'ring wing,
4. Tho sometimes He leads thru wa-ters deep, Tri-als fall a-cross the way,
5. Soon He's com-ing back to wel-come me Far be-yond the star-ry sky;

"Fear not, I am with thee— peace, be still," In all of life's ebb and flow.
Je-sus swept a-cross the bro-ken strings, Stirred the slumb'ring chords a-gain.
Al-ways look-ing on His smil-ing face— That is why I shout and sing.
Tho sometimes the path seems rough and steep, See His foot-prints all the way.
I shall wing my flight to worlds un-known, I shall reign with Him on high.

CHORUS

Je-sus, Je-sus, Je-sus— Sweet-est name I know,

Fills my ev-'ry long-ing, Keeps me sing-ing as I go.

What a Wonderful Savior!

Elisha A. Hoffman, 1839-1929

Elisha A. Hoffman, 1839-1929

1. Christ has for sin a-tone-ment made— What a won-der-ful Sav - ior!
2. I praise Him for the cleans-ing blood— What a won-der-ful Sav - ior!
3. He cleansed my heart from all its sin— What a won-der-ful Sav - ior!
4. He gives me o - ver-com-ing pow'r— What a won-der-ful Sav - ior!
5. To Him I've giv - en all my heart— What a won-der-ful Sav - ior!

We are re-deemed, the price is paid— What a won-der-ful Sav - ior!
That rec - on-ciled my soul to God— What a won-der-ful Sav - ior!
And now He reigns and rules there-in— What a won-der-ful Sav - ior!
And tri-umph in each try-ing hour— What a won-der-ful Sav - ior!
The world shall nev - er share a part— What a won-der-ful Sav - ior!

REFRAIN

What a won-der-ful Sav - ior is Je - sus, my Je - sus!

What a won-der-ful Sav - ior is Je - sus, my Lord!

455   In My Heart There Rings a Melody

ELTON M. ROTH, 1891-1951   ELTON M. ROTH, 1891-1951

1. I have a song that Je-sus gave me, It was sent from
2. I love the Christ who died on Cal-v'ry, For He washed my
3. 'Twill be my end-less theme in glo-ry, With the an-gels

heav'n a-bove; There nev-er was a sweet-er mel-o-dy, 'Tis a
sins a-way; He put with-in my heart a mel-o-dy, And I
I will sing; 'Twill be a song with glo-rious har-mo-ny, When the

CHORUS

mel-o-dy of love.
know it's there to stay.   In my heart there rings a mel-o-dy,
courts of heav-en ring.

There rings a mel-o-dy with heav-en's har-mo-ny; In my

heart there rings a mel-o-dy; There rings a mel-o-dy of love.

He Is So Precious to Me

CHARLES H. GABRIEL, 1856-1932   CHARLES H. GABRIEL, 1856-1932

1. So pre-cious is Je-sus, my Sav-ior, my King, His praise all the day
2. He stood at my heart's door 'mid sun-shine and rain, And pa-tient-ly wait-
3. I stand on the moun-tain of bless-ing at last, No cloud in the heav-
4. I praise Him be-cause He ap-point-ed a place Where some day, thru faith

long with rap-ture I sing; To Him in my weak-ness for strength I can cling,
ed an en-trance to gain; What shame that so long He en-treat-ed in vain,
ens a shad-ow to cast; His smile is up-on me, the val-ley is past,
in His won-der-ful grace, I know I shall see Him—shall look on His face,

CHORUS

For He is so pre-cious to me. For He is so pre-cious to
so
me, For He is so pre-cious to me; _____ 'Tis heav-en
pre-cious to me, so pre-cious to me;
be-low my Re-deem-er to know, For He is so pre-cious to me.

457
In My Heart

JOHN W. PETERSON, 1921-   JOHN W. PETERSON, 1921-

1. There's a mel - o - dy of glad-ness that is ring-ing in my heart,
2. I re - mem-ber how my long-ing heart was search-ing ev - 'ry-where
3. O how dark and drear my path-way when I jour-neyed all a - lone,
4. I am on my way to heav - en where our joys will be com-plete

Since I met the bless-ed Christ of Cal - va - ry; (of Cal - va - ry;)
To dis - cov - er what would take my guilt a - way; (my guilt a - way;)
With no friend di - vine to gen-tly lead the way; (to lead the way;)
In the bright e - ter - nal man-sions we will share; (yes, we will share;)

It has si - lenced ev - 'ry sad re - frain and made the joy-bells start,
Then I heard that Christ the Sav - ior all my sins Him-self did bear,
I'm so glad that I met Je - sus - that I claimed Him as my own,
Face to face I'll see my Sav - ior and I'll wor - ship at His feet,

For He took a - way my sin and set me free. (He set me free.)
And the Spir - it drew me to Him that glad day. (that hap - py day.)
Now His love is grow-ing sweet - er ev - 'ry day. (yes, ev - 'ry day.)
I will sing His praise for - ev - er o - ver there. (for - ev - er there.)

CHORUS

In my heart a mel - o - dy is ring-ing With a joy that nev - er
And an an - gel song could not be sweet - er

In My Heart

will de - part;

will not de-part; Than the song that's ring-ing in my heart.

in my heart.

Ring the Bells of Heaven! 458

WILLIAM O. CUSHING, 1823-1902

GEORGE F. ROOT, 1820-1895

1. Ring the bells of heav - en! there is joy to - day For a
2. Ring the bells of heav - en! there is joy to - day, For the
3. Ring the bells of heav - en! spread the feast to - day! An - gels,

soul re - turn-ing from the wild! See! the Fa - ther meets him
wan-d'rer now is rec - on - ciled; Yes, a soul is res - cued
swell the glad tri - um-phant strain! Tell the joy - ful ti - dings,

D.S.- 'Tis the ran-somed ar - my,

Fine

out up - on the way, Wel - com-ing His wea - ry, wan-d'ring child.
from his sin - ful way, And is born a - new a ran-somed child.
bear it far a - way! For a pre-cious soul is born a - gain.

like a might - y sea, Peal - ing forth the an - them of the free!

CHORUS

D.S.

Glo - ry! glo - ry! how the an-gels sing; Glo - ry! glo - ry! how the loud harps ring!

459

He Lifted Me

Charles H. Gabriel, 1856-1932

Charles H. Gabriel, 1856-1932

1. In lov-ing-kind-ness Je-sus came My soul in mer-cy to re-claim,
2. He called me long be-fore I heard, Be-fore my sin-ful heart was stirred,
3. His brow was pierced with man-y a thorn, His hands by cru-el nails were torn,
4. Now on a high-er plane I dwell, And with my soul I know 'tis well;

And from the depths of sin and shame Thru grace He lift-ed me.
But when I took Him at His word, For-giv'n He lift-ed me.
When from my guilt and grief, for-lorn, In love He lift-ed me.
Yet how or why, I can-not tell, He should have lift-ed me.

He lift-ed me.

CHORUS

From sink-ing sand He lift-ed me, With ten-der hand He lift-ed me;

From shades of night to plains of light, O praise His name, He lift-ed me!

Leaning on the Everlasting Arms

460

ELISHA A. HOFFMAN, 1839-1929

ANTHONY J. SHOWALTER, 1858-1924

1. What a fel-low-ship, what a joy di-vine, Lean-ing on the ev-er-
2. O how sweet to walk in this pil-grim way, Lean-ing on the ev-er-
3. What have I to dread, what have I to fear, Lean-ing on the ev-er-

last - ing arms; What a bless-ed-ness, what a peace is mine,
last - ing arms; O how bright the path grows from day to day,
last - ing arms? I have bless-ed peace with my Lord so near,

REFRAIN

Lean-ing on the ev-er-last-ing arms. Lean - ing,
Lean-ing on Je - sus,

lean - ing, Safe and se-cure from all a-larms; Lean -
lean-ing on Je - sus, Lean-ing on

ing, lean - ing, Lean-ing on the ev-er-last-ing arms.
Je-sus, lean-ing on Je - sus,

461

O It Is Wonderful!

CHARLES H. GABRIEL, 1856-1932

CHARLES H. GABRIEL, 1856-1932
Arr. by Don Peterman, 1925-

1. I stand all a - mazed at the love Je - sus of - fers me,
2. I mar - vel that He would de - scend from His throne di - vine
3. I think of His hands pierced and bleed - ing to pay the debt!

Con - fused at the grace that so ful - ly He prof - fers me;
To res - cue a soul so re - bel-lious and proud as mine;
Such mer - cy, such love and de - vo - tion can I for - get?

I trem-ble to know that for me He was cru - ci - fied—
That He should ex - tend His great love un - to such as I—
No, no! I will praise and a - dore at the mer-cy-seat,

That for me, a sin - ner, He suf - fered, He bled, and died.
Suf - fi - cient to own, to re - deem, and to jus - ti - fy.
Un - til at the glo - ri - fied throne I kneel at His feet.

CHORUS

O it is won-der-ful— That He should care for me E-nough to

O It Is Wonderful!

die for me! O it is won-der-ful— Won-der-ful to me!

Sunshine in My Soul

462

JOHN R. SWENEY, 1837-1899
Arr. by Jon Drevits, 1928-

ELIZA E. HEWITT, 1851-1920

1. There is sun-shine in my soul to-day, More glo - ri - ous and bright
2. There is mu - sic in my soul to-day, A car - ol to my King,
3. There is spring-time in my soul to-day, For when the Lord is near
4. There is glad-ness in my soul to-day, And hope and praise and love,

Than glows in an - y earth-ly sky, For Je - sus is my light.
And Je - sus, lis-ten-ing can hear The songs I can - not sing.
The dove of peace sings in my heart, The flow'rs of grace ap - pear.
For bless-ings which He gives me now, For joys "laid up" a - bove.

CHORUS

O there's sun-shine, bless-ed sun-shine, When the peace-ful, hap - py mo-ments

roll; When Je-sus shows His smil-ing face, There is sun-shine in my soul.

463 All That Thrills My Soul

THORO HARRIS, 1874-1955   THORO HARRIS, 1874-1955

1. Who can cheer the heart like Je - sus, By His pres-ence all di - vine?
2. Love of Christ so free - ly giv - en, Grace of God be-yond de - gree,
3. What a won-der-ful re-demp-tion! Nev - er can a mor-tal know
4. Ev - 'ry need His hand sup-ply - ing, Ev - 'ry good in Him I see;
5. By the crys-tal flow-ing riv - er With the ran-somed I will sing,

True and ten-der, pure and pre - cious, O how blest to call Him mine!
Mer - cy high-er than the heav - en, Deep - er than the deep-est sea!
How my sin, tho red like crim - son, Can be whit-er than the snow.
On His strength di-vine re - ly - ing, He is all in all to me.
And for - ev - er and for - ev - er Praise and glo-ri-fy the King.

REFRAIN

All that thrills my soul is Je - sus, He is more than life to me;

to me;

And the fair-est of ten thou - sand In my bless-ed Lord I see.

I Will Praise Him!

MARGARET J. HARRIS, 19th century

MARGARET J. HARRIS, 19th century

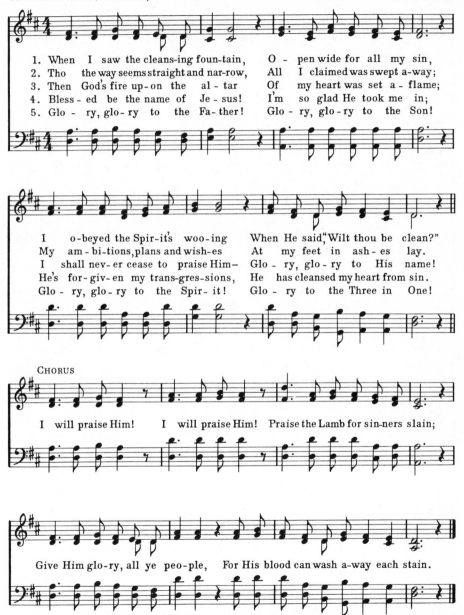

1. When I saw the cleans-ing foun-tain, O - pen wide for all my sin,
2. Tho the way seems straight and nar-row, All I claimed was swept a-way;
3. Then God's fire up-on the al - tar Of my heart was set a - flame;
4. Bless - ed be the name of Je - sus! I'm so glad He took me in;
5. Glo - ry, glo-ry to the Fa-ther! Glo - ry, glo-ry to the Son!

I o-beyed the Spir-it's woo-ing When He said,"Wilt thou be clean?"
My am - bi-tions, plans and wish-es At my feet in ash - es lay.
I shall nev-er cease to praise Him— Glo - ry, glo-ry to His name!
He's for-giv-en my trans-gres-sions, He has cleansed my heart from sin.
Glo - ry, glo-ry to the Spir-it! Glo - ry to the Three in One!

CHORUS

I will praise Him! I will praise Him! Praise the Lamb for sin-ners slain;

Give Him glo-ry, all ye peo-ple, For His blood can wash a-way each stain.

465 Springs of Living Water

JOHN W. PETERSON, 1921-

JOHN W. PETERSON, 1921-

1. I thirst-ed in the bar-ren land of sin and shame, And noth-ing sat - is -
2. How sweet the liv-ing wa-ter from the hills of God, It makes me glad and
3. O sin - ner, won't you come to-day to Cal - va - ry? A foun-tain there is

fy - ing there I found; But to the bless-ed cross of Christ one
hap - py all the way; Now glo - ry, grace and bless-ing mark the
flow-ing deep and wide; The Sav - ior now in-vites you to the

day I came, Where springs of liv - ing wa - ter did a - bound.
path I've trod, I'm shout-ing "Hal - le - lu - jah" ev - 'ry day.
wa - ter free, Where thirst - ing spir-its can be sat - is - fied.

CHORUS

Drink-ing at the springs of liv - ing wa - ter, Hap - py now am
Hap - py

I, My soul they sat - is - fy; Drink-ing at the
now am I, My soul they sat - is - fy; I'm

Springs of Living Water

springs of liv- ing wa - ter, O won-der-ful and boun-ti-ful sup - ply!

Christ Liveth in Me
466

DANIEL W. WHITTLE, 1840-1901   JAMES McGRANAHAN, 1840-1907

1. Once far from God and dead in sin, No light my heart could see,
2. As rays of light from yon - der sun The flow'rs of earth set free,
3. As lives the flow'r with-in the seed, As in the cone the tree,
4. With long-ing all my heart is filled That like Him I may be,

But in God's Word the light I found—Now Christ liv-eth in me.
So life and light and love came forth From Christ liv- ing in me.
So, praise the God of truth and grace, His Spir- it dwell-eth in me.
As on the won-drous thought I dwell, That Christ liv-eth in me.

CHORUS

Christ liv-eth in me, ___ Christ liv-eth in me; ___
Christ liv-eth in me, Christ liv-eth in
me; O

O what a sal - va-tion this— That Christ liv-eth in me.

467 Since I Have Been Redeemed

Edwin O. Excell, 1851-1921   Edwin O. Excell, 1851-1921

1. I have a song I love to sing, Since I have been re-deemed,
2. I have a Christ that sat-is-fies, Since I have been re-deemed;
3. I have a wit-ness bright and clear, Since I have been re-deemed,
4. I have a home pre-pared for me, Since I have been re-deemed,

Of my Re-deem-er, Sav-ior, King— Since I have been re-deemed.
To do His will my high-est prize— Since I have been re-deemed.
Dis-pel-ling ev-'ry doubt and fear— Since I have been re-deemed.
Where I shall dwell e-ter-nal-ly— Since I have been re-deemed.

CHORUS

Since I have been re-deemed, Since I have been re-
Since I have been re-deemed, Since I have been re-deemed,

deemed, I will glo-ry in His name; Since I have been re-
Since I have been re-deemed, Since

deemed, I will glo-ry in my Sav-ior's name.
I have been re-deemed,

I Will Sing the Wondrous Story

468

FRANCIS H. ROWLEY, 1854-1952

PETER P. BILHORN, 1865-1936

1. I will sing the won-drous sto-ry Of the Christ who died for me—
2. I was lost but Je-sus found me— Found the sheep that went a-stray,
3. I was bruised but Je-sus healed me— Faint was I from man-y a fall;
4. Days of dark-ness still come o'er me, Sor-row's paths I oft-en tread;
5. He will keep me till the riv-er Rolls its wa-ters at my feet;

How He left His home in glo-ry For the cross of Cal-va-ry.
Threw His lov-ing arms a-round me, Drew me back in-to His way.
Sight was gone and fears pos-sessed me, But He freed me from them all.
But the Sav-ior still is with me— By His hand I'm safe-ly led.
Then He'll bear me safe-ly o-ver, Where the loved ones I shall meet.

CHORUS

Yes, I'll sing the wondrous sto-ry Of the Christ
Yes, I'll sing the wondrous sto-ry Of the Christ

who died for me, Sing it with the saints in
who died for me, Sing it with

glo-ry, Gath-ered by the crys-tal sea.
the saints in glo-ry, Gath-ered by the crys-tal sea, the crys-tal sea.

469 I've Found a Friend

JAMES G. SMALL, 1817-1888

GEORGE C. STEBBINS, 1846-1945

1. I've found a Friend, O such a Friend! He loved me ere I knew Him;
2. I've found a Friend, O such a Friend! He bled, He died to save me;
3. I've found a Friend, O such a Friend! All pow'r to Him is giv - en
4. I've found a Friend, O such a Friend! So kind and true and ten - der,

He drew me with the cords of love, And thus He bound me to Him.
And not a - lone the gift of life, But His own self He gave me.
To guard me on my on-ward course And bring me safe to heav - en.
So wise a Coun - sel - lor and Guide, So might - y a De - fend - er!

And round my heart still close-ly twine Those ties which naught can sev - er,
Naught that I have my own I call, I hold it for the Giv - er:
Th'e - ter - nal glo - ries gleam a - far To nerve my faint en - deav - or:
From Him who loves me now so well, What pow'r my soul can sev - er?

For I am His and He is mine, For - ev - er and for - ev - er.
My heart, my strength, my life, my all Are His, and His for - ev - er.
So now to watch, to work, to war, And then to rest for - ev - er.
Shall life or death or earth or hell? No— I am His for - ev - er.

Jesus Is All the World to Me

470

WILL L. THOMPSON, 1847-1909

WILL L. THOMPSON, 1847-1909

1. Je - sus is all the world to me, My life, my joy, my all;
2. Je - sus is all the world to me, My Friend in tri - als sore;
3. Je - sus is all the world to me, And true to Him I'll be;
4. Je - sus is all the world to me, I want no bet - ter friend;

He is my strength from day to day, With - out Him I would fall.
I go to Him for bless-ings,and He gives them o'er and o'er.
O how could I this Friend de - ny, When He's so true to me?
I trust Him now, I'll trust Him when Life's fleet-ing days shall end.

When I am sad to Him I go, No oth - er one can
He sends the sun - shine and the rain, He sends the har - vest's
Fol - low - ing Him I know I'm right, He watch-es o'er me
Beau - ti - ful life with such a Friend, Beau - ti - ful life that

cheer me so; When I am sad He makes me glad— He's my Friend.
gold - en grain; Sun-shine and rain, har-vest of grain— He's my Friend.
day and night; Fol - low - ing Him by day and night— He's my Friend.
has no end; E - ter - nal life, e - ter - nal joy— He's my Friend.

471 Love Found a Way

Avis B. Christiansen, 1895-   Harry Dixon Loes, 1892-1965

1. Won-der-ful love that res-cued me, Sunk deep in sin, Guilt-y and
2. Love bro't my Sav-ior here to die On Cal-va-ry, For such a
3. Love o-pened wide the gates of light To heav'n's do-main, Where in e-

vile as I could be— No hope with-in; When ev-'ry ray of light had fled,
sin-ful wretch as I— How can it be? Love bridged the gulf 'twixt me and heav'n,
ter-nal pow'r and might Je-sus shall reign; Love lift-ed me from depths of woe

O glo-rious day! Rais-ing my soul from out the dead, Love found a way.
Taught me to pray; I am re-deemed, set free, for-giv'n— Love found a way.
To end-less day; There was no help in earth be-low— Love found a way.

CHORUS

Love found a way to re-deem my soul, Love found a
a way, to re-deem my soul,

way that could make me whole; Love sent my Lord to the
a way could make me whole; my Lord

Love Found a Way

cross of shame, Love found a way— O praise His ho-ly name!
to the cross of shame,

Heavenly Sunlight 472

HENRY J. ZELLEY, 1859-1942   GEORGE H. COOK, ?-1948

1. Walk-ing in sun-light all of my jour-ney, O-ver the moun-tains,
2. Shad-ows a-round me, shad-ows a-bove me, Nev-er con-ceal my
3. In the bright sun-light, ev-er re-joic-ing, Press-ing my way to

thru the deep vale: Je-sus has said, "I'll nev-er for-sake thee"—
Sav-ior and Guide; He is the Light, in Him is no dark-ness—
man-sions a-bove; Sing-ing His prais-es, glad-ly I'm walk-ing—

D.S. Hal-le-lu-jah! I am re-joic-ing,

Fine CHORUS

Prom-ise di-vine that nev-er can fail.
Ev-er I'm walk-ing close to His side. Heav-en-ly sun-light,
Walk-ing in sun-light, sun-light of love.

Sing-ing His prais-es— Je-sus is mine!

D.S.

heav-en-ly sun-light—Flood-ing my soul with glo-ry di-vine;

473 Heaven Came Down and Glory Filled My Soul

JOHN W. PETERSON, 1921-   JOHN W. PETERSON, 1921-

1. O what a won-der-ful, won-der-ful day— Day I will nev-er for-get;
2. Born of the Spir-it with life from a-bove In-to God's fam'-ly di-vine,
3. Now I've a hope that will sure-ly en-dure Aft-er the pass-ing of time;

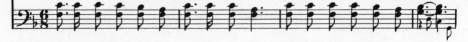

Aft-er I'd wan-dered in dark-ness a-way, Je-sus my Sav-ior I met.
Jus-ti-fied ful-ly thru Cal-va-ry's love, O what a stand-ing is mine!
I have a fu-ture in heav-en for sure, There in those man-sions sub-lime.

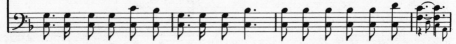

O what a ten-der, com-pas-sion-ate friend—He met the need of my heart;
And the trans-ac-tion so quick-ly was made When as a sin-ner I came,
And it's be-cause of that won-der-ful day When at the cross I be-lieved;

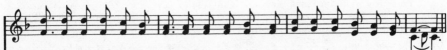

Shad-ows dis-pel-ling, With joy I am tell-ing, He made all the dark-ness de-part!
Took of the of-fer Of grace He did prof-fer— He saved me, O praise His dear name!
Rich-es e-ter-nal And bless-ings su-per-nal From His pre-cious hand I re-ceived.

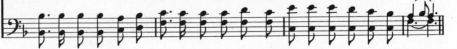

Heaven Came Down and Glory Filled My Soul

CHORUS

Heav-en came down and glo-ry filled my soul,

filled my soul, —

When at the cross the Sav-ior made me whole; — My

made me whole; —

sins were washed a - way.— And my night was turned to day—

Heav-en came down and glo-ry filled my soul! —

filled my soul! —

CODA (*after last chorus only*)

Heav-en came down and glo-ry filled my soul! —

474 Only a Sinner

JAMES M. GRAY, 1851-1935

DANIEL B. TOWNER, 1850-1919

1. Naught have I got-ten but what I re-ceived, Grace hath be-stowed it since
2. Once I was fool-ish, and sin ruled my heart, Caus-ing my foot-steps from
3. Tears un-a-vail-ing, no mer-it had I, Mer-cy had saved me or
4. Suf-fer a sin-ner whose heart o-ver-flows, Lov-ing His Sav-ior, to

I have be-lieved; Boast-ing ex-clud-ed, pride I a-base— I'm
God to de-part; Je-sus hath found me, hap-py my case— I
else I must die; Sin had a-larmed me, fear-ing God's face— But
tell what he knows; Once more to tell it would I em-brace— I'm

CHORUS

on-ly a sin-ner saved by grace!
now am a sin-ner saved by grace!
now I'm a sin-ner saved by grace!
on-ly a sin-ner saved by grace!

On-ly a sin-ner saved by grace!

On-ly a sin-ner saved by grace! This is my sto-ry, To

God be the glo-ry— I'm on-ly a sin-ner saved by grace!

Redeemed

FANNY J. CROSBY, 1820-1915

WILLIAM J. KIRKPATRICK, 1838-1921

1. Re - deemed—how I love to pro - claim it! Re - deemed by the
2. Re - deemed and so hap - py in Je - sus, No lan - guage my
3. I think of my bless - ed Re - deem - er, I think of Him
4. I know I shall see in His beau - ty The King in whose

blood of the Lamb; Re - deemed thru His in - fin - ite mer - cy— His
rap - ture can tell; I know that the light of His pres - ence With
all the day long; I sing, for I can - not be si - lent, His
law I de - light, Who lov - ing - ly guard - eth my foot - steps And

CHORUS

child, and for - ev - er, I am.
me doth con - tin - ual - ly dwell. Re - deemed, ____ re -
love is the theme of my song. re - deemed,
giv - eth me songs in the night.

deemed, ____ Re - deemed by the blood of the Lamb; Re -
re - deemed,

deemed, ____ re - deemed, ____ His child, and for - ev - er, I am.
re - deemed, re - deemed,

476 It Is Glory Just to Walk with Him

AVIS B. CHRISTIANSEN, 1895-   HALDOR LILLENAS, 1885-1959

1. It is glo - ry just to walk with Him whose blood has ran-somed me,
2. It is glo - ry when the shad-ows fall to know that He is near,
3. 'Twill be glo - ry when I walk with Him on heav-en's gold-en shore,

It is rap-ture for my soul each day; It is joy di-vine to feel Him
O what joy to sim-ply trust and pray! It is glo-ry to a-bide in
Nev-er from His side a-gain to stray; 'Twill be glo-ry, won-drous glo-ry

near wher-e'er my path may be— Bless the Lord, it's glo-ry all the way!
Him when skies a-bove are clear—Yes, with Him it's glo-ry all the way!
with the Sav-ior ev-er-more—Ev-er-last-ing glo-ry all the way!

CHORUS

It is glo-ry just to walk with Him, It is glo-ry
with Him,

just to walk with Him; He will guide my steps a-right Thru the
with Him;

It Is Glory Just to Walk with Him

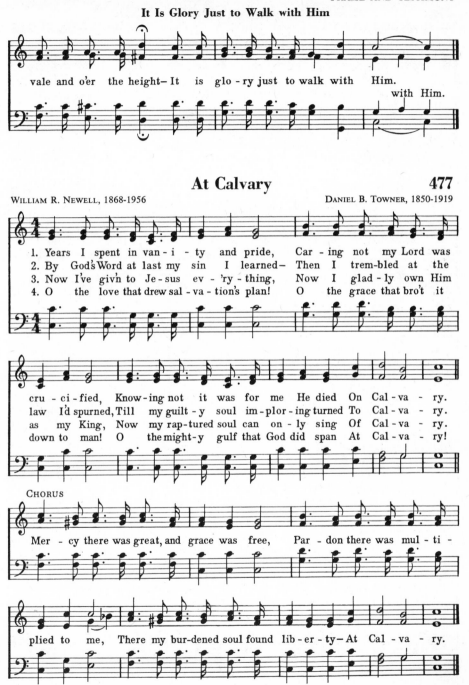

vale and o'er the height— It is glo - ry just to walk with Him.

with Him.

At Calvary

477

WILLIAM R. NEWELL, 1868-1956

DANIEL B. TOWNER, 1850-1919

1. Years I spent in van - i - ty and pride, Car - ing not my Lord was
2. By God's Word at last my sin I learned— Then I trem-bled at the
3. Now I've giv'n to Je - sus ev - 'ry - thing, Now I glad - ly own Him
4. O the love that drew sal - va - tion's plan! O the grace that bro't it

cru - ci - fied, Know-ing not it was for me He died On Cal - va - ry.
law I'd spurned, Till my guilt - y soul im - plor - ing turned To Cal - va - ry.
as my King, Now my rap-tured soul can on - ly sing Of Cal - va - ry.
down to man! O the might-y gulf that God did span At Cal - va - ry!

CHORUS

Mer - cy there was great, and grace was free, Par - don there was mul - ti -

plied to me, There my bur-dened soul found lib - er - ty— At Cal - va - ry.

478 Constantly Abiding

ANNE S. MURPHY, ?-1942   ANNE S. MURPHY, ?-1942

1. There's a peace in my heart that the world nev-er gave, A peace it can
2. All the world seemed to sing of a Sav-ior and King When peace sweet-ly
3. This treas-ure I have in a tem-ple of clay While here on His

not take a-way; Tho the tri-als of life may sur-round like a
came to my heart; Trou-bles all fled a-way and my night turned to
foot-stool I roam; But He's com-ing to take me, some glo-ri-ous

CHORUS

cloud, I've a peace that has come there to stay!
day— Bless-ed Je-sus, how glo-rious Thou art!
day, O-ver there to my heav-en-ly home!

Con - - - stant-ly a-bid - ing— Je-sus is mine;
Con-stant-ly a-bid-ing, con-stant-ly a-bid-ing— Je-sus is mine, yes, Je-sus is mine;

Con - - stant-ly a-bid - ing— Rap-ture di-
Con-stant-ly a-bid-ing, con-stant-ly a-bid-ing— Rap-ture di-vine, O

Constantly Abiding

vine! He nev-er leaves me lone - ly— Whis-pers
rap-ture di-vine! He nev-er leaves me, nev-er leaves me lone-ly—Whis-pers,

O so kind, "I will nev-er leave thee!" Je - sus is mine.
whis-pers O so kind, "I will nev-er, nev-er leave thee!" Je-sus, Je-sus is mine.

Jesus Loves Me 479

ANNA B. WARNER, 1820-1915   WILLIAM B. BRADBURY, 1816-1868

1. Je - sus loves me! this I know, For the Bi - ble tells me so; Lit - tle
2. Je - sus loves me! He who died Heav-en's gate to o - pen wide; He will
3. Je - sus loves me! He will stay Close be-side me all the way; Thou hast

CHORUS

ones to Him be-long, They are weak but He is strong.
wash a - way my sin, Let His lit - tle child come in. Yes, Je-sus loves me!
bled and died for me, I will hence-forth live for Thee.

Yes, Je - sus loves me! Yes, Je-sus loves me! The Bi - ble tells me so.

480 In Tenderness He Sought Me

W. SPENCER WALTON, 1850-1906   ADONIRAM J. GORDON, 1836-1895

1. In ten-der-ness He sought me, Wea-ry and sick with sin, And
2. He washed the bleed-ing sin-wounds And poured in oil and wine; He
3. He point-ed to the nail-prints— For me His blood was shed; A
4. I'm sit-ting in His pres-ence, The sun-shine of His face, While
5. So while the hours are pass-ing, All now is per-fect rest; I'm

on His shoul-ders brought me Back to His fold a - gain; While
whispered to as-sure me, "I've found thee, thou art Mine:" I
mock-ing crown, so thorn-y, Was placed up-on His head: I
with a-dor-ing won-der His bless-ings I re-trace: It
wait-ing for the morn-ing, The bright-est and the best, When

an-gels in His pres-ence sang Un-til the courts of heav-en rang.
nev-er heard a sweet-er voice— It made my ach-ing heart re-joice!
won-dered what He saw in me, To suf-fer such deep ag-o-ny.
seems as if e-ter-nal days Are far too short to sound His praise.
He will call us to His side To be with Him, His spot-less bride.

CHORUS

O the love that sought me! O the blood that bought me! O the grace that

brought me to the fold, Won-drous grace that brought me to the fold!

Sunlight

JUDSON W. VAN DE VENTER, 1855-1939

WINFIELD S. WEEDEN, 1847-1908

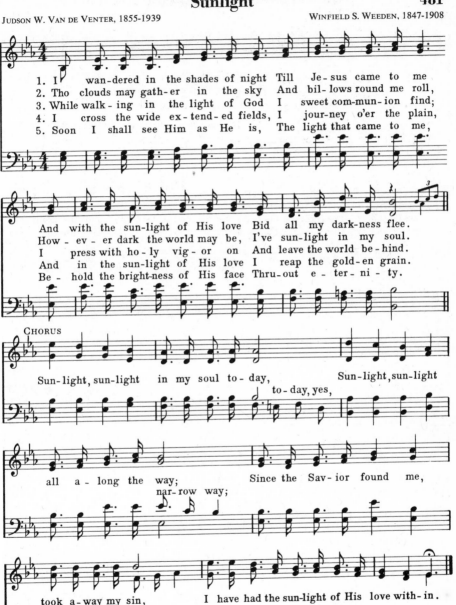

1. I wan-dered in the shades of night Till Je-sus came to me
2. Tho clouds may gath-er in the sky And bil-lows round me roll,
3. While walk-ing in the light of God I sweet com-mun-ion find;
4. I cross the wide ex-tend-ed fields, I jour-ney o'er the plain,
5. Soon I shall see Him as He is, The light that came to me,

And with the sun-light of His love Bid all my dark-ness flee.
How-ev-er dark the world may be, I've sun-light in my soul.
I press with ho-ly vig-or on And leave the world be-hind.
And in the sun-light of His love I reap the gold-en grain.
Be-hold the bright-ness of His face Thru-out e-ter-ni-ty.

CHORUS

Sun-light, sun-light in my soul to-day,   Sun-light, sun-light
to-day, yes,

all a-long the way;   Since the Sav-ior found me,
nar-row way;

took a-way my sin,   I have had the sun-light of His love with-in.
load of sin,

482 Walking in the Light

John W. Peterson, 1921-   John W. Peterson, 1921-

1. No more I'll wan-der in the dread-ful night of sin and shame— I'm
2. I'm un-a-fraid as on I go, for Je-sus walks with me— I'm
3. The fel-low-ship is won-der-ful, it's glo-ry all the way— I'm

walk-ing in the light, I'm walk-ing in the light; I'm on the road to
walk-ing in the light, I'm walk-ing in the light; He led me from my
walk-ing in the light, I'm walk-ing in the light; The pre-cious blood has

heav-en— O the truth I must pro-claim— I'm walk-ing in the Sav-ior's
dark-ness, from my sins He set me free— I'm walk-ing in the Sav-ior's
cleansed me and keeps cleansing ev-'ry day— I'm walk-ing in the Sav-ior's

CHORUS

light. Walk-ing in the light, walk-ing in the light,
I am O I am

Walk-ing on to glo-ry where there is no night; I'm sing-ing "hal-le-

Walking in the Light

lu-jah!" as I trav-el on my way, Walk-ing in the Sav-ior's light.

bless-ed light.

O How I Love Jesus

483

American melody
Arr. by John W. Peterson, 1921-

FREDERICK WHITFIELD, 1829-1904

1. There is a name I love to hear, I love to sing its worth;
2. It tells me of a Sav-ior's love, Who died to set me free;
3. It tells me what my Fa-ther hath In store for ev-'ry day,
4. It tells of One whose lov-ing heart Can feel my deep-est woe,

It sounds like mu-sic in mine ear, The sweet-est name on earth.
It tells me of His pre-cious blood, The sin-ner's per-fect plea.
And, tho I tread a dark-some path, Yields sun-shine all the way.
Who in each sor-row bears a part That none can bear be-low.

CHORUS

O how I love Je - sus, O how I love Je - sus,

O how I love Je - sus— Be - cause He first loved me!

484 Still Sweeter Every Day

W. C. MARTIN, 19th century

C. AUSTIN MILES, 1868-1946

1. To Jesus ev-'ry day I find my heart is clos-er drawn,
2. His glo-ry broke up-on me when I saw Him from a-far,
3. My heart is some-times heav-y but He comes with sweet re-lief,

He's fair-er than the glo-ry of the gold and pur-ple dawn;
He's fair-er than the lil-y, bright-er than the morn-ing star;
He folds me to His bos-om when I droop with blight-ing grief;

He's all my fan-cy pic-tures in its fair-est dreams, and more —
He fills and sat-is-fies my long-ing spir-it o'er and o'er —
I love the Christ who all my bur-dens in His bod-y bore —

Each day He grows still sweet-er than He was the day be-fore.
Each day He grows still sweet-er than He was the day be-fore.
Each day He grows still sweet-er than He was the day be-fore.

CHORUS

The half can-not be fan-cied this
The half can-not be fan-cied on this side the gold-en shore, The

Still Sweeter Every Day

side . . . . the gold-en shore; O there
half can-not be fan-cied on this side the gold-en shore; O there He'll be still

He'll be still sweet - er than He ev-er was be-fore.
sweet-er than He ev-er was be-fore, than He ev-er was be-fore.

Revive Us Again

485

WILLIAM P. MACKAY, 1839-1885

JOHN J. HUSBAND, 1760-1825

1. We praise Thee, O God, for the Son of Thy love, For Je - sus who
2. We praise Thee, O God, for Thy Spir-it of light, Who has shown us our
3. All glo - ry and praise to the Lamb that was slain, Who has borne all our
4. Re - vive us a - gain—fill each heart with Thy love; May each soul be re -

CHORUS

died and is now gone a - bove.
Sav - ior and scat-tered our night. Hal-le - lu-jah, Thine the glo-ry! Hal-le -
sins and has cleansed ev-'ry stain.
kin - dled with fire from a - bove.

lu-jah, a - men! Hal-le - lu-jah, Thine the glo-ry! Re-vive us a - gain.

486 Sweeter as the Years Go By

LELIA N. MORRIS, 1862-1929   LELIA N. MORRIS, 1862-1929

1. Of Je - sus' love that sought me When I was lost in sin —
2. He trod in old Ju - de - a Life's path - way long a - go —
3. 'Twas won - drous love which led Him For us to suf - fer loss —

Of won - drous grace that brought me Back to His fold a - gain —
The peo - ple thronged a - bout Him His sav - ing grace to know;
To bear with - out a mur - mur The an - guish of the cross;

Of heights and depths of mer - cy Far deep - er than the sea
He healed the bro - ken - heart - ed And caused the blind to see;
With saints re - deemed in glo - ry Let us our voic - es raise,

And high - er than the heav - ens, My theme shall ev - er be.
And still His great heart yearn - eth In love for e - ven me.
Till heav'n and earth re - ech - o With our Re - deem - er's praise.

CHORUS

Sweet - er as the years go by, Sweet - er as the years go by;
Sweet - er as the years go by, 'Tis sweet - er as the years go by;

Sweeter as the Years Go By

Rich-er, full-er, deep-er, Je-sus' love is sweet-er, Sweet-er as the years go by.

Now I Belong to Jesus

487

NORMAN J. CLAYTON, 1903-

NORMAN J. CLAYTON, 1903-

1. Je - sus my Lord will love me for - ev - er, From Him no pow'r of
2. Once I was lost in sin's deg - ra - da - tion, Je - sus came down to
3. Joy floods my soul, for Je - sus has saved me, Freed me from sin that

e - vil can sev - er; He gave His life to ran - som my soul —
bring me sal - va - tion, Lift - ed me up from sor - row and shame —
long had en - slaved me; His pre-cious blood He gave to re - deem —

CHORUS

Now I be-long to Him! Now I be-long to Je - sus, Je - sus be-

longs to me — Not for the years of time a-lone, But for e - ter - ni - ty.

488 My Redeemer

PHILIP P. BLISS, 1838-1876

JAMES McGRANAHAN, 1840-1907

1. I will sing of my Re-deem-er And His won - drous love to me;
2. I will tell the won-drous sto - ry, How, my lost es - tate to save,
3. I will praise my dear Re-deem-er, His tri - um - phant pow'r I'll tell,
4. I will sing of my Re-deem-er And His heav'n - ly love to me;

On the cru - el cross He suf-fered, From the curse to set me free.
In His bound-less love and mer - cy, He the ran - som free-ly gave.
How the vic - to - ry He giv-eth O - ver sin and death and hell.
He from death to life hath bro't me, Son of God with Him to be.

CHORUS

Sing, O sing of my Re-deem - er,
of my Re-deem-er, Sing, O sing of my Re-deem-er,

With His blood He pur-chased me;
He pur-chased me, With His blood He pur-chased me;

On the cross He sealed my par - don,
He sealed my par-don, On the cross He sealed my par-don,

Alternate tune: HYFRYDOL — 49 (84)

My Redeemer

Paid the debt and made me free.

and made me free,

and made me free.

Glory to His Name

489

ELISHA A. HOFFMAN, 1839-1929

JOHN H. STOCKTON, 1813-1877

1. Down at the cross where my Sav-ior died, Down where for cleans-ing from
2. I am so won-drous-ly saved from sin, Je-sus so sweet-ly a-
3. O pre-cious foun-tain that saves from sin, I am so glad I have
4. Come to this foun-tain so rich and sweet, Cast thy poor soul at the

sin I cried, There to my heart was the blood ap-plied—
bides with-in; There at the cross where He took me in-
en-tered in; There Je-sus saves me and keeps me clean-
Sav-ior's feet; Plunge in to-day, and be made com-plete—

REFRAIN

Glo-ry to His name. Glo-ry to His name, Glo-ry to His name;

There to my heart was the blood ap-plied— Glo-ry to His name.

490

When Love Shines In

Carrie E. Breck, 1855-1934

William J. Kirkpatrick, 1838-1921

1. Je - sus comes with pow'r to glad-den, When love shines in, Ev - 'ry
2. How the world will grow with beau-ty, When love shines in, And the
3. Dark-est sor - row will grow brighter, When love shines in, And the
4. We may have un - fad-ing splen-dor, When love shines in, And a

life that woe can sad-den, When love shines in. Love will teach us
heart re - joice in du - ty, When love shines in. Tri - als may be
heav - iest bur - den light-er, When love shines in. 'Tis the glo - ry
friend-ship true and ten - der, When love shines in. When earth's vic- t'ries

how to pray, Love will drive the gloom a - way, Turn our dark-ness in-to day—
sanc-ti - fied, And the soul in peace a-bide, Life will all be glo-ri-fied—
that will throw Light to show us where to go; O the heart shall bless-ing know—
shall be won, And our life in heav'n be-gun, There will be no need of sun—

CHORUS

When love shines in. When love shines in, When love shines
When love, when love shines in, When love shines

in, How the heart is tuned to sing-ing, When love shines

When Love Shines In

in,   When love shines in,   When love   shines   in,
When love, when love shines in,   When love shines in,

Joy and peace to   oth–ers bring-ing— When love   shines   in!

Heavenly Joy Is Ringing   491

ALFREDO COLOM M., 1904-
Arr. by Harold DeCou, 1932-

ROBERT C. SAVAGE, 1914-

1. Heav'n-ly joy is ring-ing, And our hearts are sing-ing, For His blood hath
2. Hail, Thou bless-ed Sav-ior! We thru Thee find fa-vor; Thou for us art
3. Now with sins for-giv-en We can en-ter heav-en; There we'll all a-

CHORUS

bought us — When con-demned, He sought us. { Men of ev-'ry na-tion Sing the
plead-ing, Ev-er in-ter-ced-ing. { O the joy be-fore us, There in
dore Thee, Sov-reign King of glo-ry.

great sal-va-tion Of our bless-ed Je-sus, Who in mer-cy freed us.
heav'n-ly cho-rus; Prais-es we'll be blend-ing For all time un-end-ing!

492

Jesus Loves Even Me

PHILIP P. BLISS, 1838-1876

PHILIP P. BLISS, 1838-1876

1. I am so glad that our Fa-ther in heav'n Tells of His love in the Book He has giv'n; Won-der-ful things in the Bi-ble I see— This is the dear-est, that Je-sus loves me.

2. Tho I for-get Him and wan-der a-way, Still He doth love me wher-ev-er I stray; Back to His dear lov-ing arms would I flee When I re-mem-ber that Je-sus loves me.

3. O if there's on-ly one song I can sing When in His beau-ty I see the great King, This shall my song in e-ter-ni-ty be: "O what a won-der that Je-sus loves me!"

CHORUS

I am so glad that Je-sus loves me, Je-sus loves me, Je-sus loves me;

I am so glad that Je-sus loves me, Je-sus loves e-ven me.

Since the Savior Found Me

EDGAR J. HASKINS, 1906-

EDGAR J. HASKINS, 1906-

1. Since the Sav-ior found me, par-doned all my sin, I have had the
2. Since the Sav-ior found me all to Him I owe, For His pre-cious
3. Since the Sav-ior found me I have per-fect rest, Liv-ing in the

joy and liv-ing hope with-in; Gone is all the shame and sor-row
blood has washed me white as snow; Now no con-dem-na-tion, hap-py
realms of joy and hap-pi-ness; Lean-ing on my Sav-ior, look-ing

Fine

of the past— They're un-der-neath the pre-cious blood of Christ at last.
as can be— I'm glad that Je-sus jus-ti-fies and sets me free.
for that day When He shall come to catch His wait-ing bride a-way.

D. S. — saves and keeps and sanc-ti-fies me by His pow'r.

CHORUS

Saved, saved, saved— I'm hap-py on the way, Saved, saved, saved— I

D.S.

love Him more each day; Saved, saved, saved—I know He's mine each hour: He

494 It's Just Like His Great Love

EDNA R. WORRELL, 19th century

CLARENCE B. STROUSE, 19th century
Arr. by Harold DeCou, 1932-

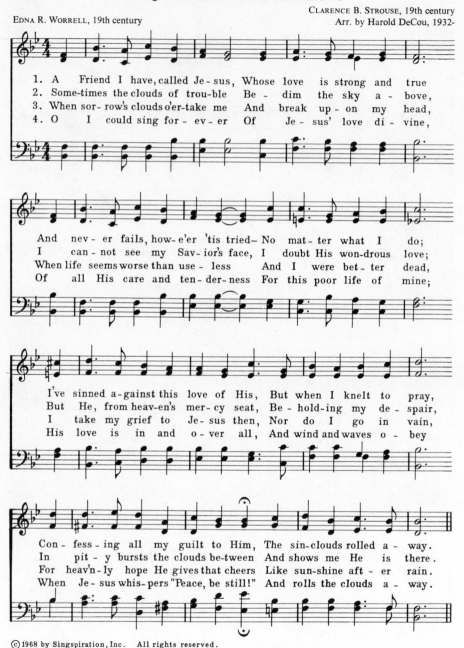

1. A Friend I have, called Je-sus, Whose love is strong and true
2. Some-times the clouds of trou-ble Be - dim the sky a - bove,
3. When sor - row's clouds o'er-take me And break up - on my head,
4. O I could sing for - ev - er Of Je - sus' love di - vine,

And nev - er fails, how-e'er 'tis tried— No mat - ter what I do;
I can - not see my Sav-ior's face, I doubt His won-drous love;
When life seems worse than use - less And I were bet - ter dead,
Of all His care and ten - der-ness For this poor life of mine;

I've sinned a-gainst this love of His, But when I knelt to pray,
But He, from heav-en's mer - cy seat, Be - hold-ing my de - spair,
I take my grief to Je - sus then, Nor do I go in vain,
His love is in and o - ver all, And wind and waves o - bey

Con - fess - ing all my guilt to Him, The sin-clouds rolled a - way.
In pit - y bursts the clouds be-tween And shows me He is there.
For heav'n-ly hope He gives that cheers Like sun-shine aft - er rain.
When Je - sus whis-pers "Peace, be still!" And rolls the clouds a - way.

It's Just Like His Great Love

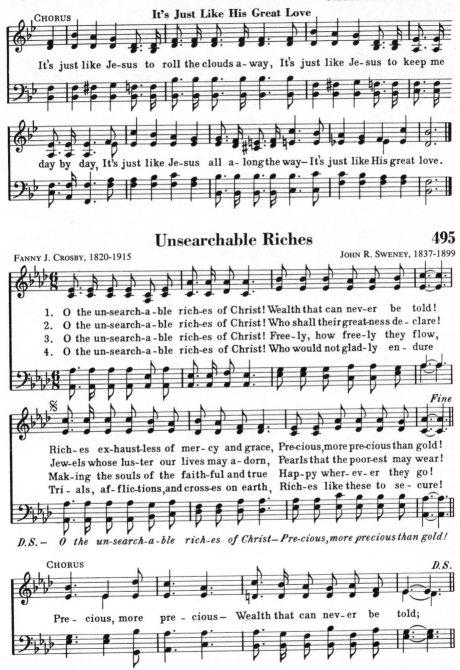

CHORUS

It's just like Je-sus to roll the clouds a-way, It's just like Je-sus to keep me day by day, It's just like Je-sus all a-long the way—It's just like His great love.

Unsearchable Riches 495

FANNY J. CROSBY, 1820-1915

JOHN R. SWENEY, 1837-1899

1. O the un-search-a-ble rich-es of Christ! Wealth that can nev-er be told!
2. O the un-search-a-ble rich-es of Christ! Who shall their great-ness de-clare!
3. O the un-search-a-ble rich-es of Christ! Free-ly, how free-ly they flow,
4. O the un-search-a-ble rich-es of Christ! Who would not glad-ly en-dure

Fine

Rich-es ex-haust-less of mer-cy and grace, Pre-cious, more pre-cious than gold!
Jew-els whose lus-ter our lives may a-dorn, Pearls that the poor-est may wear!
Mak-ing the souls of the faith-ful and true Hap-py wher-ev-er they go!
Tri-als, af-flic-tions, and cross-es on earth, Rich-es like these to se-cure!

D.S.— O the un-search-a-ble rich-es of Christ—Pre-cious, more precious than gold!

CHORUS

D.S.

Pre-cious, more pre-cious— Wealth that can nev-er be told;

Victory in Jesus

Eugene M. Bartlett, 1885-1941

Eugene M. Bartlett, 1885-1941

1. I heard an old, old sto-ry, how a Sav-ior came from glo-ry,
2. I heard a-bout His heal-ing, of His cleans-ing pow'r re-veal-ing,
3. I heard a-bout a man-sion He has built for me in glo-ry,

How He gave His life on Cal-va-ry to save a wretch like me:
How He made the lame to walk a-gain and caused the blind to see;
And I heard a-bout the streets of gold be-yond the crys-tal sea;

I heard a-bout His groan-ing, of His pre-cious blood's a-ton-ing,
And then I cried,"Dear Je-sus, come and heal my bro-ken spir-it,"
A-bout the an-gels sing-ing and the old re-demp-tion sto-ry,

Then I re-pent-ed of my sins and won the vic-to-ry.
And some-how Je-sus came and brought to me the vic-to-ry.
And some sweet day I'll sing up there the song of vic-to-ry.

Chorus

O vic-to-ry in Je-sus, my Sav-ior, for-ev-er! He sought me and

Victory in Jesus

bought me with His re-deem-ing blood; He loved me ere I knew Him, and all my

love is due Him—He plunged me to vic-to-ry be-neath the cleans-ing flood.

When I Can Read My Title Clear 497

PISGAH

Isaac Watts, 1674-1748

Attr. to Joseph C. Lowry, 19th century
Arr. by Harold DeCou, 1932-

1. When I can read my ti-tle clear To man-sions in the skies,
2. Should earth a-gainst my soul en-gage, And fi-ery darts be hurled,
3. Let cares, like a wild de-luge come, And storms of sor-row fall!
4. There shall I bathe my wea-ry soul In seas of heav'n-ly rest,

D.S.— I'll bid fare-well to ev-'ry fear And wipe my weep-ing eyes.
D.S.— Then I can smile at Sa-tan's rage And face a frown-ing world.
D.S.— May I but safe-ly reach my home, My God, my heav'n, my all.
D.S.— And not a wave of trou-ble roll A-cross my peace-ful breast.

Fine

And wipe my weep-ing eyes, And wipe my weep-ing eyes,
And face a frown-ing world, And face a frown-ing world,
My God, my heav'n, my all, My God, my heav'n, my all,
A-cross my peace-ful breast, A-cross my peace-ful breast,

D.S.

Alternate tune: CLEANSING FOUNTAIN—222

498 When We All Get to Heaven

ELIZA E. HEWITT, 1851-1920   EMILY D. WILSON, 1865-1942

1. Sing the won-drous love of Je-sus, Sing His mer-cy and His grace;
2. While we walk the pil - grim path-way Clouds will o - ver- spread the sky;
3. Let us then be true and faith-ful, Trust-ing, serv-ing ev - 'ry day;
4. On-ward to the prize be-fore us! Soon His beau-ty we'll be-hold;

In the man-sions bright and bless-ed He'll pre-pare for us a place.
But when trav-'ling days are o - ver Not a shad-ow, not a sigh.
Just one glimpse of Him in glo - ry Will the toils of life re- pay.
Soon the pearl-y gates will o - pen— We shall tread the streets of gold.

CHORUS

When we all get to heav - en, What a day of re-
When we all   What a

joic-ing that will be! When we all see
day of re-joic-ing that will be! When we all

Je - sus, We'll sing and shout the vic-to - ry.
shout, and shout the vic-to - ry.

I've a Home Beyond the River

JOHN W. PETERSON, 1921-

JOHN W. PETERSON, 1921-

1. O the bless - ed con-tem-pla-tion, When with trou - ble here I sigh:
2. Just a lit - tle more to la - bor, Tell the sto - ry, watch and pray;
3. O how sweet 'twill be to meet them—All the ran - somed host a - bove;
4. Tho the world is filled with sor-row, And the tear - drops oft-en fall,
5. Tho the hills are rough and ston-y, And the val - leys dark and cold,

I've a home be-yond the riv - er, That I'll en - ter by and by.
Just a few more earth-ly sor-rows, Then to heav'n we'll fly a - way.
Sweet-er still to see the Sav-ior, Praise Him for re - deem-ing love.
There will be but joy and glad-ness, Safe in - side the jas - per wall.
I must walk the path be - fore me— It will some day turn to gold.

CHORUS

I've a home be-yond the riv - er, I've a
I've a home be-yond the riv - er,

man - - - sion bright and fair; I've a home
I've a man-sion bright and fair; (bright and fair;) home, a hap - py

be - yond the riv - er— I will dwell with Je - sus there.
home be - yond the riv - er—

500 When the Roll Is Called Up Yonder

JAMES M. BLACK, 1856-1938   JAMES M. BLACK, 1856-1938

1. When the trum-pet of the Lord shall sound and time shall be no more, And the
2. On that bright and cloudless morning when the dead in Christ shall rise And the
3. Let us la - bor for the Mas-ter from the dawn till set-ting sun, Let us

morn-ing breaks e - ter-nal, bright and fair— When the saved of earth shall gath-er
glo - ry of His res - ur - rec-tion share— When His cho-sen ones shall gath-er
talk of all His won-drous love and care; Then when all of life is o - ver

o - ver on the oth - er shore, And the roll is called up yon-der—
to their home be-yond the skies, And the roll is called up yon-der—
and our work on earth is done, And the roll is called up yon-der—

CHORUS

I'll be there! When the roll is called up yon - der, When the
I'll be there!   When the roll is called up yon-der I'll be there,
I'll be there!

roll is called up yon - der, When the roll
When the roll is called up yon-der I'll be there,   When the roll

When the Roll Is Called Up Yonder

is called up yon - der—When the roll is called up yon-der I'll be there!

After

501

N. B. VANDALL, 1896-

N. B. VANDALL, 1896-

1. Aft-er the toil and the heat of the day, Aft-er my trou-bles are past,
2. Aft-er the heart-aches and sighing shall cease, Aft-er the cold win-ter's blast,
3. Aft-er the shad-ows of evening shall fall, Aft-er my an-chor is cast,

Aft-er the sor-rows are tak-en a-way, I shall see Je-sus at last.
Aft-er the con-flict comes glo-ri-ous peace— I shall see Je-sus at last.
Aft-er I list to my Sav-ior's last call, I shall see Je-sus at last.

REFRAIN

He will be wait-ing for me— Je-sus, so kind and true; On His
for me— so kind and true;

beau-ti-ful throne, He will wel-come me home— Aft-er the day is through.

502
My Savior First of All

FANNY J. CROSBY, 1820-1915

JOHN R. SWENEY, 1837-1899

1. When my life-work is end-ed and I cross the swell-ing tide,
2. O the soul-thrill-ing rap-ture when I view His bless-ed face
3. O the dear ones in glo-ry, how they beck-on me to come,
4. Thru the gates to the cit-y, in a robe of spot-less white,

When the bright and glo-rious morn-ing I shall see, I shall know my Re-
And the lus-ter of His kind-ly beam-ing eye; How my full heart will
And our part-ing at the riv-er I re-call; To the sweet vales of
He will lead me where no tears will ev-er fall; In the glad song of

deem-er when I reach the oth-er side, And His smile will be the
praise Him for the mer-cy, love and grace That pre-pare for me a
E-den they will sing my wel-come home— But I long to meet my
a-ges I shall min-gle with de-light— But I long to meet my

CHORUS

first to wel-come me.
man-sion in the sky.   I shall know   Him, I shall
Sav-ior first of all.   I shall know Him,
Sav-ior first of all.

know Him, And re-deemed by His side I shall stand, I shall

My Savior First of All

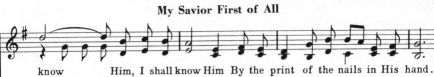

know   Him, I shall know Him By the print of the nails in His hand.
I shall know Him,

My Home, Sweet Home   503

N. B. VANDALL, 1896-   N. B. VANDALL, 1896-

1. Walk - ing a - long life's road one day, I heard a voice so sweet-ly say, "A
2. Loved ones up-on that shore I'll meet, Casting their crowns at Je - sus' feet; I'll
3. Life's day is short— I soon shall go To be with Him who loved me so; I

place up in heav'n I am build-ing thee, A beau-ti-ful, beau-ti-ful home."
wor-ship and praise Him for - ev - er-more In my beau-ti-ful, beau-ti-ful home.
see in the dis-tance that shin-ing shore, My beau-ti-ful, beau-ti-ful home.

CHORUS

Home, sweet home, home, sweet home— Where I'll nev - er roam!

I see the light of that cit-y so bright— My home, sweet home.

504

Sweet By and By

Sanford F. Bennett, 1836-1898

Joseph P. Webster, 1819-1875

1. There's a land that is fair-er than day, And by faith we can
2. We shall sing on that beau-ti-ful shore The me-lo-di-ous
3. To our boun-ti-ful Fa-ther a-bove We will of-fer our

see it a-far, For the Fa-ther waits o-ver the way To pre-
songs of the blest; And our spir-its shall sor-row no more— Not a
trib-ute of praise, For the glo-ri-ous gift of His love And the

CHORUS

pare us a dwell-ing-place there.
sigh for the bless-ing of rest.
bless-ings that hal-low our days.

In the sweet by and
In the sweet

by, We shall meet on that beau-ti-ful shore; In the
by and by, by and by,

sweet by and by, We shall meet on that beau-ti-ful shore.
In the sweet by and by,

O That Will Be Glory

Charles H. Gabriel, 1856-1932

Charles H. Gabriel, 1856-1932

1. When all my la-bors and tri-als are o'er And I am safe on that
2. When, by the gift of His in-fi-nite grace, I am ac-cord-ed in
3. Friends will be there I have loved long a-go, Joy like a riv-er a-

beau-ti-ful shore, Just to be near the dear Lord I a-dore
heav-en a place, Just to be there and to look on His face
round me will flow; Yet, just a smile from my Sav-ior, I know,

Chorus

Will thru the a-ges be glo-ry for me.

O that will be

O that will

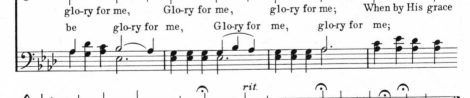

glo-ry for me, Glo-ry for me, glo-ry for me; When by His grace

be glo-ry for me, Glo-ry for me, glo-ry for me;

rit.

I shall look on His face, That will be glo-ry, be glo-ry for me!

506
Meet Me There

HENRIETTA E. BLAIR, 19th century

WILLIAM J. KIRKPATRICK, 1838-1921

1. On the hap-py, gold-en shore Where the faith-ful part no more, When the
2. Here our fond-est hopes are vain, Dear-est links are rent in twain, But in
3. Where the harps of an-gels ring And the blest for - ev - er sing, In the

storms of life are o'er, Meet me there; Where the night dis-solves a - way
heav'n no throb of pain— Meet me there; By the riv - er spark-ling bright
pal - ace of the King, Meet me there; Where in sweet com-mun-ion blend

In - to pure and per-fect day, I am go - ing home to stay— Meet me
In the cit - y of de-light, Where our faith is lost in sight, Meet me
Heart with heart and friend with friend, In a world that ne'er shall end, Meet me

CHORUS

there. Meet me there, Meet me there, Where the tree of
there. Meet me there, Meet me there,
there.

life is bloom-ing, Meet me there; When the storms of life are o'er,
Meet me there;

Meet Me There

On the hap-py, gold-en shore, Where the faith-ful part no more, Meet me there.

When We All Get Home 507

JOHN W. PETERSON, 1921-

JOHN W. PETERSON, 1921-

1. Tho like pil-grims here we wan-der, It is won-der-ful to pon-der All the bless-ings wait-ing yon-der— When we all get home.
2. There will be no pain nor dy-ing, There will be no grief nor cry-ing, Not a sound of an-xious sigh-ing— When we all get home.
3. On-ly heav-en's bliss be-fore us, On-ly glo-ry shin-ing o'er us, We will be a hap-py cho-rus— When we all get home.

CHORUS

When we all get home,
get home,
Nev-er more to roam;
to roam;

What a day of glad re-joic-ing— When we all get home.
get home.

508

For All the Saints

SINE NOMINE

William W. How, 1823-1897

Ralph Vaughan Williams, 1872-1958

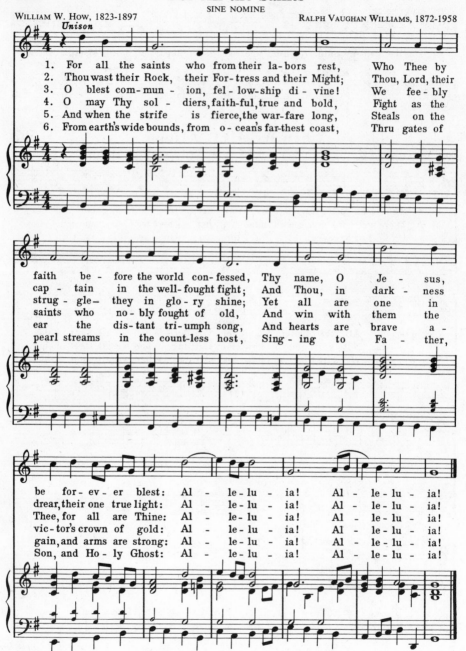

1. For all the saints who from their la-bors rest, Who Thee by faith be-fore the world con-fessed, Thy name, O Je - sus, be for-ev-er blest: Al - le-lu - ia! Al - le-lu - ia!

2. Thou wast their Rock, their For-tress and their Might; Thou, Lord, their cap - tain in the well-fought fight; And Thou, in dark - ness drear, their one true light: Al - le-lu - ia! Al - le-lu - ia!

3. O blest com-mun - ion, fel - low-ship di - vine! We fee - bly strug - gle— they in glo - ry shine; Yet all are one in Thee, for all are Thine: Al - le-lu - ia! Al - le-lu - ia!

4. O may Thy sol - diers, faith-ful, true and bold, Fight as the saints who no - bly fought of old, And win with them the vic - tor's crown of gold: Al - le-lu - ia! Al - le-lu - ia!

5. And when the strife is fierce, the war-fare long, Steals on the ear the dis - tant tri-umph song, And hearts are brave a - gain, and arms are strong: Al - le-lu - ia! Al - le-lu - ia!

6. From earth's wide bounds, from o - cean's far-thest coast, Thru gates of pearl streams in the count-less host, Sing - ing to Fa - ther, Son, and Ho - ly Ghost: Al - le-lu - ia! Al - le-lu - ia!

Tune from "The English Hymnal." Used by permission Oxford University Press, London.

The Sands of Time Are Sinking

RUTHERFORD

ANNE ROSS COUSIN, 1824-1906

CHRÉTIEN URHAN, 1790-1845
Arr. by Edward F. Rimbault, 1816-1876

1. The sands of time are sink- ing, The dawn of heav - en breaks;
2. O Christ, He is the foun- tain, The deep, sweet well of love!
3. O I am my Be - lov- ed's, And my Be - lov - ed's mine!
4. The Bride eyes not her gar - ment But her dear Bride-groom's face;

The sum-mer morn I've sighed for— The fair, sweet morn a - wakes:
The streams on earth I've tast - ed More deep I'll drink a - bove:
He brings a poor vile sin - ner In - to His "house of wine."
I will not gaze at glo - ry But on my King of grace.

Dark, dark hath been the mid - night, But day-spring is at hand,
There to an o - cean ful - ness His mer - cy doth ex - pand,
I stand up - on His mer - it— I know no oth - er stand,
Not at the crown He giv - eth But on His pierc - ed hand:

And glo - ry, glo - ry dwell - eth In Im - man - uel's land.
And glo - ry, glo - ry dwell - eth In Im - man - uel's land.
Not e'en where glo - ry dwell - eth In Im - man - uel's land.
The Lamb is all the glo - ry Of Im - man - uel's land.

510   Shall We Gather at the River?

ROBERT LOWRY, 1826-1899   ROBERT LOWRY, 1826-1899

1. Shall we gath-er at the riv - er, Where bright an-gel feet have trod,
2. On the bos-om of the riv - er, Where the Sav-ior-King we own,
3. Ere we reach the shin-ing riv - er, Lay we ev - 'ry bur-den down;
4. Soon we'll reach the shin-ing riv - er, Soon our pil-grim-age will cease;

With its crys-tal tide for - ev - er Flow-ing by the throne of God?
We shall meet and sor-row nev - er 'Neath the glo-ry of the throne.
Grace our spir-its will de - liv - er And pro-vide a robe and crown.
Soon our hap-py hearts will quiv-er With the mel - o - dy of peace.

CHORUS

Yes, we'll gath-er at the riv - er, The beau-ti-ful, the beau-ti - ful riv - er,

Gath-er with the saints at the riv - er That flows by the throne of God.

Face to Face

Carrie E. Breck, 1855-1934

Grant Colfax Tullar, 1869-1950

1. Face to face with Christ, my Sav-ior, Face to face—what will it be?
2. On-ly faint-ly now I see Him, With the dark-ling veil be-tween;
3. What re-joic-ing in His pres-ence, When are ban-ished grief and pain,
4. Face to face—O bliss-ful mo-ment! Face to face—to see and know;

When with rap-ture I be-hold Him, Je-sus Christ who died for me!
But a bless-ed day is com-ing, When His glo-ry shall be seen.
When the crook-ed ways are straightened And the dark things shall be plain.
Face to face with my Re-deem-er, Je-sus Christ who loves me so!

CHORUS

Face to face I shall be-hold Him, Far be-yond the star-ry sky;

Face to face, in all His glo-ry, I shall see Him by and by!

Saved by Grace

GEORGE C. STEBBINS, 1846-1945
Arr. by Norman Johnson, 1928-

FANNY J. CROSBY, 1820-1915

1. Some day the sil - ver cord will break, And I no more as now shall sing;
2. Some day my earth - ly house will fall— I can-not tell how soon 'twill be;
3. Some day, when fades the gold-en sun Be-neath the ros - y - tint - ed west,
4. Some day—till then I'll watch and wait, My lamp all trimmed and burn-ing bright,

But O the joy when I shall wake With-in the pal-ace of the King!
But this I know— my All in All Has now a place in heav'n for me.
My bless-ed Lord will say, "Well done!" And I shall en-ter in - to rest.
That when my Sav - ior opes the gate, My soul to Him may take its flight.

CHORUS

And I shall see Him face to face, And tell the sto - ry— Saved by grace;

And I shall see Him face to face, And tell the sto - ry— Saved by grace.

He the Pearly Gates Will Open

FREDRICK A. BLOM, 1867-1927
Trans. by Nathaniel Carlson, 1879-1957

ELSIE AHLWÉN, 1905-
Arr. by Norman Johnson, 1928-

1. Love di-vine, so great and won-drous, Deep and might-y, pure, sub-lime!
2. Like a dove when hunt-ed, fright-ened, As a wound-ed fawn was I;
3. Love di-vine, so great and won-drous! All my sins He then for-gave!
4. In life's e-ven-tide, at twi-light, At His door I'll knock and wait;

Com-ing from the heart of Je-sus— Just the same thru tests of time.
Bro-ken-heart-ed, yet He healed me— He will heed the sin-ner's cry.
I will sing His praise for-ev-er, For His blood, His pow'r to save.
By the pre-cious love of Je-sus I shall en-ter heav-en's gate.

CHORUS

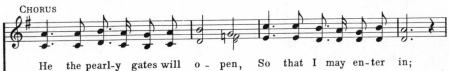

He the pearl-y gates will o-pen, So that I may en-ter in;

For He pur-chased my re-demp-tion And for-gave me all my sin.

514 We're Marching to Zion

Isaac Watts, 1674-1748
Chorus — Robert Lowry, 1826-1899

Robert Lowry, 1826-1899

1. Come, we that love the Lord, And let our joys be known; Join
2. Let those re - fuse to sing Who nev - er knew our God; But
3. The hill of Zi - on yields A thou-sand sa - cred sweets Be -
4. Then let our songs a - bound And ev - 'ry tear be dry; We're

in a song with sweet ac - cord, Join in a song with sweet ac - cord,
chil-dren of the heav'n-ly King, But chil-dren of the heav'n-ly King
fore we reach the heav'n-ly fields, Be - fore we reach the heav'n-ly fields
march-ing thru Im- man-uel's ground, We're march-ing thru Im- man-uel's ground

And thus sur - round the throne, And thus sur-round the throne.
May speak their joys a - broad, May speak their joys a - broad.
Or walk the gold- en streets, Or walk the gold - en streets.
To fair - er worlds on high, To fair - er worlds on high.

1. And thus sur-round the throne, And thus sur - round the throne.

CHORUS

We're march - ing to Zi - on, Beau-ti - ful, beau-ti-ful Zi - on; We're
We're march-ing on to Zi - on,

march-ing up-ward to Zi - on, The beau-ti-ful cit-y of God.
Zi - on, Zi - on,

Beulah Land

EDGAR PAGE STITES, 1836-1921

JOHN R. SWENEY, 1837-1899

1. I've reached the land of corn and wine, And all its rich-es free-ly mine;
2. My Sav-ior comes and walks with me, And sweet com-mun-ion here have we;
3. A sweet per-fume up-on the breeze Is borne from ev-er-ver-nal trees
4. The zeph-yrs seem to float to me Sweet sounds of heav-en's mel-o-dy,

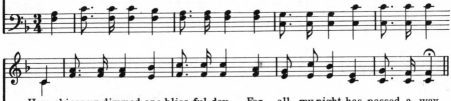

Here shines un-dimmed one bliss-ful day, For all my night has passed a-way.
He gen-tly leads me by His hand, For this is heav-en's bor-der-land.
And flow'rs that nev-er-fad-ing grow, Where streams of life for-ev-er flow.
As an-gels with the white-robed throng Join in the sweet Re-demp-tion song.

CHORUS

O Beu-lah Land, sweet Beu-lah Land! As on thy high-est mount I stand,

I look a-way a-cross the sea, Where man-sions are pre-pared for me,

And view the shin-ing glo-ry-shore— My heav'n, my home for-ev-er-more!

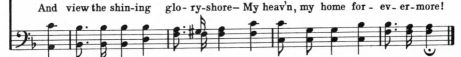

516 I'm Going Home
MILLER

WILLIAM HUNTER, 1811-1877

WILLIAM MILLER, 19th century
Arr. by William McDonald, 1820-1901

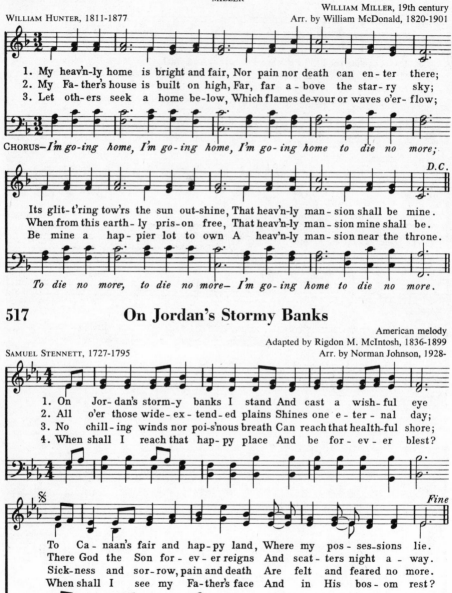

1. My heav'n-ly home is bright and fair, Nor pain nor death can en-ter there;
2. My Fa-ther's house is built on high, Far, far a-bove the star-ry sky;
3. Let oth-ers seek a home be-low, Which flames de-vour or waves o'er-flow;

CHORUS—I'm go-ing home, I'm go-ing home, I'm go-ing home to die no more;

Its glit-t'ring tow'rs the sun out-shine, That heav'n-ly man-sion shall be mine.
When from this earth-ly pris-on free, That heav'n-ly man-sion mine shall be.
Be mine a hap-pier lot to own A heav'n-ly man-sion near the throne.

To die no more, to die no more— I'm go-ing home to die no more.

517 On Jordan's Stormy Banks

American melody
Adapted by Rigdon M. McIntosh, 1836-1899

SAMUEL STENNETT, 1727-1795

Arr. by Norman Johnson, 1928-

1. On Jor-dan's storm-y banks I stand And cast a wish-ful eye
2. All o'er those wide-ex-tend-ed plains Shines one e-ter-nal day;
3. No chill-ing winds nor poi-s'nous breath Can reach that health-ful shore;
4. When shall I reach that hap-py place And be for-ev-er blest?

To Ca-naan's fair and hap-py land, Where my pos-ses-sions lie.
There God the Son for-ev-er reigns And scat-ters night a-way.
Sick-ness and sor-row, pain and death Are felt and feared no more.
When shall I see my Fa-ther's face And in His bos-om rest?

D.S.— O who will come and go with me? I am bound for the prom-ised land.

On Jordan's Stormy Banks

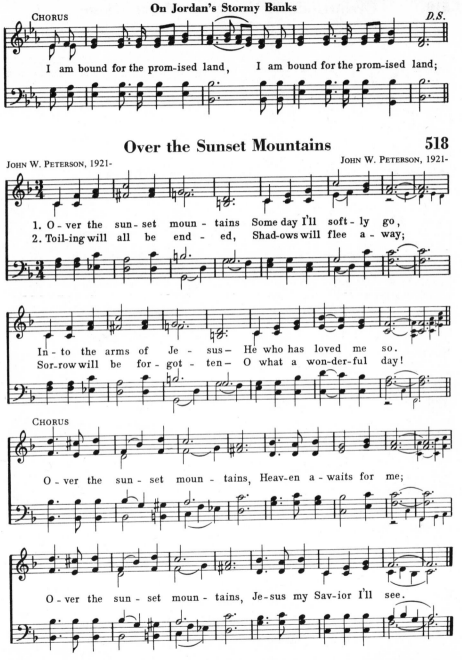

CHORUS   *D.S.*

I am bound for the prom-ised land,   I am bound for the prom-ised land;

Over the Sunset Mountains   518

JOHN W. PETERSON, 1921-   JOHN W. PETERSON, 1921-

1. O - ver the sun - set moun - tains Some day I'll soft - ly go,
2. Toil-ing will all be end - ed, Shad-ows will flee a - way;

In - to the arms of Je - sus— He who has loved me so.
Sor-row will be for - got - ten— O what a won-der-ful day!

CHORUS

O — ver the sun - set moun - tains, Heav-en a - waits for me;

O — ver the sun - set moun - tains, Je-sus my Sav-ior I'll see.

519 Great God, We Sing That Mighty Hand

ST. CRISPIN

GEORGE J. ELVEY, 1816-1893
Arr. by Eldon Burkwall, 1928-

PHILIP DODDRIDGE, 1702-1751

1. Great God, we sing that might-y hand   By which sup-port-ed still we stand;
2. By   day, by night, at   home, a-broad,   Still are we guard-ed   by   our God;
3. With grate-ful hearts the past we   own;   The fu-ture, all   to   us   un-known,
4. In scenes ex-alt-ed   or   de-pressed Thou art our joy, and Thou our rest;

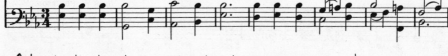

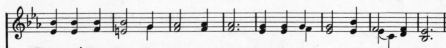

The o-p'ning year Thy mer-cy shows, That mer-cy crowns it   till   it close.
By   His in-ces-sant boun-ty   fed, By His un-err-ing coun-sel led.
We   to Thy guard-ian care com-mit, And, peaceful, leave be-fore Thy feet.
Thy good-ness all   our hopes shall raise, A-dored thru all our chang-ing days.

Alternate tune: GERMANY - 217 (521)

520 Another Year Is Dawning

FRANCES R. HAVERGAL, 1836-1879

To be sung to the tune AURELIA – 186

1. Another year is dawning!
   Dear Father, let it be,
   In working or in waiting,
   Another year with Thee;
   Another year of leaning
   Upon Thy loving breast;
   Another year of trusting,
   Of quiet, happy rest;

2. Another year of mercies,
   Of faithfulness and grace;
   Another year of gladness
   In the shining of Thy face;
   Another year of progress,
   Another year of praise;
   Another year of proving
   Thy presence all the days;

3. Another year of service,
   Of witness for Thy love;
   Another year of training
   For holier work above.
   Another year is dawning!
   Dear Father, let it be
   On earth, or else in heaven,
   Another year for Thee.

Alternate tunes: MENDEBRAS—68, MISSIONARY HYMN—433

Where Cross the Crowded Ways of Life   521

GERMANY

FRANKLIN MASON NORTH, 1850-1935   From Gardiner's *Sacred Melodies*, 1815

1. Where cross the crowd-ed ways of life, Where sound the cries of race and clan,
2. In haunts of wretch-ed-ness and need, On shad-owed thresholds dark with fears,
3. The cup of wa-ter giv'n for Thee Still holds the fresh-ness of Thy grace;
4. O Mas-ter, from the moun-tain side, Make haste to heal these hearts of pain,
5. Till sons of men shall learn Thy love And fol-low where Thy feet have trod;

A-bove the noise of self-ish strife, We hear Thy voice, O Son of man!
From paths where hide the lures of greed, We catch the vi-sion of Thy tears.
Yet long these mul-ti-tudes to see The sweet com-pas-sion of Thy face.
A-mong these rest-less throngs a-bide, O tread the cit-y streets a-gain:
Till glo-rious, from Thy heav'n a-bove, Shall come the cit-y of our God.

This tune in a lower key: 217

Our Thanks, O God, for Fathers   522

SOLIE

LOIS S. JOHNSON, 1925-   LOIS S. JOHNSON, 1925-

1. Our thanks, O God, for fa-thers Who fol-low in Thy way,
2. Our thanks, O God, for fa-thers Who show, by word and deed,
3. Our thanks, O God, for fa-thers Who meet Thee oft in prayer,
4. How bless-ed are the chil-dren Who in their fa-thers see

And who, with glad and trust-ing hearts, Ex-alt Thee ev-'ry day.
Com-mit-ment to Thy will and plan, And Thy com-mand-ments heed.
And who, for all life's toil and care, Find strength and wis-dom there.
The ten-der Fa-ther-love of God, And find their way to Thee.

The word "mothers" or "parents" may be substituted for other occasions.

523   Happy the Home When God Is There

BEATITUDO

HENRY WARE, the younger, 1794-1843   JOHN B. DYKES, 1823-1876

1. Hap-py the home when God is there, And love fills ev - 'ry breast,
2. Hap-py the home where Je - sus' name Is sweet to ev - 'ry ear,
3. Hap-py the home where prayer is heard And praise is wont to rise,
4. Lord, let us in our homes a - gree This bless-ed peace to gain;

When one their wish and one their prayer And one their heav'n - ly rest.
Where chil-dren ear - ly lisp His fame And par - ents hold Him dear.
Where pa-rents love the sa - cred Word And all its wis - dom prize.
U - nite our hearts in love to Thee, And love to all will reign.

This tune in a lower key: 336

524   Gracious Savior, Who Didst Honor

NELSON

EMILY L. SHIRREFF, 1814-1897 — alt.   JOHN W. PETERSON, 1921-

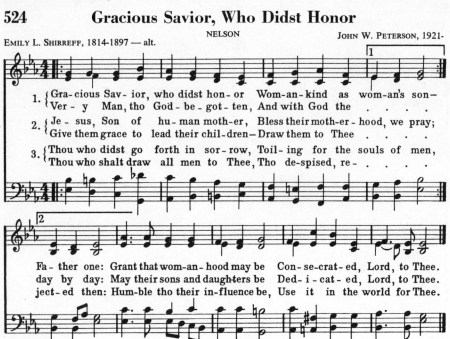

1   1. { Gra-cious Sav - ior, who didst hon - or Wom-an-kind as wom-an's son—
{ Ver - y Man, tho God - be - got - ten, And with God the . . . .

2. { Je - sus, Son of hu-man moth-er, Bless their moth-er - hood, we pray;
{ Give them grace to lead their chil-dren— Draw them to Thee . . . .

3. { Thou who didst go forth in sor - row, Toil- ing for the souls of men,
{ Thou who shalt draw all men to Thee, Tho de-spised, re - . . . .

2

Fa - ther one: Grant that wom-an-hood may be Con - se-crat - ed, Lord, to Thee.
day by day: May their sons and daugh-ters be Ded - i - cat - ed, Lord, to Thee.
ject- ed then: Hum-ble tho their in-fluence be, Use it in the world for Thee.

A Christian Home

FINLANDIA

Barbara B. Hart, 1916-

Jean Sibelius, 1865-1957

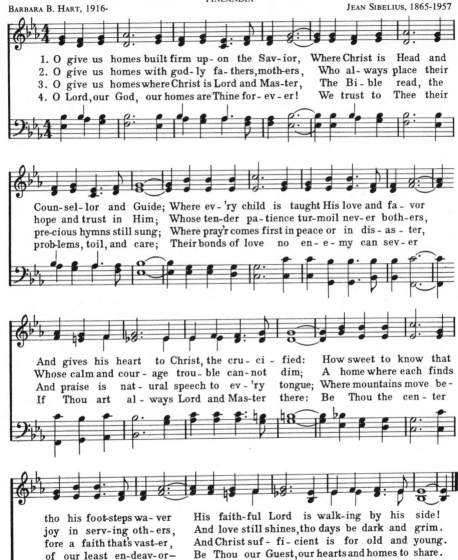

1. O give us homes built firm up-on the Sav-ior, Where Christ is Head and Coun-sel-lor and Guide; Where ev-'ry child is taught His love and fa-vor And gives his heart to Christ, the cru-ci-fied: How sweet to know that tho his foot-steps wa-ver His faith-ful Lord is walk-ing by his side!

2. O give us homes with god-ly fa-thers, moth-ers, Who al-ways place their hope and trust in Him; Whose ten-der pa-tience tur-moil nev-er both-ers, Whose calm and cour-age trou-ble can-not dim; A home where each finds joy in serv-ing oth-ers, And love still shines, tho days be dark and grim.

3. O give us homes where Christ is Lord and Mas-ter, The Bi-ble read, the pre-cious hymns still sung; Where pray'r comes first in peace or in dis-as-ter, And praise is nat-ural speech to ev-'ry tongue; Where mountains move be-fore a faith that's vast-er, And Christ suf-fi-cient is for old and young.

4. O Lord, our God, our homes are Thine for-ev-er! We trust to Thee their problems, toil, and care; Their bonds of love no en-e-my can sev-er If Thou art al-ways Lord and Mas-ter there: Be Thou the cen-ter of our least en-deav-or— Be Thou our Guest, our hearts and homes to share.

This tune in a higher key: 290

526 Come, Ye Thankful People

ST. GEORGE'S, WINDSOR

HENRY ALFORD, 1810-1871

GEORGE J. ELVEY, 1816-1893

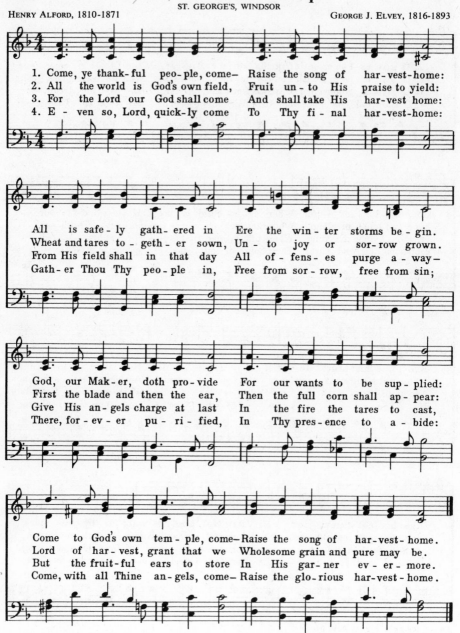

1. Come, ye thank-ful peo-ple, come— Raise the song of har-vest-home:
2. All the world is God's own field, Fruit un-to His praise to yield:
3. For the Lord our God shall come And shall take His har-vest home:
4. E-ven so, Lord, quick-ly come To Thy fi-nal har-vest-home:

All is safe-ly gath-ered in Ere the win-ter storms be-gin.
Wheat and tares to-geth-er sown, Un-to joy or sor-row grown.
From His field shall in that day All of-fens-es purge a-way—
Gath-er Thou Thy peo-ple in, Free from sor-row, free from sin;

God, our Mak-er, doth pro-vide For our wants to be sup-plied:
First the blade and then the ear, Then the full corn shall ap-pear:
Give His an-gels charge at last In the fire the tares to cast,
There, for-ev-er pu-ri-fied, In Thy pres-ence to a-bide:

Come to God's own tem-ple, come—Raise the song of har-vest-home.
Lord of har-vest, grant that we Wholesome grain and pure may be.
But the fruit-ful ears to store In His gar-ner ev-er-more.
Come, with all Thine an-gels, come—Raise the glo-rious har-vest-home.

Thanks to God!

HULTMAN

August Ludvig Storm, 1862-1914
Freely translated by Norman Johnson, 1928-

John Alfred Hultman, 1861-1942
Arr. by Norman Johnson, 1928-

1. Thanks, O God, for bound-less mer-cy From Thy gra-cious throne a-bove;
2. Thanks for thorns as well as ros-es, Thanks for weak-ness and for health;
3. Thanks, O God, for home and fire-side, Where we share our dai-ly bread;

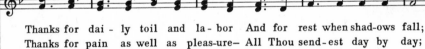

Thanks for ev-'ry need pro-vid-ed From the full-ness of Thy love!
Thanks for clouds as well as sun-shine, Thanks for pov-er-ty and wealth!
Thanks for hours of sweet com-mun-ion, When by Thee our souls are fed!

Thanks for dai-ly toil and la-bor And for rest when shad-ows fall;
Thanks for pain as well as pleas-ure- All Thou send-est day by day;
Thanks for grace in time of sor-row And for joy and peace in Thee;

Thanks for love of friend and neigh-bor And Thy good-ness un-to all!
And Thy Word, our dear-est treas-ure, Shed-ding light up-on our way.
Thanks for hope to-day, to-mor-row, And for all e-ter-ni-ty!

The Star-Spangled Banner

FRANCIS SCOTT KEY, 1779-1843

Attributed to
John Stafford Smith, 1750-1836

1. O say, can you see, by the dawn's ear-ly light, What so proud-ly we
2. O thus be it ev - er, when free men shall stand Be - tween their loved

hailed at the twi-light's last gleam-ing, Whose broad stripes and bright stars, thru the
homes and the war's des - o - la - tion! Blest with vic - t'ry and peace, may the

per - il - ous fight, O'er the ram-parts we watched, were so gal-lant-ly stream-ing?
heav'n-res-cued land Praise the Pow'r that hath made and pre-served us a na - tion!

And the rock-ets' red glare, the bombs burst-ing in air, Gave proof thru the
Then con-quer we must, when our cause it is just; And this be our

night that our flag was still there. O say, does that star-span-gled
mot - to: "In God is our trust!" And the star-span-gled ban - ner in

The Star-Spangled Banner

ban - ner yet wave O'er the land of the free and the home of the brave?
tri - umph shall wave O'er the land of the free and the home of the brave!

My Country, 'Tis of Thee   529

AMERICA

Samuel Francis Smith, 1808-1895

Source unknown
From *Thesaurus Musicus*, 1744

1. My coun - try, 'tis of thee, Sweet land of lib - er - ty,
2. My na - tive coun - try, thee, Land of the no - ble free,
3. Let mu - sic swell the breeze, And ring from all the trees
4. Our fa - thers' God, to Thee, Au - thor of lib - er - ty,

Of thee I sing: Land where my fa - thers died, Land of the
Thy name I love: I love thy rocks and rills, Thy woods and
Sweet free-dom's song: Let mor - tal tongues a - wake, Let all that
To Thee we sing: Long may our land be bright With free-dom's

pil - grims' pride, From ev - 'ry moun-tain side Let free-dom ring!
tem - pled hills; My heart with rap - ture thrills Like that a - bove.
breathe par-take; Let rocks their si - lence break, The sound pro - long.
ho - ly light; Pro - tect us by Thy might, Great God, our King!

530 Battle Hymn of the Republic

JULIA WARD HOWE, 1819-1910

American melody, c. 1852

1. Mine eyes have seen the glo-ry of the com-ing of the Lord, He is
2. I have seen Him in the watch-fires of a hun-dred cir-cling camps, They have
3. He has sound-ed forth the trum-pet that shall nev-er sound re-treat, He is
4. In the beau-ty of the lil-ies Christ was born a-cross the sea, With a

tram-pling out the vin-tage where the grapes of wrath are stored; He hath loosed the
build-ed Him an al-tar in the eve-ning dews and damps; I can read His
sift-ing out the hearts of men be-fore His judg-ment seat; O be swift, my
glo-ry in His bos-om that trans-fig-ures you and me; As He died to

fate-ful light-ning of His ter-ri-ble swift sword—His truth is march-ing on.
righteous sen-tence by the dim and flar-ing lamps— His day is march-ing on.
soul, to an-swer Him! be ju-bi-lant, my feet!— Our God is march-ing on.
make men ho-ly, let us die to make men free, While God is march-ing on.

REFRAIN

Glo-ry! glo-ry, hal-le-lu-jah! Glo-ry! glo-ry, hal-le-lu-jah!

Glo-ry! glo-ry, hal-le-lu-jah! His truth is march-ing on.

America the Beautiful

MATERNA

KATHARINE LEE BATES, 1859-1929

SAMUEL A. WARD, 1847-1903

1. O beau-ti-ful for spa-cious skies, For am-ber waves of grain,
2. O beau-ti-ful for pil-grim feet, Whose stern, im-pas-sioned stress
3. O beau-ti-ful for he-roes proved In lib-er-at-ing strife,
4. O beau-ti-ful for pa-triot dream That sees, be-yond the years,

For pur-ple moun-tain maj-es-ties A-bove the fruit-ed plain!
A thor-ough-fare for free-dom beat A-cross the wil-der-ness!
Who more than self their coun-try loved And mer-cy more than life!
Thine al-a-bas-ter cit-ies gleam— Un-dimmed by hu-man tears!

A-mer-i-ca! A-mer-i-ca! God shed His grace on thee,
A-mer-i-ca! A-mer-i-ca! God mend thine ev-'ry flaw,
A-mer-i-ca! A-mer-i-ca! May God thy gold re-fine,
A-mer-i-ca! A-mer-i-ca! God shed His grace on thee,

And crown thy good with broth-er-hood From sea to shin-ing sea.
Con-firm thy soul in self-con-trol, Thy lib-er-ty in law.
Till all suc-cess be no-ble-ness, And ev-'ry gain di-vine.
And crown thy good with broth-er-hood From sea to shin-ing sea.

532

God of Our Fathers

NATIONAL HYMN

DANIEL C. ROBERTS, 1841-1907

GEORGE W. WARREN, 1828-1902

Trumpets,
before each verse

1. God of our fa - thers, whose al-might-y hand
2. Thy love di - vine hath led us in the past,
3. From war's a - larms, from dead - ly pes - ti - lence,
4. Re - fresh Thy peo - ple on their toil-some way,

Leads forth in beau - ty all the star - ry band   Of shin - ing worlds in
In this free land by Thee our lot is cast;   Be Thou our rul - er,
Be Thy strong arm our ev - er - sure de - fense;   Thy true re - li - gion
Lead us from night to nev - er - end - ing day;   Fill all our lives with

splen-dor thru the skies,   Our grate-ful songs be-fore Thy throne a - rise.
guard-ian, guide, and stay,   Thy word our law, Thy paths our cho - sen way.
in our hearts in - crease,   Thy boun-teous good-ness nour-ish us in peace.
love and grace di - vine,   And glo - ry, laud, and praise be ev - er Thine!

533

We Bid Thee Welcome

SMOLAN

JAMES MONTGOMERY, 1771-1854

ELDON BURKWALL, 1928-

1. We bid thee wel - come in the name Of Je - sus, our ex - alt - ed Head:
2. Come as a shep-herd—guard and keep This fold from harm of earth and sin;
3. Come as a teach - er sent from God, Charged His whole coun-sel to de - clare;

Alternate tunes: MARYTON—437, MISSIONARY CHANT—415

We Bid Thee Welcome

Come as a serv-ant— so He came, And we re-ceive thee in His stead.
Nour-ish the lambs and feed the sheep, The wounded heal, the lost bring in.
Lift o'er our ranks the proph-et's rod, While we up-hold thy hands with prayer.

Let All the World in Every Corner Sing　534

GEORGE HERBERT, 1593-1632

ROBERT G. McCUTCHAN, 1877-1958

Unison

1. Let all the world in ev-'ry cor-ner sing: My God and King!
2. Let all the world in ev-'ry cor-ner sing: My God and King!

The heav'ns are not too high, His praise may thith-er fly; The
The church with psalms must shout, No door can keep them out; But,

earth is not too low, His prais-es there may grow. Let
more than all, the heart Must bear the long-est part. Let

all the world in ev-'ry cor-ner sing: My God and King!
all the world in ev-'ry cor-ner sing: My God and King!

535

Hear Our Prayer, O Lord

GEORGE WHELPTON, 1847-1930

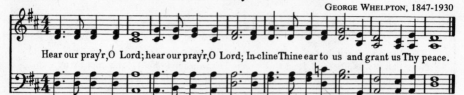

Hear our pray'r, O Lord; hear our pray'r, O Lord; In-cline Thine ear to us and grant us Thy peace.

536

Almighty Father, Hear Our Prayer

FELIX MENDELSSOHN, 1809-1847

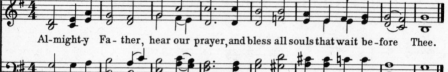

Al-might-y Fa-ther, hear our prayer, and bless all souls that wait be-fore Thee.

537

All Things Come of Thee

I Chronicles 29:14

Attr. to Ludwig van Beethoven, 1770-1827

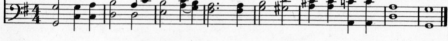

All things come of Thee, O Lord, and of Thine own have we giv-en Thee.

538

We Give Thee But Thine Own

SCHUMANN

WILLIAM W. How, 1823-1897

From Mason & Webb's *Cantica Laudis*, 1850

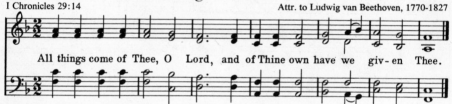

1. We give Thee but Thine own, What-e'er the gift may be: All
2. May we Thy boun-ties thus As stew-ards true re - ceive, And

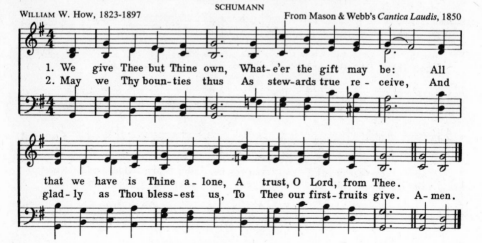

that we have is Thine a - lone, A trust, O Lord, from Thee.
glad-ly as Thou bless-est us, To Thee our first-fruits give. A - men.

SELECTIONS FROM SCRIPTURE

for responsive, antiphonal, or unison reading

---

1 A Call to Worship

O magnify the Lord with me, and let us exalt his name together.

Make a joyful noise unto God, all ye lands:

Sing forth the honor of his name: make his praise glorious.

Say unto God, How terrible art thou in thy works! through the greatness of thy power shall thine enemies submit themselves unto thee.

All the earth shall worship thee, and shall sing unto thee; they shall sing to thy name.

Let the people praise thee, O God; let all the people praise thee.

O let the nations be glad and sing for joy: for thou shalt judge the people righteously, and govern the nations upon earth.

Let the people praise thee, O God; let all the people praise thee.
Psalm 34:3; 66:1-4; 67:3-5

2 Creation

In the beginning God created the heaven and the earth.

And the earth was without form, and void; and darkness was upon the face of the deep.

And the Spirit of God moved upon the face of the waters.

And God said, Let there be light: and there was light.

And God created every living creature that moveth, after his kind.

And God blessed them, saying, Be fruitful, and multiply in the earth . . . and it was so.

And God said, Let us make man in our image, after our likeness:

So God created man in his own image, in the image of God created he him.
From Genesis 1:1-27

By the word of the Lord were the heavens made; and all the host of them by the breath of his mouth.

He gathereth the waters of the sea together as an heap: he layeth up the depth in storehouses.

Let all the earth fear the Lord: let all the inhabitants of the world stand in awe of him.

For he spake, and it was done; he commanded, and it stood fast.
Psalm 33:6-9

3 The Word of God

All scripture is given by inspiration of God, and is profitable for doctrine, for reproof, for correction, for instruction in righteousness:

That the man of God may be perfect, thoroughly furnished unto all good works.
II Timothy 3:16, 17

The law of the Lord is perfect, converting the soul:

The testimony of the Lord is sure, making wise the simple.

The statutes of the Lord are right, rejoicing the heart:

The commandment of the Lord is pure, enlightening the eyes.

The fear of the Lord is clean, enduring for ever:

The judgments of the Lord are true and righteous altogether.

More to be desired are they than gold, yea, than much fine gold: sweeter also than honey and the honeycomb.

Moreover by them is thy servant warned: and in keeping of them there is great reward. *Psalm 19:7-11*

Thy word is a lamp unto my feet, and a light unto my path.

The entrance of thy words giveth light; it giveth understanding unto the simple. *Psalm 119:105, 130*

For the word of God is quick, and powerful, and sharper than any two-edged sword, piercing even to the dividing asunder of soul and spirit, and of the joints and marrow, and is a discerner of the thoughts and intents of the heart. *Hebrews 4:12*

But these are written, that ye might believe that Jesus is the Christ, the Son of God; and that believing ye might have life through his name. *John 20:31*

4 The Commandments

And God spake all these words, saying,

I am the Lord thy God, which have brought thee out of the land of Egypt, out of the house of bondage.

Thou shalt have no other gods before me.

Thou shalt not make unto thee any graven image, or any likeness of any thing that is in heaven above, or that is in the earth beneath, or that is in the water under the earth:

Thou shalt not bow down thyself to them, nor serve them: for I the Lord thy God am a jealous God, visiting the iniquity of the fathers upon the children unto the third and fourth generation of them that hate me;

And showing mercy unto thousands of them that love me, and keep my commandments.

Thou shalt not take the name of the Lord thy God in vain: for the Lord will not hold him guiltless that taketh his name in vain.

Remember the sabbath day, to keep it holy.

Six days shalt thou labor, and do all thy work:

But the seventh day is the sabbath of the Lord thy God: in it thou shalt not do any work, thou, nor thy son, nor thy daughter, thy manservant, nor thy maidservant, nor thy cattle, nor thy stranger that is within thy gates:

For in six days the Lord made heaven and earth, the sea, and all that in them is, and rested the seventh day: wherefore the Lord blessed the sabbath day, and hallowed it.

Honor thy father and thy mother: that thy days may be long upon the land which the Lord thy God giveth thee.

Thou shalt not kill.

Thou shalt not commit adultery.

Thou shalt not steal.

Thou shalt not bear false witness against thy neighbor.

Thou shalt not covet thy neighbor's house, thou shalt not covet thy neighbor's wife, nor his manservant, nor his maidservant, nor his ox, nor his ass, nor any thing that is thy neighbor's. *Exodus 20:1-17*

Jesus said . . . Thou shalt love the Lord thy God with all thy heart, and with all thy soul, and with all thy mind. This is the first and great commandment.

And the second is like unto it, Thou shalt love thy neighbor as thyself.

On these two commandments hang all the law and the prophets. *Matthew 22:37-40*

5 The Blessed Man

Blessed is the man that walketh not in the counsel of the ungodly, nor standeth in the way of sinners, nor sitteth in the seat of the scornful.

But his delight is in the law of the Lord; and in his law doth he meditate day and night.

And he shall be like a tree planted by the rivers of water, that bringeth forth his fruit in his season; his leaf also shall not wither; and whatsoever he doeth shall prosper.

The ungodly are not so; but are like the chaff which the wind driveth away.

Therefore the ungodly shall not stand in the judgment, nor sinners in the congregation of the righteous.

For the Lord knoweth the way of the righteous; but the way of the ungodly shall perish. Psalm 1

6 The Glory of God

The heavens declare the glory of God; and the firmament showeth his handiwork.

Day unto day uttereth speech, and night unto night showeth knowledge.

There is no speech nor language, where their voice is not heard.

Their line is gone out through all the earth, and their words to the end of the world. In them hath he set a tabernacle for the sun,

Which is as a bridegroom coming out of his chamber, and rejoiceth as a strong man to run a race.

His going forth is from the end of the heaven, and his circuit unto the ends of it: and there is nothing hid from the heat thereof.

The law of the Lord is perfect, converting the soul: the testimony of the Lord is sure, making wise the simple.

The statutes of the Lord are right, rejoicing the heart: the commandment of the Lord is pure, enlightening the eyes.

The fear of the Lord is clean, enduring for ever: the judgments of the Lord are true and righteous altogether.

More to be desired are they than gold, yea, than much fine gold: sweeter also than honey and the honeycomb.

Moreover by them is thy servant warned: and in keeping of them there is great reward.

Who can understand his errors? cleanse thou me from secret faults.

Keep back thy servant also from presumptuous sins; let them not have dominion over me: then shall I be upright, and I shall be innocent from the great transgression.

Let the words of my mouth, and the meditation of my heart, be acceptable in thy sight, O Lord, my strength, and my redeemer. Psalm 19

7 The Shepherd Psalm

The Lord is my shepherd; I shall not want.

He maketh me to lie down in green pastures: he leadeth me beside the still waters.

He restoreth my soul: he leadeth me in the paths of righteousness for his name's sake.

Yea, though I walk through the valley of the shadow of death, I will fear no evil: for thou art with me; thy rod and thy staff they comfort me.

Thou preparest a table before me in the presence of mine enemies: thou anointest my head with oil; my cup runneth over.

Surely goodness and mercy shall follow me all the days of my life: and I will dwell in the house of the Lord for ever. Psalm 23

8 The King of Glory

The earth is the Lord's and the fulness thereof; the world, and they that dwell therein.

For he hath founded it upon the seas, and established it upon the floods.

Who shall ascend into the hill of the Lord? or who shall stand in his holy place?

He that hath clean hands, and a pure heart; who hath not lifted up his soul unto vanity, nor sworn deceitfully.

He shall receive the blessing from the Lord, and righteousness from the God of his salvation.

This is the generation of them that seek him, that seek thy face, O Jacob.

Lift up your heads, O ye gates; and be ye lifted up, ye everlasting doors; and the King of glory shall come in.

Who is this King of glory? The Lord strong and mighty, the Lord mighty in battle.

Lift up your heads, O ye gates; even lift them up, ye everlasting doors; and the King of glory shall come in.

Who is this King of glory? The Lord of hosts, he is the King of glory.

Psalm 24

9 Faith and Trust

The Lord is my light and my salvation; whom shall I fear? the Lord is the strength of my life; of whom shall I be afraid?

When the wicked, even mine enemies and my foes, came upon me to eat up my flesh, they stumbled and fell.

Though an host should encamp against me, my heart shall not fear: though war should rise against me, in this will I be confident.

One thing have I desired of the Lord, that will I seek after; that I may dwell in the house of the Lord all the days of my life, to behold the beauty of the Lord, and to enquire in his temple.

For in the time of trouble he shall hide me in his pavilion: in the secret of his tabernacle shall he hide me; he shall set me up upon a rock.

And now shall mine head be lifted up above mine enemies round about me: therefore will I offer in his tabernacle sacrifices of joy; I will sing, yea, I will sing praises unto the Lord.

Hear, O Lord, when I cry with my voice: have mercy also upon me, and answer me.

When thou saidst, Seek ye my face; my heart said unto thee, Thy face, Lord, will I seek.

Hide not thy face far from me; put not thy servant away in anger: thou hast been my help; leave me not, neither forsake me, O God of my salvation.

When my father and my mother forsake me, then the Lord will take me up.

Teach me thy way, O Lord, and lead me in a plain path, because of mine enemies.

Deliver me not over unto the will of mine enemies: for false witnesses are risen up against me, and such as breathe out cruelty.

I had fainted, unless I had believed to see the goodness of the Lord in the land of the living.

Wait on the Lord: be of good courage, and he shall strengthen thine heart: wait, I say, on the Lord.

Psalm 27

10 The Joy of Forgiveness

Blessed is he whose transgression is forgiven, whose sin is covered.

Blessed is the man unto whom the Lord imputeth not iniquity, and in whose spirit there is no guile.

When I kept silence, my bones waxed old through my roaring all the day long.

For day and night thy hand was heavy upon me: my moisture is turned into the drought of summer.

I acknowledged my sin unto thee, and mine iniquity have I not hid.

I said, I will confess my transgressions unto the Lord; and thou forgavest the iniquity of my sin.

For this shall every one that is godly pray unto thee in a time when thou mayest be found: surely in the floods of great waters they shall not come nigh unto him.

Thou art my hiding place; thou shalt preserve me from trouble; thou shalt compass me about with songs of deliverance.

I will instruct thee and teach thee in the way which thou shalt go: I will guide thee with mine eye.

Be ye not as the horse, or as the mule, which have no understanding: whose mouth must be held in with bit and bridle, lest they come near unto thee.

Many sorrows shall be to the wicked: but he that trusteth in the Lord, mercy shall compass him about.

Be glad in the Lord, and rejoice, ye righteous: and shout for joy, all ye that are upright in heart. Psalm 32

11 The Goodness of God

O taste and see that the Lord is good: blessed is the man that trusteth in him.

O fear the Lord, ye his saints: for there is no want to them that fear him.

The young lions do lack, and suffer hunger: but they that seek the Lord shall not want any good thing.

The eyes of the Lord are upon the righteous, and his ears are open unto their cry.

The face of the Lord is against them that do evil, to cut off the remembrance of them from the earth.

The righteous cry, and the Lord heareth, and delivereth them out of all their troubles.

The Lord is nigh unto them that are of a broken heart; and saveth such as be of a contrite spirit.

Many are the afflictions of the righteous: but the Lord delivereth him out of them all.

The Lord redeemeth the soul of his servants: and none of them that trust in him shall be desolate. Psalm 34:8-10, 15-19, 22

Oh that men would praise the Lord for his goodness, and for his wonderful works to the children of men!

For he satisfieth the longing soul and filleth the hungry soul with goodness.

Whoso is wise, and will observe these things, even they shall understand the lovingkindess of the Lord. Psalm 107:8, 9, 43

12 Thirsting for God

As the hart panteth after the water brooks, so panteth my soul after thee, O God.

My soul thirsteth for God, for the living God: when shall I come and appear before God?

My tears have been my meat day and night, while they continually say unto me, Where is thy God?

When I remember these things, I pour out my soul in me: for I had gone with the multitude, I went with them to the house of God, with the voice of joy and praise, with a multitude that kept holyday.

Why art thou cast down, O my soul? and why art thou disquieted in me? hope thou in God: for I shall yet praise him for the help of his countenance.

Yet the Lord will command his lovingkindness in the daytime, and in the night his song shall be with me, and my prayer unto the God of my life.

I will say unto God my rock, Why hast thou forgotten me? why go I mourning because of the oppression of the enemy?

As with a sword in my bones, mine enemies reproach me; while they say daily unto me, Where is thy God?

Why art thou cast down, O my soul? and why art thou disquieted within me?

Hope thou in God: for I shall yet praise him, who is the health of my countenance, and my God. Psalm 42:1-5, 8-11

13 Prayer of Penitence

Have mercy upon me, O God, according to thy lovingkindness: according to the multitude of thy tender mercies blot out my transgressions.

Wash me thoroughly from mine iniquity, and cleanse me from my sin. For I acknowledge my transgressions: and my sin is ever before me.

Against thee, thee only, have I sinned, and done this evil in thy sight: that thou mightest be justified when thou speakest, and be clear when thou judgest.

Behold, I was shapen in iniquity; and in sin did my mother conceive me.

Behold, thou desirest truth in the inward parts: and in the hidden part thou shalt make me to know wisdom.

Purge me with hyssop, and I shall be clean: wash me, and I shall be whiter than snow.

Make me to hear joy and gladness; that the bones which thou has broken may rejoice.

Hide thy face from my sins, and blot out all mine iniquities.

Create in me a clean heart, O God; and renew a right spirit within me.

Cast me not away from thy presence; and take not thy holy spirit from me.

Restore unto me the joy of thy salvation; and uphold me with thy free spirit.

Then will I teach transgressors thy ways; and sinners shall be converted unto thee.

For thou desirest not sacrifice; else would I give it: thou delightest not in burnt offering.

The sacrifices of God are a broken spirit: a broken and a contrite heart, O God, thou wilt not despise.

Psalm 51:1-13, 16, 17

14   The Lord Our Refuge

He that dwelleth in the secret place of the most High shall abide under the shadow of the Almighty.

I will say of the Lord, He is my refuge and my fortress: my God; in him will I trust.

Surely he shall deliver thee from the snare of the fowler, and from the noisome pestilence.

He shall cover thee with his feathers, and under his wings shalt thou trust: his truth shall be thy shield and buckler.

Thou shalt not be afraid for the terror by night; nor for the arrow that flieth by day;

Nor for the pestilence that walketh in darkness; nor for the destruction that wasteth at noonday.

A thousand shall fall at thy side, and ten thousand at thy right hand; but it shall not come nigh thee.

Only with thine eyes shalt thou behold and see the reward of the wicked.

Because thou hast made the Lord, which is my refuge, even the most High, thy habitation;

There shall no evil befall thee, neither shall any plague come nigh thy dwelling.

For he shall give his angels charge over thee, to keep thee in all thy ways.

They shall bear thee up in their hands, lest thou dash thy foot against a stone.

Thou shalt tread upon the lion and adder: the young lion and the dragon shalt thou trample under feet.

Because he hath set his love upon me, therefore will I deliver him; I will set him on high, because he hath known my name.

He shall call upon me, and I will answer him: I will be with him in trouble; I will deliver him, and honor him.

With long life will I satisfy him, and show him my salvation.   Psalm 91

15   A Call to Thanksgiving

It is a good thing to give thanks unto the Lord, and to sing praises unto thy name, O most High:

To show forth thy lovingkindness in the morning, and thy faithfulness every night.

For thou, Lord, hast made me glad through thy work: I will triumph in the works of thy hands.

O come, let us sing unto the Lord: let us make a joyful noise to the rock of our salvation.

Let us come before his presence with thanksgiving, and make a joyful noise unto him with psalms.

For the Lord is a great God, and a great King above all gods.

Serve the Lord with gladness: come before his presence with singing.

Know ye that the Lord he is God: it is he that hath made us, and not we ourselves; we are his people, and the sheep of his pasture.

Enter into his gates with thanksgiving and into his courts with praise:

Be thankful unto him, and bless his name.   Psalm 92:1,2,4; 95:1-3; 100:2-4

16   God of the Nations

O sing unto the Lord a new song: sing unto the Lord, all the earth.

Sing unto the Lord, bless his name; show forth his salvation from day to day.

Declare his glory among the heathen, his wonders among all people.

For the Lord is great, and greatly to be praised: he is to be feared above all gods.

For all the gods of the nations are idols: but the Lord made the heavens.

Honor and majesty are before him: strength and beauty are in his sanctuary.

Give unto the Lord, O ye kindreds of the people, give unto the Lord glory and strength.

Give unto the Lord the glory due unto his name: bring an offering, and come into his courts.

O worship the Lord in the beauty of holiness: fear before him, all the earth.

Say among the heathen that the Lord reigneth:

The world also shall be established that it shall not be moved: he shall judge the people righteously.

Let the heavens rejoice, and let the earth be glad; let the sea roar, and the fulness thereof.

Let the field be joyful, and all that is therein: then shall all the trees of the wood rejoice before the Lord:

For he cometh, for he cometh to judge the earth: he shall judge the world with righteousness, and the people with his truth.   Psalm 96

17   A Call to Praise

Bless the Lord, O my soul: and all that is within me, bless his holy name.

Bless the Lord, O my soul, and forget not all his benefits:

Who forgiveth all thine iniquities; who healeth all thy diseases;

Who redeemeth thy life from destruction; who crowneth thee with lovingkindness and tender mercies;

Who satisfieth thy mouth with good things; so that thy youth is renewed like the eagle's.

The Lord executeth righteousness and judgment for all that are oppressed.

He made known his ways unto Moses, his acts unto the children of Israel.

The Lord is merciful and gracious, slow to anger, and plenteous in mercy.

He will not always chide: neither will he keep his anger for ever.

He hath not dealt with us after our sins; nor rewarded us according to our iniquities.

For as the heaven is high above the earth, so great is his mercy toward them that fear him.

As far as the east is from the west, so far hath he removed our transgressions from us.

Like as a father pitieth his children, so the Lord pitieth them that fear him.

For he knoweth our frame; he remembereth that we are dust.

As for man, his days are as grass: as a flower of the field, so he flourisheth.

For the wind passeth over it, and it is gone; and the place thereof shall know it no more.

But the mercy of the Lord is from everlasting to everlasting upon them that fear him, and his righteousness unto children's children;

To such as keep his covenant, and to those that remember his commandments to do them.

The Lord hath prepared his throne in the heavens; and his kingdom ruleth over all.

Bless the Lord, ye his angels, that excel in strength, that do his commandments, hearkening unto the voice of his word.

Bless ye the Lord, all ye hosts; ye ministers of his, that do his pleasure.

Bless the Lord, all his work in all places of his dominion: bless the Lord, O my soul.
Psalm 103

18   A Psalm of Praise

I will extol thee, my God, O king; and I will bless thy name for ever and ever.

Every day will I bless thee; and I will praise thy name for ever and ever.

Great is the Lord, and greatly to be praised; and his greatness is unsearchable.

One generation shall praise thy works to another, and shall declare thy mighty acts.

I will speak of the glorious honor of thy majesty, and of thy wondrous works.

And men shall speak of the might of thy terrible acts: and I will declare thy greatness.

They shall abundantly utter the memory of thy great goodness, and shall sing of thy righteousness.

The Lord is gracious, and full of compassion; slow to anger, and of great mercy.

The Lord is good to all: and his tender mercies are over all his works.

All thy works shall praise thee, O Lord; and thy saints shall bless thee.

They shall speak of the glory of thy kingdom, and talk of thy power;

To make known to the sons of men his mighty acts, and the glorious majesty of his kingdom.

Thy kingdom is an everlasting kingdom, and thy dominion endureth throughout all generations.

My mouth shall speak the praise of the Lord; and let all flesh bless his holy name for ever and ever.   Psalm 145:1-13, 21

19   The Secret of Strength

Fret not thyself because of evil-doers, neither be thou envious against the workers of iniquity.

For they shall soon be cut down like the grass, and wither as the green herb.

Trust in the Lord, and do good; so shalt thou dwell in the land, and verily thou shalt be fed.

Delight thyself also in the Lord; and he shall give thee the desires of thine heart.

Commit thy way unto the Lord; trust also in him; and he shall bring it to pass.

And he shall bring forth thy righteousness as the light, and thy judgment as the noonday.

Rest in the Lord, and wait patiently for him: fret not thyself because of him who prospereth in his way, because of the man who bringeth wicked devices to pass.

Cease from anger, and forsake wrath: fret not thyself in any wise to do evil.

Psalm 37:1-8

Hast thou not known? hast thou not heard, that the everlasting God, the Lord, the Creator of the ends of the earth, fainteth not, neither is weary? there is no searching of his understanding.

He giveth power to the faint; and to them that have no might he increaseth strength.

Even the youths shall faint and be weary, and the young men shall utterly fall:

But they that wait upon the Lord shall renew their strength; they shall mount up with wings as eagles; they shall run, and not be weary; and they shall walk, and not faint.

Isaiah 40:28-31

20 The Prince of Peace

The people that walked in darkness have seen a great light:

They that dwell in the land of the shadow of death, upon them hath the light shined.

Thou hast multiplied the nation, and not increased the joy:

They joy before thee according to the joy in harvest, and as men rejoice when they divide the spoil.

For thou hast broken the yoke of his burden, and the staff of his shoulder, the rod of his oppressor, as in the day of Midian.

For every battle of the warrior is with confused noise, and garments rolled in blood; but this shall be with burning and fuel of fire.

For unto us a child is born, unto us a son is given: and the government shall be upon his shoulder:

And his name shall be called Wonderful, Counsellor, The mighty God, The everlasting Father, The Prince of Peace.

Of the increase of his government and peace there shall be no end, upon the throne of David, and upon his kingdom, to order it, and to establish it with judgment and with justice from henceforth even for ever.

The zeal of the Lord of hosts will perform this.

Isaiah 9:2-7

21 The Incarnate Word

In the beginning was the Word, and the Word was with God, and the Word was God.

The same was in the beginning with God.

All things were made by him; and without him was not any thing made that was made.

In him was life; and the life was the light of men.

And the light shineth in darkness; and the darkness comprehended it not.

There was a man sent from God, whose name was John.

The same came for a witness, to bear witness of the Light, that all men through him might believe.

He was not that Light, but was sent to bear witness of that Light.

That was the true Light, which lighteth every man that cometh into the world.

He was in the world, and the world was made by him, and the world knew him not.

He came unto his own, and his own received him not.

But as many as received him, to them gave he power to become the sons of God, even to them that believe on his name:

Which were born, not of blood, nor of the will of the flesh, nor of the will of man, but of God.

And the Word was made flesh, and dwelt among us, (and we beheld his glory, the glory as of the only begotten of the Father,) full of grace and truth.

John 1:1-14

22 The Christmas Story

And it came to pass in those days, that there went out a decree from Caesar Augustus, that all the world should be taxed.

And this taxing was first made when Cyrenius was governor of Syria.

And all went to be taxed, every one into his own city.

And Joseph also went up from Galilee, out of the city of Nazareth, into Judaea, unto the city of David, which is called Bethlehem; because he was of the house and lineage of David:

To be taxed with Mary his espoused wife, being great with child.

And so it was, that, while they were there, the days were accomplished that she should be delivered.

And she brought forth her firstborn son, and wrapped him in swaddling clothes, and laid him in a manger; because there was no room for them in the inn.

And there were in the same country shepherds abiding in the field, keeping watch over their flock by night.

And, lo, the angel of the Lord came upon them, and the glory of the Lord shone round about them; and they were sore afraid.

And the angel said unto them, Fear not: for, behold, I bring you good tidings of great joy, which shall be to all people.

For unto you is born this day in the city of David a Savior, which is Christ the Lord.

And this shall be a sign unto you; Ye shall find the babe wrapped in swaddling clothes, lying in a manger.

And suddenly there was with the angel a multitude of the heavenly host praising God, and saying,

Glory to God in the highest, and on earth peace, good will toward men.
Luke 2:1-14

23 The Triumphal Entry

And when they came nigh to Jerusalem, unto Bethphage and Bethany, at the mount of Olives, he sendeth forth two of his disciples,

And saith unto them, Go your way into the village over against you: and as soon as ye be entered into it, ye shall find a colt tied, whereon never man sat; loose him, and bring him.

And if any man say unto you, Why do ye this? say ye that the Lord hath need of him; and straightway he will send him hither.

And they went their way, and found the colt tied by the door without in a place where two ways met; and they loose him.

And certain of them that stood there said unto them, What do ye, loosing the colt?

And they said unto them even as Jesus had commanded: and they let them go.

And they brought the colt to Jesus, and cast their garments on him; and he sat upon him.

And many spread their garments in the way: and others cut down branches off the trees, and strewed them in the way.

And they that went before, and they that followed, cried, saying, Hosanna; Blessed is he that cometh in the name of the Lord:

Blessed be the kingdom of our father David, that cometh in the name of the Lord: Hosanna in the highest. And Jesus entered into Jerusalem, and into the temple.
Mark 11:1-11

24 The Suffering Lamb

Who hath believed our report? and to whom is the arm of the Lord revealed?

For he shall grow up before him as a tender plant, and as a root out of a dry ground:

He hath no form nor comeliness; and when we shall see him, there is no beauty that we should desire him.

He is despised and rejected of men; a man of sorrows, and acquainted with grief: and we hid as it were our faces from him; he was despised, and we esteemed him not.

Surely he hath borne our griefs, and carried our sorrows: yet we did esteem him stricken, smitten of God, and afflicted.

But he was wounded for our transgressions, he was bruised for our iniquities: the chastisement of our peace was upon him, and with his stripes we are healed.

All we like sheep have gone astray; we have turned every one to his own way; and the Lord hath laid on him the iniquity of us all.

He was oppressed, and he was afflicted, yet he opened not his mouth; he is brought as a lamb to the slaughter, and as a sheep before her shearers is dumb, so he openeth not his mouth.

He was taken from prison and from judgment: and who shall declare his generation?

For he was cut off out of the land of the living: for the transgression of my people was he stricken.

And he made his grave with the wicked, and with the rich in his death; because he had done no violence, neither was any deceit in his mouth.

Yet it pleased the Lord to bruise him; he hath put him to grief:

When thou shalt make his soul an offering for sin, he shall see his seed, he shall prolong his days, and the pleasure of the Lord shall prosper in his hand.

He shall see of the travail of his soul, and shall be satisfied: by his knowledge shall my righteous servant justify many; for he shall bear their iniquities.

Therefore will I divide him a portion with the great, and he shall divide the spoil with the strong; because he hath poured out his soul unto death:

And he was numbered with the transgressors; and he bare the sin of many, and made intercession for the transgressors.
Isaiah 53

25 The Crucifixion

Then Pilate took Jesus, and scourged him.

And the soldiers platted a crown of thorns, and put it on his head, and they put on him a purple robe.

And said, Hail, King of the Jews! and they smote him with their hands.

Pilate therefore went forth again, and saith unto them, Behold, I bring him forth to you, that ye may know that I find no fault in him.

Then came Jesus forth, wearing the crown of thorns, and the purple robe. And Pilate saith unto them, Behold the man!

When the chief priests therefore and officers saw him, they cried out, saying, Crucify him, crucify him. Pilate saith unto them, Take ye him, and crucify him: for I find no fault in him.

Then delivered he him therefore unto them to be crucified. And they took Jesus, and led him away.

And he bearing his cross went forth into a place called the place of a skull, which is called in the Hebrew Golgotha:

Where they crucified him, and two other with him, on either side one, and Jesus in the midst.

And Pilate wrote a title, and put it on the cross. And the writing was, JESUS OF NAZARETH THE KING OF THE JEWS.
John 19:1-6, 16-19

26 The Resurrection

In the end of the sabbath, as it began. to dawn toward the first day of the week,

475

came Mary Magdalene and the other Mary to see the sepulchre.

And, behold, there was a great earthquake; for the angel of the Lord descended from heaven, and came and rolled back the stone from the door, and sat upon it.

His countenance was like lightning, and his raiment white as snow:

And for fear of him the keepers did shake, and became as dead men.

And the angel answered and said unto the women, Fear not ye: for I know that ye seek Jesus, which was crucified.

He is not here: for he is risen, as he said. Come, see the place where the Lord lay.

And go quickly, and tell his disciples that he is risen from the dead; and, behold, he goeth before you into Galilee; there shall ye see him: lo, I have told you.

And they departed quickly from the sepulchre with fear and great joy, and did run to bring his disciples word.

And as they went to tell his disciples, behold, Jesus met them, saying, All hail. And they came and held him by the feet, and worshipped him.

Then said Jesus unto them, Be not afraid: go tell my brethren that they go into Galilee, and there shall they see me.
Matthew 28:1-10

27 The Ascension

The former treatise have I made, O Theophilus, of all that Jesus began both to do and teach, until the day in which he was taken up, after that he through the Holy Ghost had given commandments unto the apostles whom he had chosen:

To whom also he shewed himself alive after his passion by many infallible proofs, being seen of them forty days, and speaking of the things pertaining to the kingdom of God:

And, being assembled together with them, commanded them that they should not depart from Jerusalem, but wait for the promise of the Father, which, saith he, ye have heard of me.

For John truly baptized with water; but ye shall be baptized with the Holy Ghost not many days hence.

When they therefore were come together, they asked of him, saying, Lord, wilt thou at this time restore again the kingdom to Israel?

And he said unto them, It is not for you to know the times or the seasons, which the Father hath put in his own power.

But ye shall receive power, after that the Holy Ghost is come upon you: and ye shall be witnesses unto me both in Jerusalem, and in all Judaea, and in Samaria, and unto the uttermost part of the earth.

And when he had spoken these things, while they beheld, he was taken up; and a cloud received him out of their sight.

And while they looked stedfastly toward heaven as he went up, behold, two men stood by them in white apparel;

Which also said, Ye men of Galilee, why stand ye gazing up into heaven? this same Jesus, which is taken up from you into heaven, shall so come in like manner as ye have seen him go into heaven.
Acts 1:1-11

28 Christ, Our High Priest

Wherefore, holy brethren, partakers of the heavenly calling, consider the Apostle and High Priest of our profession, Christ Jesus.

We have not an high priest which cannot be touched with the feeling of our infirmities; but was in all points tempted like as we are, yet without sin.

Let us therefore come boldly unto the throne of grace, that we may obtain mercy, and find grace to help in time of need.

This man, because he continueth ever, hath an unchangeable priesthood.

Wherefore he is able also to save them to the uttermost that come unto God by him, seeing he ever liveth to make intercession for them.

For such an high priest became us, who is holy, harmless, undefiled, separate from sinners, and made higher than the heavens;

Who needeth not daily, as those high priests, to offer up sacrifice, first for his own sins, and then for the people's:

For this he did once, when he offered up himself.

And every priest standeth daily ministering and offering oftentimes the same sacrifices, which can never take away sins:

But this man, after he had offered one sacrifice for sins for ever, sat down on the right hand of God;

From henceforth expecting till his enemies be made his footstool.

For by one offering he hath perfected for ever them that are sanctified.

Having therefore, brethren, boldness to enter into the holiest by the blood of Jesus,

By a new and living way, which he hath consecrated for us, through the veil, that is to say, his flesh;

And having an high priest over the house of God;

Let us draw near with a true heart in full assurance of faith, having our hearts sprinkled from an evil conscience, and our bodies washed with pure water.
Hebrews 3:1;4:15,16;7:24-27;10:11-14,19-22

29 The Exaltation of Christ

Let this mind be in you, which was also in Christ Jesus:

Who, being in the form of God, thought it not robbery to be equal with God:

But made himself of no reputation, and took upon him the form of a servant, and was made in the likeness of men:

And being found in fashion as a man, he humbled himself, and became obedient unto death, even the death of the cross.

Wherefore God also hath highly exalted him, and given him a name which is above every name:

That at the name of Jesus every knee should bow, of things in heaven, and things in earth, and things under the earth;

And that every tongue should confess that Jesus Christ is Lord, to the glory of God the Father.   Philippians 2:5-11

And I beheld, and I heard the voice of many angels round about the throne and the beasts and the elders: and the number of them was ten thousand times ten thousand, and thousands of thousands; saying with a loud voice,

Worthy is the Lamb that was slain to receive power, and riches, and wisdom, and strength, and honor, and glory, and blessing.

And every creature which is in heaven, and on the earth, and under the earth, and such as are in the sea, and all that are in them, heard I saying, Blessing, and honor, and glory, and power, be unto him that sitteth upon the throne, and unto the Lamb for ever and ever.   Revelation 5:11-13

30 The New Jerusalem

And I saw a new heaven and a new earth: for the first heaven and the first earth were passed away; and there was no more sea.

And I John saw the holy city, new Jerusalem, coming down from God out of heaven, prepared as a bride adorned for her husband.

And I heard a great voice out of heaven saying, Behold, the tabernacle of God is with men, and he will dwell with them, and they shall be his people, and God himself shall be with them, and be their God.

And God shall wipe away all tears from their eyes; and there shall be no more

death, neither sorrow, nor crying, neither shall there be any more pain: for the former things are passed away.

And I saw no temple therein: for the Lord God Almighty and the Lamb are the temple of it.

And the city had no need of the sun, neither of the moon, to shine in it: for the glory of God did lighten it, and the Lamb is the light thereof.

And the nations of them which are saved shall walk in the light of it: and the kings of the earth do bring their glory and honor into it.

And the gates of it shall not be shut at all by day: for there shall be no night there.

And they shall bring the glory and honor of the nations into it.

And there shall in no wise enter into it any thing that defileth, neither whatsoever worketh abomination, or maketh a lie: but they which are written in the Lamb's book of life. Revelation 21:1-4, 22-27

31 The Beautitudes

And seeing the multitudes, he went up into a mountain: and when he was set, his disciples came unto him:

And he opened his mouth, and taught them, saying,

Blessed are the poor in spirit: for theirs is the kingdom of heaven.

Blessed are they that mourn: for they shall be comforted.

Blessed are the meek: for they shall inherit the earth.

Blessed are they which do hunger and thirst after righteousness: for they shall be filled.

Blessed are the merciful: for they shall obtain mercy.

Blessed are the pure in heart: for they shall see God.

Blessed are the peacemakers: for they shall be called the children of God.

Blessed are they which are persecuted for righteousness' sake: for theirs is the kingdom of heaven.

Blessed are ye, when men shall revile you, and persecute you, and shall say all manner of evil against you falsely, for my sake.

Rejoice, and be exceeding glad: for great is your reward in heaven: for so persecuted they the prophets which were before you. Matthew 5:1-12

32 Salt and Light

Ye are the salt of the earth: but if the salt have lost his savor, wherewith shall it be salted?

It is thenceforth good for nothing, but to be cast out, and to be trodden under foot of men.

Ye are the light of the world. A city that is set on an hill cannot be hid.

Neither do men light a candle, and put it under a bushel, but on a candlestick; and it giveth light unto all that are in the house.

Let your light so shine before men, that they may see your good works, and glorify your Father which is in heaven.

Think not that I am come to destroy the law, or the prophets: I am not come to destroy, but to fulfil.

For verily I say unto you, Till heaven and earth pass, one jot or one tittle shall in no wise pass from the law, till all be fulfilled.

Whosoever therefore shall break one of these least commandments, and shall teach men so, he shall be called the least in the kingdom of heaven: but whosoever shall do and teach them, the same shall be called great in the kingdom of heaven. Matthew 5:13-20

33 The Good Samaritan

And, behold, a certain lawyer stood up, and tempted him, saying, Master, what shall I do to inherit eternal life?

He said unto him, What is written in the law? how readest thou?

And he answering said, Thou shalt love the Lord thy God with all thy heart, and with all thy soul, and with all thy strength, and with all thy mind; and thy neighbor as thyself.

And he said unto him, Thou hast answered right: this do, and thou shalt live.

But he, willing to justify himself, said unto Jesus, And who is my neighbor?

And Jesus answering said, A certain man went down from Jerusalem to Jericho, and fell among thieves, which stripped him of his raiment, and wounded him, and departed, leaving him half dead.

And by chance there came down a certain priest that way: and when he saw him, he passed by on the other side.

And likewise a Levite, when he was at the place, came and looked on him, and passed by on the other side.

But a certain Samaritan, as he journeyed, came where he was: and when he saw him, he had compassion on him,

And went to him, and bound up his wounds, pouring in oil and wine, and set him on his own beast, and brought him to an inn, and took care of him.

And on the morrow when he departed, he took out two pence, and gave them to the host, and said unto him, Take care of him; and whatsoever thou spendest more, when I come again, I will repay thee.

Which now of these three, thinkest thou, was neighbor unto him that fell among the thieves?

And he said, He that showed mercy on him.

Then said Jesus unto him, Go, and do thou likewise. Luke 10:25-37

34 The Prodigal Son

And he said, A certain man had two sons:

And the younger of them said to his father, Father, give me the portion of thy substance that falleth to me. And he divided unto them his living.

And not many days after, the younger son gathered all together, and took his journey into a far country; and there he wasted his substance with riotous living.

And when he had spent all, there arose a mighty famine in that country; and he began to be in want.

And he went and joined himself to one of the citizens of that country; and he sent him into his fields to feed swine.

And he would fain have filled his belly with the husks that the swine did eat: and no man gave unto him.

But when he came to himself he said, How many hired servants of my father's have bread enough and to spare, and I perish here with hunger!

I will arise and go to my father, and will say unto him, Father, I have sinned against heaven, and in thy sight:

I am no more worthy to be called thy son: make me as one of thy hired servants.

And he arose and came to his father. But while he was yet afar off, his father saw him, and was moved with compassion, and ran, and fell on his neck, and kissed him.

And the son said unto him, Father, I have sinned against heaven, and in thy sight: I am no more worthy to be called thy son.

But the father said to his servants, Bring forth quickly the best robe, and put it on him; and put a ring on his hand, and shoes on his feet:

And bring the fatted calf, and kill it, and let us eat and be merry:

For this my son was dead, and is alive again; he was lost, and is found. And they began to be merry. Luke 15:11-24

35 The Missionary Mandate

The word is nigh thee, even in thy mouth, and in thy heart: that is, the word of faith, which we preach;

That if thou shalt confess with thy mouth the Lord Jesus, and shalt believe in thine heart that God hath raised him from the dead, thou shalt be saved.

For with the heart man believeth unto righteousness; and with the mouth confession is made unto salvation.

For the scripture saith, Whosoever believeth on him shall not be ashamed.

For there is no difference between the Jew and the Greek: for the same Lord over all is rich unto all that call upon him.

For whosoever shall call upon the name of the Lord shall be saved.

How then shall they call on him in whom they have not believed? and how shall they believe in him of whom they have not heard? and how shall they hear without a preacher?

And how shall they preach, except they be sent? as it is written, How beautiful are the feet of them that preach the gospel of peace, and bring glad tidings of good things! Romans 10:8-15

Say not ye, There are yet four months, and then cometh harvest? behold, I say unto you, Lift up your eyes, and look on the fields; for they are white already to harvest. John 4:35

All power is given unto me in heaven and in earth.

Go ye therefore, and teach all nations, baptizing them in the name of the Father, and of the Son, and of the Holy Ghost:

Teaching them to observe all things whatsoever I have commanded you: and,

lo, I am with you alway, even unto the end of the world. Amen. Matthew 28:18-20

36 The Holy Spirit

I will pray the Father, and he shall give you another Comforter, that he may abide with you for ever;

Even the Spirit of truth; whom the world cannot receive, because it seeth him not, neither knoweth him: but ye know him; for he dwelleth with you, and shall be in you.

I will not leave you comfortless: I will come to you. John 14:16-18

But now I go my way to him that sent me; and none of you asketh me, Whither goest thou?

But because I have said these things unto you, sorrow hath filled your heart.

Nevertheless I tell you the truth; It is expedient for you that I go away: for if I go not away, the Comforter will not come unto you; but if I depart, I will send him unto you.

And when he is come, he will reprove the world of sin, and of righteousness, and of judgment:

Of sin, because they believe not on me;

Of righteousness, because I go to my Father, and ye see me no more;

Of judgment, because the prince of this world is judged.

I have yet many things to say unto you, but ye cannot bear them now.

Howbeit when he, the Spirit of truth, is come, he will guide you into all truth: for he shall not speak of himself; but whatsoever he shall hear, that shall he speak: and he will show you things to come.

He shall glorify me: for he shall receive of mine, and shall show it unto you.

All things that the Father hath are mine: therefore said I, that he shall take of mine, and shall show it unto you.
John 16:5-15

37 Pentecost

And when the day of Pentecost was fully come, they were all with one accord in one place.

And suddenly there came a sound from heaven as of a rushing mighty wind, and it filled all the house where they were sitting.

And there appeared unto them cloven tongues like as of fire, and it sat upon each of them.

And they were all filled with the Holy Ghost, and began to speak with other tongues, as the Spirit gave them utterance.

And there were dwelling at Jerusalem Jews, devout men, out of every nation under heaven.

Now when this was noised abroad, the multitude came together, and were confounded, because that every man heard them speak in his own language.

And they were all amazed and marvelled, saying one to another, Behold, are not all these which speak Galilaeans?

And how hear we every man in our own tongue, wherein we were born?

We do hear them speak in our tongues the wonderful works of God.

And they were all amazed, and were in doubt, saying one to another, What meaneth this?

Others mocking said, These men are full of new wine.

But Peter, standing up with the eleven, lifted up his voice, and said unto them, Ye men of Judaea, and all ye that dwell at Jerusalem, be this known unto you, and hearken to my words:

For these are not drunken, as ye suppose, seeing it is but the third hour of the day.

But this is that which was spoken by the prophet Joel: And it shall come to pass in the last days, saith God, I will pour out of my Spirit upon all flesh:

And your sons and your daughters shall prophesy, and your young men shall see visions, and your old men shall dream dreams:

And it shall come to pass, that whosoever shall call on the name of the Lord shall be saved.   Acts 2:1-8,11-17,21

38 The New Birth

There was a man of the Pharisees, named Nicodemus, a ruler of the Jews:

The same came to Jesus by night, and said unto him, Rabbi, we know that thou art a teacher come from God: for no man can do these miracles that thou doest, except God be with him.

Jesus answered and said unto him, Verily, verily, I say unto thee, Except a man be born again, he cannot see the kingdom of God.

Nicodemus saith unto him, How can a man be born when he is old? can he enter the second time into his mother's womb, and be born?

Jesus answered, Verily, verily, I say unto thee, Except a man be born of water and of the Spirit, he cannot enter into the kingdom of God.

That which is born of the flesh is flesh; and that which is born of the Spirit is spirit.

Marvel not that I said unto thee, Ye must be born again.

The wind bloweth where it listeth, and thou hearest the sound thereof, but canst not tell whence it cometh, and whither it goeth: so is every one that is born of the Spirit.

And as Moses lifted up the serpent in the wilderness, even so must the Son of Man be lifted up:

That whosoever believeth in him should not perish, but have eternal life.

For God so loved the world, that he gave his only begotten Son, that whosoever believeth in him should not perish, but have everlasting life.

For God sent not his Son into the world to condemn the world; but that the world through him might be saved. John 3:1-8,14-17

39 Justification

Therefore being justified by faith, we have peace with God through our Lord Jesus Christ:

By whom also we have access by faith into this grace wherein we stand, and rejoice in hope of the glory of God.

And not only so, but we glory in tribulations also: knowing that tribulation worketh patience; and patience, experience; and experience, hope;

And hope maketh not ashamed; because the love of God is shed abroad in our hearts by the Holy Ghost which is given unto us.

For when we were yet without strength, in due time Christ died for the ungodly.

For scarcely for a righteous man will one die: yet peradventure for a good man some would even dare to die.

But God commendeth his love toward us, in that, while we were yet sinners, Christ died for us.

Much more then, being now justified by his blood, we shall be saved from wrath through him.

For if, when we were enemies, we were reconciled to God by the death of his Son, much more, being reconciled, we shall be saved by his life.

And not only so, but we also joy in God through our Lord Jesus Christ, by whom we have now received the atonement.

Therefore as by the offence of one judgment came upon all men to condemnation; even so by the righteousness of one the free gift came upon all men unto justification of life. Romans 5:1-11, 18

There is therefore now no condemnation to them which are in Christ Jesus, who walk not after the flesh, but after the **Spirit.** Romans 8:1

40 Assurance

We know that all things work together for good to them that love God, to them who are the called according to his purpose.

For whom he did foreknow, he also did predestinate to be conformed to the image of his Son, that he might be the firstborn among many brethren.

Moreover whom he did predestinate, them he also called: and whom he called, them he also justified: and whom he justified, them he also glorified.

What shall we then say to these things? If God be for us, who can be against us?

He that spared not his own Son, but delivered him up for us all, how shall he not with him also freely give us all things?

Who shall lay any thing to the charge of God's elect? It is God that justifieth.

Who is he that condemneth? It is Christ that died, yea rather, that is risen again, who is even at the right hand of God, who also maketh intercession for us.

Who shall separate us from the love of Christ? shall tribulation, or distress, or persecution, or famine, or nakedness, or peril, or sword?

As it is written, For thy sake we are killed all the day long; we are accounted as sheep for the slaughter.

Nay, in all these things we are more than conquerors through him that loved us.

For I am persuaded, that neither death, nor life, nor angels, nor principalities, nor powers, nor things present, nor things to come,

Nor height, nor depth, nor any other creature, shall be able to separate us from the love of God, which is in Christ Jesus our Lord. Romans 8:28-39

41 Life and Victory

What shall we say then? Shall we continue in sin, that grace may abound?

God forbid. How shall we, that are dead to sin, live any longer therein?

Know ye not, that so many of us as were baptized into Jesus Christ were baptized into his death?

Therefore we are buried with him by baptism into death: that like as Christ was raised up from the dead by the glory of the Father, even so we also should walk in newness of life.

For if we have been planted together in the likeness of his death, we shall be also in the likeness of his resurrection:

Knowing this, that our old man is crucified with him, that the body of sin might be destroyed, that henceforth we should not serve sin.

For he that is dead is freed from sin.

Now if we be dead with Christ, we believe that we shall also live with him:

Knowing that Christ being raised from the dead dieth no more; death hath no more dominion over him.

For in that he died, he died unto sin once: but in that he liveth, he liveth unto God.

Likewise reckon ye also yourselves to be dead indeed unto sin, but alive unto God through Jesus Christ our Lord.

Let not sin therefore reign in your mortal body, that ye should obey it in the lusts thereof.

Neither yield ye your members as instruments of unrighteousness unto sin:

But yield yourselves unto God, as those that are alive from the dead, and your members as instruments of righteousness unto God. Romans 6:1-13

42 A Living Sacrifice

I beseech you therefore, brethren, by the mercies of God, that ye present your bodies a living sacrifice, holy, acceptable unto God, which is your reasonable service.

And be not conformed to this world: but be ye transformed by the renewing of your mind, that ye may prove what is that good, and acceptable, and perfect, will of God.

For I say, through the grace given unto me, to every man that is among you, not to think of himself more highly than he ought to think; but to think soberly, according as God hath dealt to every man the measure of faith.

For as we have many members in one body, and all members have not the same office:

So we, being many, are one body in Christ, and every one members one of another.

Let love be without dissimulation. Abhor that which is evil: cleave to that which is good.

Be kindly affectioned one to another with brotherly love; in honor preferring one another;

Not slothful in business; fervent in spirit; serving the Lord;

Rejoicing in hope; patient in tribulation; continuing instant in prayer;

Distributing to the necessity of saints; given to hospitality.

Bless them which persecute you: bless, and curse not.

Rejoice with them that do rejoice, and weep with them that weep.

Be of the same mind one toward another. Mind not high things, but condescend to men of low estate. Be not wise in your own conceits.

Recompense to no man evil for evil. Provide things honest in the sight of all men.

If it be possible, as much as lieth in you, live peaceably with all men.

Be not overcome of evil, but overcome evil with good. Romans 12:1-5,9-18,21

43 The True Vine

I am the true vine, and my Father is the husbandman.

Every branch in me that beareth not fruit he taketh away: and every branch that beareth fruit, he purgeth it, that it may bring forth more fruit.

Now ye are clean through the word which I have spoken unto you.

Abide in me, and I in you. As the branch cannot bear fruit of itself, except it abide in the vine; no more can ye, except ye abide in me.

I am the vine, ye are the branches: He that abideth in me, and I in him, the same bringeth forth much fruit: for without me ye can do nothing.

If a man abide not in me, he is cast forth as a branch, and is withered; and men gather them, and cast them into the fire, and they are burned.

If ye abide in me, and my words abide in you, ye shall ask what ye will, and it shall be done unto you.

Herein is my Father glorified, that ye bear much fruit; so shall ye be my disciples.

As the Father hath loved me, so have I loved you: continue ye in my love.

If ye keep my commandments, ye shall abide in my love; even as I have kept my Father's commandments, and abide in his love.

These things have I spoken unto you, that my joy might remain in you, and that your joy might be full.

Ye have not chosen me, but I have chosen you, and ordained you, that ye should go and bring forth fruit, and that your fruit should remain: that whatsoever ye shall ask of the Father in my name, he may give it you.   John 15:1-11,16

44 Pattern for Prayer

When thou prayest, thou shalt not be as the hypocrites are: for they love to pray standing in the synagogues and in the corners of the streets, that they may be seen of men. Verily I say unto you, They have their reward.

But thou, when thou prayest, enter into thy closet, and when thou hast shut thy door, pray to thy Father which is in secret; and thy Father which seeth in secret shall reward thee openly.

But when ye pray, use not vain repetitions, as the heathen do: for they think that they shall be heard for their much speaking.

Be not ye therefore like unto them: for your Father knoweth what things ye have need of, before ye ask him.

After this manner therefore pray ye: Our Father which art in heaven, Hallowed be thy name.

Thy kingdom come. Thy will be done in earth, as it is in heaven.

Give us this day our daily bread.

And forgive us our debts, as we forgive our debtors.

And lead us not into temptation, but deliver us from evil:

For thine is the kingdom, and the power, and the glory, for ever. Amen.

For if ye forgive men their trespasses, your heavenly Father will also forgive you:

But if ye forgive not men their trespasses, neither will your Father forgive your trespasses.   Matthew 6:5-15

45 Our Father's Care

No man can serve two masters: for either he will hate the one, and love the other; or else he will hold to the one, and despise the other. Ye cannot serve God and mammon.

Therefore I say unto you, Take no thought for your life, what ye shall eat, or what ye shall drink; nor yet for your body, what ye shall put on. Is not the life more than meat, and the body than raiment?

Behold the fowls of the air: for they sow not, neither do they reap, nor gather into barns; yet your heavenly Father feedeth them. Are ye not much better than they?

Which of you by taking thought can add one cubit unto his stature?

And why take ye thought for raiment? Consider the lilies of the field, how they grow; they toil not, neither do they spin:

And yet I say unto you, That even Solomon in all his glory was not arrayed like one of these.

Wherefore, if God so clothe the grass of the field, which today is, and tomorrow is cast into the oven, shall he not much more clothe you, O ye of little faith?

Therefore take no thought, saying, What shall we eat? or, What shall we drink? or, Wherewithal shall we be clothed?

For your heavenly Father knoweth that ye have need of all these things.

But seek ye first the kingdom of God, and his righteousness; and all these things shall be added unto you. Matthew 6:24-33

46 Comfort in Affliction

Blessed be God, even the Father of our Lord Jesus Christ, the Father of mercies, and the God of all comfort;

Who comforteth us in all our tribulation, that we may be able to comfort them which are in any trouble, by the comfort wherewith we ourselves are comforted of God.

For as the sufferings of Christ abound in us, so our consolation also aboundeth by Christ.

And whether we be afflicted, it is for your consolation and salvation, which is effectual in the enduring of the same sufferings which we also suffer:

Or whether we be comforted, it is for your consolation and salvation.

And our hope of you is stedfast, knowing, that as ye are partakers of the sufferings, so shall ye be also of the consolation.
II Corinthians 1:3-7

Beloved, think it not strange concerning the fiery trial which is to try you, as though some strange thing happened unto you:

But rejoice, inasmuch as ye are partakers of Christ's sufferings; that, when his glory shall be revealed, ye may be glad also with exceeding joy.

Yet if any man suffer as a Christian, let him not be ashamed; but let him glorify God on this behalf.

Wherefore let them that suffer according to the will of God commit the keeping of their souls to him in well doing, as unto a faithful Creator. I Peter 4:12,13,16,19

47 The Christian Armor

Finally, my brethren, be strong in the Lord, and in the power of his might. Put on the whole armor of God, that ye may be able to stand against the wiles of the devil.

For we wrestle not against flesh and blood, but against principalities, against powers, against the rulers of the darkness of this world, against spiritual wickedness in high places.

Wherefore take unto you the whole armor of God, that ye may be able to withstand in the evil day, and having done all, to stand.

Stand therefore, having your loins girt about with truth, and having on the breastplate of righteousness;

And your feet shod with the preparation of the gospel of peace;

Above all, taking the shield of faith, wherewith ye shall be able to quench all the fiery darts of the wicked.

And take the helmet of salvation, and the sword of the Spirit, which is the word of God:

Praying always with all prayer and supplication in the Spirit, and watching thereunto with all perseverance and supplication for all saints. Ephesians 6:10-18

48 Christian Love

Beloved, let us love one another: for love is of God; and every one that loveth is born of God, and knoweth God.

He that loveth not knoweth not God; for God is love.

In this was manifested the love of God toward us, because that God sent his only begotten Son into the world, that we might live through him.

Herein is love, not that we loved God, but that he loved us, and sent his Son to be the propitiation for our sins.

Beloved, if God so loved us, we ought also to love one another.

No man hath seen God at any time. If we love one another, God dwelleth in us, and his love is perfected in us.

If a man say, I love God, and hateth his brother, he is a liar; for he that loveth not his brother whom he hath seen, how can he love God whom he hath not seen?

And this commandment have we from him, That he who loveth God love his brother also. 1 John 4:7-12,20,21

My little children, let us not love in word, neither in tongue; but in deed and in truth.

And hereby we know that we are of the truth, and shall assure our hearts before him. 1 John 3:18,19

49 The Supremacy of Love

Though I speak with the tongues of men and of angels, and have not love, I am become as sounding brass, or a tinkling cymbal.

And though I have the gift of prophecy, and understand all mysteries, and all knowledge; and though I have all faith, so that I could remove mountains, and have not love, I am nothing.

And though I bestow all my goods to feed the poor, and though I give my body to be burned, and have not love, it profiteth me nothing.

Love suffereth long, and is kind; love envieth not; love vaunteth not itself, is not puffed up,

Doth not behave itself unseemly, seeketh not her own, is not easily provoked, thinketh no evil;

Rejoiceth not in iniquity, but rejoiceth in the truth;

Beareth all things, believeth all things, hopeth all things, endureth all things.

Love never faileth: but whether there be prophecies, they shall fail; whether there be tongues, they shall cease; whether there be knowledge, it shall vanish away.

For we know in part and we prophesy in part.

But when that which is perfect is come, then that which is in part shall be done away.

When I was a child, I spake as a child, I understood as a child, I thought as a child: but when I became a man, I put away childish things.

For now we see through a glass, darkly; but then face to face:

Now I know in part; but then shall I know even as also I am known.

And now abideth faith, hope, love, these three; but the greatest of these is love. I Corinthians 13

50 The Unity of the Spirit

I therefore, the prisoner of the Lord, beseech you that ye walk worthy of the vocation wherewith ye are called,

With all lowliness and meekness, with longsuffering, forbearing one another in love;

Endeavoring to keep the unity of the Spirit in the bond of peace.

There is one body, and one Spirit, even as ye are called in one hope of your calling;

One Lord, one faith, one baptism,

One God and Father of all, who is above all, and through all, and in you all.

But unto every one of us is given grace according to the measure of the gift of Christ.

And he gave some, apostles; and some, prophets; and some, evangelists; and some, pastors and teachers;

For the perfecting of the saints, for the work of the ministry, for the edifying of the body of Christ:

Till we all come in the unity of the faith, and of the knowledge of the Son of God, unto a perfect man, unto the measure of the stature of the fulness of Christ:

That we henceforth be no more children, tossed to and fro, and carried about with every wind of doctrine, by the sleight of men, and cunning craftiness, whereby they lie in wait to deceive;

But speaking the truth in love, may grow up into him in all things, which is the head, even Christ.   Ephesians 4:1-7,11-15

51 The Blessed Hope

Let not your heart be troubled: ye believe in God, believe also in me.

In my Father's house are many mansions: if it were not so, I would have told you. I go to prepare a place for you.

And if I go and prepare a place for you, I will come again, and receive you unto myself; that where I am, there ye may be also.

And whither I go ye know, and the way ye know.

Thomas saith unto him, Lord, we know not whither thou goest; and how can we know the way?

Jesus saith unto him, I am the way, the truth, and the life: no man cometh unto the Father, but by me.   John 14:1-6

But I would not have you to be ignorant, brethren, concerning them which are asleep, that ye sorrow not, even as others which have no hope.

For if we believe that Jesus died and rose again, even so them also which sleep in Jesus will God bring with him.

For this we say unto you by the word of the Lord, that we which are alive and remain unto the coming of the Lord shall not precede them which are asleep.

For the Lord himself shall descend from heaven with a shout, with the voice of the archangel, and with the trump of God: and the dead in Christ shall rise first:

Then we which are alive and remain shall be caught up together with them in the clouds, to meet the Lord in the air: and so shall we ever be with the Lord.

Wherefore comfort one another with these words.   I Thessalonians 4:13-18

52 The Hope of Resurrection

If in this life only we have hope in Christ, we are of all men most miserable.

But now is Christ risen from the dead, and become the firstfruits of them that slept.

For since by man came death, by man came also the resurrection of the dead.

For as in Adam all die, even so in Christ shall all be made alive.

But some man will say, How are the dead raised up? and with what body do they come?

Thou fool, that which thou sowest is not quickened, except it die:

And that which thou sowest, thou sowest not that body that shall be,

But God giveth it a body as it hath pleased him, and to every seed his own body.

It is sown in corruption; it is raised in incorruption:

It is sown in dishonor; it is raised in glory:

It is sown in weakness; it is raised in power:

It is sown a natural body; it is raised a spiritual body.

For this corruptible must put on incorruption, and this mortal must put on immortality.

So when this corruptible shall have put on incorruption, and this mortal shall have put on immortality, then shall be brought to pass the saying that is written, Death is swallowed up in victory.

O death, where is thy sting? O grave, where is thy victory?

The sting of death is sin; and the strength of sin is the law.

But thanks be to God, which giveth us the victory through our Lord Jesus Christ.

Therefore, my beloved brethren, be ye stedfast, unmoveable, always abounding in the work of the Lord, forasmuch as ye know that your labor is not in vain in the Lord.   I Corinthians 15:19-22,35-38,42-44,53-58

53   Faith in Action

Now faith is the substance of things hoped for, the evidence of things not seen.

For by it the elders obtained a good report.

Through faith we understand that the worlds were framed by the word of God, so that things which are seen were not made of things which do appear.

By faith Abel offered unto God a more excellent sacrifice than Cain, by which he obtained witness that he was righteous, God testifying of his gifts: and by it he being dead yet speaketh.

By faith Enoch was translated that he should not see death; and was not found, because God had translated him: for before his translation he had this testimony, that he pleased God.

But without faith it is impossible to please him: for he that cometh to God must believe that he is, and that he is a rewarder of them that diligently seek him.

By faith Noah, being warned of God of things not seen as yet, moved with fear, prepared an ark to the saving of his house; by the which he condemned the world, and became heir of the righteousness which is by faith.

By faith Abraham, when he was called to go out into a place which he should after receive for an inheritance, obeyed; and he went out, not knowing whither he went.

By faith Isaac blessed Jacob and Esau concerning things to come.

By faith Moses, when he was come to years, refused to be called the son of Pharaoh's daughter;

Choosing rather to suffer affliction with the people of God, than to enjoy the pleasures of sin for a season;

Esteeming the reproach of Christ greater riches than the treasures in Egypt: for he had respect unto the recompence of the reward.
                        Hebrews 11:1-8,20,24-26

These all died in faith, not having received the promises, but having seen them afar off, and were persuaded of them, and embraced them, and confessed that they were strangers and pilgrims on the earth.

For they that say such things declare plainly that they seek a country . . . that is, an heavenly: wherefore God is not ashamed to be called their God: for he hath prepared for them a city.

Hebrews 11:13,14,16

Wherefore seeing we also are compassed about with so great a cloud of witnesses, let us lay aside every weight, and the sin which doth so easily beset us, and let us run with patience the race that is set before us,

Looking unto Jesus the author and finisher of our faith; who for the joy that was set before him endured the cross, despising the shame, and is set down at the right hand of the throne of God.

Hebrews 12:1,2

54 The Christian Family

Wives, submit yourselves unto your own husbands, as unto the Lord.

For the husband is the head of the wife, even as Christ is the head of the church: and he is the savior of the body.

Therefore as the church is subject unto Christ, so let the wives be to their own husbands in every thing.

Husbands, love your wives, even as Christ also loved the church, and gave himself for it;

So ought men to love their wives as their own bodies.

He that loveth his wife loveth himself.

For no man ever yet hated his own flesh; but nourisheth and cherisheth it, even as the Lord the church:

For we are members of his body, of his flesh, and of his bones.

For this cause shall a man leave his father and mother, and shall be joined unto his wife, and they two shall be one flesh.

Ephesians 5:22-25, 28-31

Children, obey your parents in the Lord: for this is right.

Honor thy father and mother; which is the first commandment with promise;

That it may be well with thee, and thou mayest live long on the earth.

And, ye fathers, provoke not your children to wrath: but bring them up in the nurture and admonition of the Lord.

Ephesians 6:1-4

Train up a child in the way he should go: and when he is old, he will not depart from it.

Proverbs 22:6

55 Christian Motherhood

Who can find a virtuous woman? for her price is far above rubies.

The heart of her husband doth safely trust in her, so that he shall have no need of spoil.

She will do him good and not evil all the days of her life.

She seeketh wool, and flax, and worketh willingly with her hands.

She is like the merchants' ships; she bringeth her food from afar.

She riseth also while it is yet night, and giveth meat to her household, and a portion to her maidens.

She considereth a field, and buyeth it: with the fruit of her hands she planteth a vineyard.

She girdeth her loins with strength, and strengtheneth her arms.

She perceiveth that her merchandise is good: her candle goeth not out by night.

She layeth her hands to the spindle, and her hands hold the distaff.

She stretcheth out her hand to the poor; yea, she reacheth forth her hands to the needy.

She is not afraid of the snow for her household: for all her household are clothed with scarlet.

She maketh herself coverings of tapestry; her clothing is silk and purple.

Her husband is known in the gates, when he sitteth among the elders of the land.

She maketh fine linen, and selleth it; and delivereth girdles unto the merchant.

Strength and honor are her clothing; and she shall rejoice in time to come.

She openeth her mouth with wisdom; and in her tongue is the law of kindness.

She looketh well to the ways of her household, and eateth not the bread of idleness.

Her children arise up, and call her blessed; her husband also, and he praiseth her.

Many daughters have done virtuously, but thou excellest them all.

Favor is deceitful, and beauty is vain: but a woman that feareth the Lord, she shall be praised.

Give her of the fruit of her hands; and let her own works praise her in the gates. Proverbs 31:10-31

56 Christ and the Children

At the same time came the disciples unto Jesus, saying, Who is the greatest in the kingdom of heaven?

And Jesus called a little child unto him, and set him in the midst of them,

And said, Verily I say unto you, Except ye be converted, and become as little children, ye shall not enter into the kingdom of heaven.

Whosoever therefore shall humble himself as this little child, the same is greatest in the kingdom of heaven.

And whoso shall receive one such little child in my name receiveth me.

But whoso shall offend one of these little ones which believe in me, it were better for him that a millstone were hanged about his neck, and that he were drowned in the depth of the sea. Matthew 18:1-6

And they brought young children to him, that he should touch them: and his disciples rebuked those that brought them.

But when Jesus saw it, he was much displeased, and said unto them, Suffer the little children to come unto me, and forbid them not: for of such is the kingdom of God.

Verily I say unto you, Whosoever shall not receive the kingdom of God as a little child, he shall not enter therein.

And he took them up in his arms, put his hands upon them, and blessed them. Mark 10:13-16

57 Counsel for Youth

My son, if sinners entice thee, consent thou not.

If they say, Come with us, let us lay wait for blood, let us lurk privily for the innocent without cause:

Let us swallow them up alive as the grave; and whole, as those that go down into the pit:

We shall find all precious substance, we shall fill our houses with spoil:

Cast in thy lot among us; let us all have one purse:

My son, walk not thou in the way with them; refrain thy foot from their path: Proverbs 1:10-15

My son, forget not my law; but let thine heart keep my commandments:

For length of days, and long life, and peace, shall they add to thee.

Let not mercy and truth forsake thee: bind them about thy neck; write them upon the table of thine heart:

So shalt thou find favor and good understanding in the sight of God and man. Proverbs 3:1-4

Remember now thy Creator in the days of thy youth, while the evil days come not, nor the years draw nigh, when thou shalt say, I have no pleasure in them;

While the sun, or the light, or the moon, or the stars, be not darkened, nor the clouds return after the rain:

Let us hear the conclusion of the whole matter: Fear God, and keep his commandments: for this is the whole duty of man.

For God shall bring every work into judgment, with every secret thing, whether it be good, or whether it be evil.
Ecclesiastes 12:1,2,13,14

58 God and Country

All the commandments which I command thee this day shall ye observe to do, that ye may live . . .

And thou shalt remember all the way which the Lord thy God led thee . . .

For the Lord thy God bringeth thee into a good land, a land of brooks of water, of fountains and depths that spring out of valleys and hills;

A land of wheat, and barley, and vines, and fig trees, and pomegranates; a land of oil olive, and honey;

A land wherein thou shalt eat bread without scarceness, thou shalt not lack any thing in it; a land whose stones are iron, and out of whose hills thou mayest dig brass.

When thou hast eaten and art full, then thou shalt bless the Lord thy God

for the good land which he hath given thee.

Beware that thou forget not the Lord thy God, in not keeping his commandments, and his judgments, and his statutes, which I command thee this day:

Lest when thou hast eaten and art full, and hast built goodly houses, and dwelt therein;

And when thy herds and thy flocks multiply, and thy silver and thy gold is multiplied, and all that thou hast is multiplied;

Then thine heart be lifted up, and thou forget the Lord thy God . . .

And thou say in thine heart, My power and the might of mine hand hath gotten me this wealth.

But thou shalt remember the Lord thy God: for it is he that giveth thee power to get wealth.

And it shall be, if thou do at all forget the Lord thy God, and walk after other gods, and serve them, and worship them, I testify against you this day that ye shall surely perish.

As the nations which the Lord destroyeth before your face, so shall ye perish; because ye would not be obedient unto the voice of the Lord your God.
Deuteronomy 8:1,2,7-14,17-20

---

59 Calls to Worship

1 — The Lord is in his holy temple: let all the earth keep silence before him.   Hab. 2:20

2 — This is the day which the Lord hath made; we will rejoice and be glad in it.
Psalm 118:24

3 — I was glad when they said unto me, Let us go into the house of the Lord. Psalm 122:1

4 — How amiable are thy tabernacles, O Lord of hosts! My soul longeth, yea, even fainteth for the courts of the Lord: my heart and my flesh crieth out for the living God. Blessed are they that dwell in thy house: they will be still praising thee.   Psalm 84:1,2,4

5 — O sing unto the Lord a new song: sing unto the Lord, all the earth. Give unto the Lord the glory due unto his name: bring an offering, and come into his courts. O worship the Lord in the beauty of holiness: fear before him, all the earth.   Psalm 96:1,8,9

6 — Serve the Lord with gladness: come before his presence with singing. Enter into his gates with thanksgiving, and into his courts with praise: be thankful unto him, and bless his name.   Psalm 100:2,4

7 — The hour cometh, and now is, when the true worshippers shall worship the Father in spirit and in truth: for the Father seeketh such to worship him. God is a Spirit: and they that worship him must worship him in spirit and in truth.   John 4:23,24

1 — The grace of the Lord Jesus Christ, and the love of God, and the communion of the Holy Ghost, be with you all. Amen.

II Corinthians 13:14

2 — Now unto the King eternal, immortal, invisible, the only wise God, be honor and glory for ever and ever. Amen.

I Timothy 1:17

3 — Now unto him that is able to keep you from falling, and to present you faultless before the presence of his glory with exceeding joy, to the only wise God our Savior, be glory and majesty, dominion and power, both now and ever. Amen.   Jude 24,25

4 — Now the God of peace, that brought again from the dead our Lord Jesus, that great shepherd of the sheep, through the blood of the everlasting covenant, make you perfect in every good work to do his will, working in you that which is wellpleasing in his sight, through Jesus Christ; to whom be glory for ever and ever. Amen.   Hebrews 13:20,21

5 — Now unto him that is able to do exceeding abundantly above all that we ask or think, according to the power that worketh in us, unto him be glory in the church by Christ Jesus throughout all ages, world without end. Amen.   Ephesians 3:20,21

6 — And the very God of peace sanctify you wholly; and I pray God your whole spirit and soul and body be preserved blameless unto the coming of our Lord Jesus Christ. The grace of our Lord Jesus Christ be with you. Amen.   I Thessalonians 5:23,28

7 — The Lord bless thee, and keep thee: the Lord make his face shine upon thee, and be gracious unto thee: the Lord lift up his countenance upon thee, and give thee peace. Amen.

Numbers 6:24-26

THE APOSTLES' CREED

I believe in God the Father Almighty, maker of heaven and earth;

And in Jesus Christ, His only begotten Son, our Lord, who was conceived by the Holy Spirit[1], born of the Virgin Mary, suffered under Pontius Pilate, was crucified, dead and buried; He descended into hell; the third day He rose again from the dead; He ascended into heaven, and sitteth at the right hand of God the Father Almighty; from thence He shall come to judge the quick and the dead.

I believe in the Holy Spirit, the holy Christian church[2], the communion of saints, the forgiveness of sins, the resurrection of the body, and the life everlasting. Amen.

[1] Or "Holy Ghost."   [2] Or "holy catholic church," meaning universal.

TITLE INDEX OF SELECTIONS FROM SCRIPTURE

SUBJECT INDEX OF SELECTIONS FROM SCRIPTURE

SCRIPTURAL INDEX OF SELECTIONS FROM SCRIPTURE

SUGGESTED SCRIPTURE PASSAGES FOR UNISON READING

Advent.............................Isaiah 11:1-9; Isaiah 40:1-11
Anniversaries ....Psalm 98
Annunciation ....Luke 1:26-38
Child Jesus..Luke 2:40-52
Chosen of God.................................Ephesians 1:3-14
Church...............................I Kings 8:22-30; Psalm 84;
　　　　　　　　　　　　　Psalm 115; Ephesians 2
Church Leaders...............................I Timothy 3:1-13
Divine Help.......................Psalm 121, Psalm 130
Easter...Luke 24:13-35
Education............................Deuteronomy 6:4-25;
　　　　　　　　　　Proverbs 2:1-9; Proverbs 4:1-13
Eternal Christ...............................Hebrews 1:1-12
Eternal Destiny — see Messiah's Reign
Forgiveness..Psalm 130
Good Shepherd................................John 10:1-16
Holy Spirit..Romans 8:1-17
Humility...John 13:3-17
Installation of Pastor....................II Timothy 4:1-8
Invitation to Salvation................................Isaiah 55
Judgment ....Matthew 25:31-46
Lord's Supper.....................Matthew 26:17-29;
　　　　　　　　　　　I Corinthians 11:23-32
Magnificat ....Luke 1:46-55
Memorial Days................Psalm 90; Psalm 145;
　　　　　　　　　　　　Revelation 7:9-17

Mercy...Psalm 130
Messiah's Reign.............................Isaiah 11:1-9;
　　　　　　　　　　Isaiah 42:1-12; Isaiah 35
Music ....Psalm 150
New Year...Psalm 190
New Birth..I John 5:4-15
Obedience.......................................Psalm 119:1-18
Patriotism ....Psalm 33
Praise...........................Psalm 111; Psalm 148
Prayer ....Luke 11:1-13
Providence..Psalm 34
Revival...Joel 2:12-19
Security ....Psalm 46
Second Coming........................Matthew 24:27-42;
　　　　　　　　　　　　　Matthew 25:31-46
Social Concern...................Matthew 25:31-46;
　　　　　　　　　　　I Thessalonians 5:5-24
Stewardship......................Proverbs 3:1-10, 27-35;
　　　　　　　Isaiah 58:1-12; Matthew 6:19-34;
　　　　　　　Matthew 25:14-30; I Peter 5:1-11
Temperance.........................Ecclesiastes 3:1-13;
　　　　　　　　　　　I Thessalonians 5:5-24
Thanksgiving ....Psalm 147
Trials.........................I Peter 1:3-19; I Peter 4:12-19
Worship............Psalm 100; Psalm 111; Isaiah 6:1-8
Wisdom............Job 28:12-28; Proverbs 2:1-9;
　　　　　　　Proverbs 3:1-18; Proverbs 4:1-13

INDEX OF AUTHORS, COMPOSERS AND SOURCES
including translators and arrangers

INDEX OF AUTHORS, COMPOSERS AND SOURCES

495

INDEX OF AUTHORS, COMPOSERS AND SOURCES

INDEX OF AUTHORS, COMPOSERS AND SOURCES

TUNE INDEX

(R. indicates "with Refrain;" A. indicates "with Alleluias.")

METRICAL INDEX

(Tune names in parentheses are of a different basic meter but are readily adaptable to the meter indicated. Tune names with an asterisk require an extension by repetition of text.)

TOPICAL INDEX

TOPICAL INDEX

TOPICAL INDEX

GENERAL INDEX

Titles are in SMALL CAPS, familiar first lines in lower case type.

GENERAL INDEX

511

Benediction

Revelation 22:21

JOHN W. PETERSON, 1921-

The grace of our Lord Je-sus Christ   be with you all, be with you all;
The grace of our Lord Je-sus Christ   be with you all,   A - men.

The Lord Bless You and Keep You

Numbers 6:24-26

PETER C. LUTKIN, 1858-1931

The Lord bless you and keep   you; The Lord lift His coun-te-nance up-

The

on   you,   and give you peace,   and give you peace; The Lord
and give you peace,   and give you peace;

Lord make His

make His   face to shine up-on   you, And be   gra - - - cious un-to
And be gra-cious

you,   be gra-cious,   The Lord be gra-cious, gra-cious un-to you. A - men.
and be gra-cious,